METEOR SCIENCE AND ENGINEERING
unifies the field of meteor science and
engineering by explaining the astronomical
and physical aspects of meteor studies as
well as their practical application.

Dr. D. W. R. McKinley is a Canadian scientist
who has been associated with the many
areas of meteor science and engineering
since 1947. He is the author of almost fifty
papers on the subject.

Meteor Science and Engineering

D. W. R. McKinley

McGraw-Hill Book Company, Inc.
New York   Toronto   London

METEOR SCIENCE AND ENGINEERING

45170

Preface

Most of us, outdoors on a warm summer night, have taken passing notice of the shooting stars which streak across the sky at random intervals. Perhaps once a year or so, in a given locality, a brilliant fireball may light up the countryside and thereby unleash a flood of telephone calls to newspaper offices. Rarer still are the spectacular displays of celestial fireworks associated with the really great meteor showers, which in the past have aroused emotions ranging from delighted awe to sheer superstitious terror. We know, of course, that these are the visible manifestations of the continual bombardment of our planet by objects from outer space, objects which vary in size from gigantic boulders with the latent energy of an atomic bomb—fortunately these do not occur more frequently than once or twice a century—down to particles the size of pinheads, which create a hundred thousand fleeting sparks a minute all over our globe. Beyond the limits of our telescopically aided vision, we have evidence that large numbers of still finer particles are streaming into the atmosphere; saved from fiery destruction by their very smallness, they drift leisurely down to earth. It may be that, as condensation nuclei, this microscopic meteoric material literally precipitates the gentle rain from heaven.

Although the historical records of meteoric appearances go back for three or four thousand years, it was only around the beginning of the nineteenth century that the first glimmerings of scientific interest showed. Even then, few took up the study with lasting determination, and until comparatively recently, research in meteor science was left to a small but select group of devoted specialists. In the last two decades, though, an increasing awareness of the influence that meteors have on man's activities has blossomed among scientists and engineers and, to a more diffuse extent, among the literate public. More powerful optical tools have been complemented by the new radio observing methods, with the result that rapid progress is being made, both in our fundamental understanding of meteoric phenomena and in our practical utilization of the effects.

In this book we have attempted to summarize the major observational and theoretical developments in meteor science. As defined here, meteor science embraces the spatial history of the particles and the effects they create in the upper atmosphere. Field and laboratory studies of meteorites are among the areas not covered. One of the alternative titles suggested for this book was "Meteor Science for Engineers"; in some respects, it would not have been inappropriate. In broad terms, our aim on the one hand has been to explain meteor science to the man who has not specialized in meteor research but who would like to learn something of the background—perhaps because he is engaged in scientific or engineering work in which meteors may play some part or perhaps just because he has an inquiring mind. On the other hand, the outline of the engineering side of the meteor story has been written not primarily for the communications engineer but rather for the scientific layman or even the meteor research specialist who may not be acquainted with this aspect.

Only a moderate grounding in mathematics at the undergraduate level is asked of the reader, and for much of the discussion even this is not essential. Where necessary, though, mathematical developments have been introduced without excuses either for the difficulties they might present to some readers or for the lack of rigor and completeness that might be apparent to others. A somewhat tutorial tone may be detected at times, although there are no neat problems for the student to solve with tidy answers at the back of the book. One of the themes throughout, in fact, is that we lack satisfactory solutions to a great many questions in meteor science. Some of these solutions will undoubtedly be found through the interlocking efforts of scientists in many disciplines, because the study of meteors, once the prerogative of a select group of astronomers, has spread across the borders of several sciences.

I wish to express my gratitude and appreciation to my colleagues all over the world on whose work, both published and unpublished, I have drawn freely. Personal acknowledgments are due to P. M. Millman, J. S. Greenhow, R. E. McCrosky, L. C. Parode, G. W. L. Davis, J. G. Davies, and G. S. Hawkins for the use of material in advance of publication. F. L. Whipple, A. F. Cook, J. H. Crysdale, and C. O. Hines have responded with very helpful comments on certain sections. My greatest debt is to Larry Manning, Allen McNamara, Peter Millman, and my wife Barbara, who each waded through the entire manuscript and offered highly valued, though sometimes widely divergent, advice on what should have been changed, added, or thrown out. The reader must, of course, assess me with any shortcomings that may be apparent.

D. W. R. McKinley

Contents

CHAPTER I

Historical Survey

1-1. What is a meteor? Naturally the Greeks had a word for it—
μετεωρον, or more commonly the plural μετεωρα—meaning literally
"raised beyond" or "things up in the air." As recently as the eighteenth
century the term was applied to the aurora as well, and also to many
phenomena in the lower atmosphere, such as lightning, rain, snow and
hail, cloud formations, and rainbows, which in these days are encompassed
by the science of weather known as meteorology. Contemporary
meteorologists often use the word as a prefix or suffix (for example, a
raindrop is a hydrometeor) but rarely if ever by itself in the archaic
general sense. The word meteor now refers to the streak of light or
"shooting star" that is seen in the night sky when a small object, known
as a *meteoroid*, enters the earth's atmosphere at high speed and dissipates
its energy and substance in a brief blaze. If the event is spectacularly
brilliant the term *fireball* may be used, and if the object appears to
explode it is called a detonating fireball or *bolide*. Over the entire earth
it is estimated that from one to two hundred million visible meteors burn
themselves out daily in our upper air.

Very rarely, a residual fragment of a large meteoroid may survive the
fiery plunge and drop to the ground as a *meteorite*, often breaking up into
many small pieces. Perhaps 30 meteorites may descend each day over
land and sea, but few are recovered. The actuarial statistics on the probability of being killed by one of these chunks of celestial minerals are most
reassuring. In recorded history there is no truly authenticated instance
of a human death from this cause, and only one case of injury has been
proved in recent times, when in 1954 an Alabama housewife received a
glancing blow from a meteorite which fell through the roof of her home.*
No radio record of a meteorite-dropping fireball seems to have been confirmed yet, although this should not be surprising in view of the relatively

---

* In a comprehensive and well-documented article on the effects of meteorites upon
the earth LaPaz (1958) discusses the past history and the future probabilities of hits
on human targets, and in this particular case he adds the colorful comment " . . .
in fact, even the Sylacauga [Alabama] meteorite did not score a direct hit on Mrs.
Hodges, but rather clobbered her on the first bounce!"

insignificant fraction of the earth's area which has been monitored during the short history of radio observing methods.   Recently, Czechoslovakian meteor observers were fortunate enough to photograph the luminous path of a bolide, from which several fragments were recovered (Ceplecha, Rajckl, and Sehnal, 1959).*   Much valuable information can be gleaned from laboratory examinations of meteorites, though these studies lie outside the scope of this book.

At the other end of the scale there are the minute particles which Whipple has aptly termed *micrometeorites*.   A micrometeorite has a large surface area relative to its mass.   Therefore its kinetic energy, when converted to heat by collisions with air particles, is radiated away at low temperatures and the meteoroid does not vaporize.   The larger micrometeorites may melt into small globules without much loss of mass, while the smaller ones may not reach the point of incandescence.   Micrometeorites cannot be detected by optical or radio methods but their presence is made known through suitable instrumentation borne aloft by rockets and satellites.   Some days or weeks after they enter the atmosphere they drift down to earth and may be trapped by exposed sticky surfaces.   The more general term *meteoric dust* embraces the range of micrometeorites and includes motes and finer debris which may be ascribed to a meteoric origin.

Most of the visible radiation from a meteor comes from the immediate vicinity of the vaporizing meteoroid, known as the *head* of the meteor, and the object therefore appears as a moving point of light to an observer. Sudden and brief enhancements of the light during the meteor's passage are termed *flares* or *bursts*.   A brighter meteor sometimes leaves a faintly glowing *train* along its path behind the head, which may be described as a *wake* if the glow lasts for less than a second, or as a *persistent train* if the duration is longer.   The *meteor path* is defined as the geometrical line of motion of the meteoroid; it is usually applied to the straight-line segment that is visible, or detectable by instruments, but it may be extended to any part of the orbit in space.   The projection of the visible path on the observer's celestial sphere has been called the *meteor trail* in certain reduction procedures in visual and photographic work.   In this sense the trail length is an angular measurement.   More recently, many radio observers have adopted the word *trail* when they refer to the train of ionization left in or near the path of the meteor.   We shall accept both interpretations, since the context will generally resolve any lingering ambiguity.   The phrases "visual meteors," "photographic meteors," "telescopic meteors,"

---

* The bibliography, pp. 284–296, is arranged in alphabetical order by the name of the first author, followed by the year of publication.   A listed reference is identified in the main text or in the figure captions by the name of the author (either in or out of parentheses) followed by the date (always in parentheses).

and "radio meteors" are convenient shorthand expressions which are often used to indicate the association with the particular observing technique.

The *radiant* of a meteor is the point where the meteor path intersects the celestial sphere, or, if you prefer, the point at infinity on the meteor path, assuming a linear extension backward of the visible line segment. In more down-to-earth terms the radiant is the spot in the sky from which the meteor appears to have come. This is clearly brought out when a *shower radiant* is active. In this case numbers of *shower meteors* from the same radiant are seen crossing the sky in all directions: their paths, extrapolated backward, all appear to originate in a common point. The effect is one of perspective, of course, for all of the shower meteors are actually moving in parallel paths. A *sporadic* or *nonshower meteor* is one which is not a member of a recognized shower. The term sporadic should not be taken to mean that these meteors occur infrequently. Over a period of a year it is found that the number of sporadics greatly outweighs the total number of meteors belonging to the well-known showers, particularly if the counts are extended to the very faint meteors. For this reason some preference may be expressed for the alternative designation, nonshower meteor, keeping in mind that, as techniques improve, an appreciable number of such meteors may be shown to belong to minor showers which are at present difficult to delineate.

The reader will be quick to notice that the word "meteor," as used both in this book and in much of the contemporary literature, is not confined solely to the visible streak of light in the sky. Quite frequently it is applied to other associated aspects of the phenomenon, such as the meteoroid itself. Furthermore, the word is often employed as an adjective in place of the pedantically correct "meteoric." Consciously or otherwise, scientific writers may tend to avoid the longer form of the adjective because of its popular association with any sudden or spectacular achievement. A "meteoric rise" in a man's career may well merit congratulations, but the approval should be tempered by thoughts of some other connotations of the simile. Even a moderately bright meteor can generate energy at a rate of thousands of horsepower, but its life is inevitably brief and fleeting and its trajectory is always down to earth, never upward. In discussing meteor observations and techniques we shall use the shorter form more often than not, but there will be occasions in analysing meteoric phenomena when the longer form will fall more naturally into context.

1-2. Ancient records. The chronicler of the flight of the children of Israel from Egypt may have been inspired by his own or contemporary observations of brilliant fireballs when he created the very striking metaphor "by day in a pillar of a cloud . . . and by night in a pillar of fire" (Exodus 13:20)—words which aptly describe the daylight dust clouds or nighttime glowing trains left by extremely large meteors. The Book of Joshua (10:11) relates that "the Lord cast down great stones from heaven," and while these are later described as hailstones it seems quite possible that the stones may actually have been meteorites in this case (Olivier, 1925). If so, one would be compelled to revise the rather sweeping actuarial statistics mentioned in the previous section, since the account goes on to say "they were more which died with hailstones than they whom the children of Israel slew with the sword," but it is admittedly difficult to obtain independent corroboration at this late date.

Evidence of ancient meteor occurrences is available in Chinese and Japanese records (Imoto and Hasegawa, 1958) and in Biot's (1846) catalog of *étoiles filantes*. The earliest account, dated 1809 B.C., mentions that "many stars flew, crossing each other." In 687 B.C., during the era of Chou Chuang Wang, the stars were said to fall like a shower, which appears to be the first known record of the annual Lyrid shower. Grecian writings tell of a meteorite, large as a cart, which fell in Thrace in 467 B.C. The awe and veneration accorded in many countries to these mysterious invaders are revealed by their adoption as symbols of worship by both savage and civilized peoples. In Greece and Rome temples are believed to have been erected to house them, and there is evidence to support a meteorical origin for the sacred black stone in the shrine at Mecca, toward which Mohammedans face when praying. In the Western Hemisphere meteorites have been found in the burial mounds of North American Indians and in an Aztec temple (Olivier, 1925). From the fall of Rome down through the Middle Ages, the classical literature abounds in references to very bright meteors, meteorites, and striking showers. While the language used was often allegorical and the dates and other features of the occurrences are difficult to pin down with precision, it is nevertheless possible to trace back for centuries several of the prominent meteor showers of modern times. For example, the annual Perseid shower made its imprint on history at least a dozen times between A.D. 36 and A.D. 1451, and the Delta Aquarids may claim a verified lineage extending back to A.D. 401.

Many of the Greek and Roman writers, unhampered by scientific knowledge, were quite convinced that stones did fall from outer space, and that meteor showers were displays of truly celestial fireworks. In contrast, toward the end of the eighteenth century we find the Academy of Science in France declaring unequivocally that a meteorite, which had actually been seen to fall by numerous eyewitnesses, was merely an earthly stone that had been struck by lightning. Similar disbelief and ridicule were expressed by the learned authorities in several other cases. Not until Biot carried out a careful and detailed examination of one fall of stones, and proved beyond doubt that they were indeed of extra-terrestrial origin, were the doubting scientists convinced of what the ancients had intuitively known.

1-3. Nineteenth-century observations. The astronomer Chladni put forward in 1794 the theory that space is filled with flying particles which are ignited by friction when they encounter the earth's upper atmosphere. Inspired by this suggestion, Brandes and Benzenberg, students at the University of Göttingen, carried out in 1798 simultaneous observations of meteors from two locations separated by several miles. They were able to demonstrate that the streaks of light were located about sixty miles above the earth's surface, and that the speeds of the particles were of the order of planetary velocities; hence the particles must have arrived from well outside the earth. Despite the crudeness of their triangulation methods it may safely be said that these two German students were the founders of modern observing techniques in this field. It turned out, though, that they were years ahead of their time, because enthusiasm for meteor astronomy lagged and stumbled for more than three decades after their pioneering achievements. It needed an amazing spectacle in the heavens to cause a resurgence of scientific investigation, as well as to arouse a widespread public interest.

This inspiring spectacle was the famous Leonid shower of 1833. On the night of Nov. 12–13 a tempest of falling stars broke loose all over North America. From Halifax to the Gulf of Mexico thousands of entranced observers watched as myriads of shooting stars laced across the sky and majestic fireballs lit up the ground below. The ignorant and superstitious thought the Day of Judgment had come, but the more enlightened regarded it rightly as a natural, though uncommon, event and one of most unusual splendor. Among the observers were several of scientific training who noted a remarkable feature common to all the streaks of light, namely, that they all appeared to come from the same part of the sky, in the constellation Leo. This radiant point moved in company with the stars as the night wore on, and hence it was independent of the earth and its rotation. One of the eyewitnesses, Professor Olmstead of Yale University, concluded that the meteors must therefore be traveling in parallel paths, hence the apparent divergence in the sky was simply a perspective effect. Furthermore, he was able to state that the point of origin must be at least several thousand miles above the earth. Some of Olmstead's other conclusions, such as that the velocity of the meteors was about four miles per second and that they came from a nebulous body which revolved around the sun with a period of six months, failed to stand up under more accurate observations made much later, but his bold and imaginative analysis of the phenomena firmly established meteor science as an integral part of astronomy.

In the years immediately after 1833 the activity of the November Leonids fell off markedly, but scientific attention, now aroused, was drawn to other evidences of recurrent meteor showers. From medieval times notice had been taken of the appreciable, although not startling, increase in the numbers of shooting stars seen during a few days each August. These were known as the "tears of St. Lawrence," after the saint whose festival was celebrated on the 10th of August. It was shown by Quételet of Brussels and confirmed by American observers that these meteors had their radiant point in the constellation Perseus, whence their

FIG. 1-1. A drawing by Albert Tissandier, entitled "Shooting Stars Seen from a Balloon, 1870," which originally appeared in the book "Travels in the Air," edited by James Glaisher, 1871. (*Reproduction courtesy of King Penguin Books, Ltd.*)

present name, Perseids. Other annual showers came under scrutiny in this period, for example, the Quadrantids in January, the Lyrids in April, and the Delta Aquarids of late July.

The main emphasis in the early work was on meteor counts and radiant positions. Rough values for the meteor velocities could be deduced, but these were quite inadequate for orbital calculations, for which the parabolic heliocentric velocity of 42 km/sec usually had to be assumed. At the earth's distance from the sun, particles moving with less than the parabolic velocity will follow closed elliptical orbits while higher velocities will be associated with objects in open or hyperbolic orbits. The latter therefore make only one pass around the sun and then disappear into interstellar space. Accurate measurement of meteor velocities is necessary for the computation of orbits of individual meteors. Velocity information is also required to determine the orbits of those annual showers which show little or no evidence of an orbital period. The long-standing controversy about nonshower meteors, which some have asserted to come largely from interstellar space and others have considered to belong almost entirely to the solar system, can be unequivocally settled only when precise orbital information is available for a statistically sufficient sample of the meteor population.

The great Leonid shower of 1833 revived memories of a similar display which occurred in November of 1799. Three men, H. A. Newton (1865), a professor of mathematics at Yale, A. C. Twining of West Point, N.Y., and the Italian astronomer Schiaparelli (1866) in his monumental work on meteors, known simply as *Sternschnuppen* (meaning literally "snuffed-out stars"), each independently noted that the two events might be related and, if so, the next return of the Leonids would be scheduled for 1866. This prediction was most gratifyingly confirmed by a magnificent celestial show on the night of Nov. 13, 1866. The shower came back in fair strength in 1867 and 1868 and then tapered off in succeeding years. Its anticipated return as a major spectacle in 1899 was widely heralded in the popular press, and there was bitter disappointment when the shower failed to produce more than a scattering of meteors. What had happened was not difficult to explain—in fact, computations made many years earlier by Adams of Cambridge University should have warned that the Leonids were likely to be off course in 1899—but the explanation did little to restore the layman's lost faith in scientific predictions. The orbit had been calculated with fair precision (from known data on the radiant position and the period of revolution, which was taken as 33.25 years), and it was shown that the stream would make close approaches to Saturn in 1870 and to Jupiter in 1898. The resultant perturbations by these great planets shifted the main orbit well over a million miles inside the earth's orbit on the 1899 date, and may also have scattered the individual members of the stream rather widely. Since that time a few Leonids have been seen each year, and in the years 1932 to 1935 an appreciable increase in the rates was recorded, but the intensity was insignificant in comparison with the phenomenal displays of 1799, 1833, and 1866. It is highly improbable that we shall ever again witness the full fury of the Leonid storm.

About the middle of the century several eminent scientists pointed out that the orbital elements of certain comets coincided remarkably closely with those of some meteor showers. The orbit of the Leonid meteors was identified with that of Comet 1866 I (Tempel's comet). Schiaparelli brilliantly demonstrated the agreement between the paths of Comet 1862 III and the August Perseid meteors, despite the fact that neither a good velocity measurement nor a reliable indication of the periodicity was available for this shower. The Lyrids in April were shown by Professor E. Weiss of Vienna to follow the path of Comet 1861 I. Perhaps the most conclusive evidence for cometary associations was deduced from the remarkable behavior of Biela's comet, discovered in 1826. This rather faint and unspectacular object was proved to have been seen on at least two earlier occasions, in 1772 and 1805. It reappeared in 1832, but in 1846 it was observed to have split into two parts. The pair, separated considerably, were seen again in 1852 for the last time. However, in 1872, a magnificient meteor shower occurred just as the earth passed through the comet's orbit, and this observation strongly confirmed Kirkwood's suggestion that meteor showers are the debris of ancient comets. It should be noted, though, that before the comet divided, the Bielid shower had made several appearances as far back as 1741. Therefore it should not be assumed that a comet must necessarily disintegrate before a meteor shower is produced. The comets connected with the Leonids, Lyrids, and Perseids are still moving in their courses each as a relatively compact aggregation, and these comets were discovered only in the nineteenth century, long after the showers themselves were first observed. In the case of a very old shower like the Perseids, the particles have become distributed fairly uniformly around the orbit of the parent comet so that little or no trace of the comet's own periodicity is left, and each year we encounter a shower of roughly similar strength. Younger showers, for example, the Giacobinids, show strong concentrations near the point on the orbit where the comet is, or was, located.

In the latter half of the century hundreds of lesser showers were recorded. Denning (1899) lists over 4,000 radiants in his *Catalogue*. While still serving as a qualitative guide to the general distribution of meteor showers, Denning's *Catalogue* is now mainly of historical interest, because many of his radiant positions depended upon too few data and have hence been discarded as spurious, while the value of much of the remainder of his material has been made obsolete by modern techniques.

In 1848, a German physician named Mayer proposed a "meteoric hypothesis" to account for the conservation of the sun's energy—this was long before the rise of nuclear physics. He claimed that the infall of meteors into the sun would transfer enough kinetic energy to balance the sun's radiation loss, and the suggestion even received serious consideration for a time from Lord Kelvin himself. This mechanism we now know to be hopelessly inadequate, but in those days, when the riddle of the sun's energy was sorely perplexing, any theory with even a smattering of plausibility was accorded some attention. The "meteoric hypothesis" was not confined to the sun but was extended to the creation of the planets. Sir Norman Lockyer (1890) widened the field to the entire universe by proposing that "all self-luminous bodies in the celestial space are composed either of swarms of meteorites or of masses of meteoric vapour produced by heat. New stars . . . are produced by the clash of meteor-swarms"! The "meteoric hypothesis" has long since dropped into limbo, but an occasional revival of its memory may serve to remind us that modern theories can also overreach themselves if extended too far from a firm base of observation and experiment.

1-4. Modern visual and photographic observations. It has been rather sweepingly remarked that the observational science of meteors is one in which the amateur and professional are on equal footing. This has been true for the past hundred years in visual observing, since the only basic equipment needed is a star chart and pencil, together with a reasonably accurate clock. More than any other man, Charles P. Olivier (1960) has been responsible for the activities of the American Meteor Society, which was founded in 1911 as an organization dedicated to the collection of visual data on meteors and fireballs. Small groups of amateur observers all over the country report on their meteor counts and magnitudes, which are usually taken during well-known shower periods, and in some cases they furnish plots of the meteor trails done on a simplified mimeographed star chart. A similar clearing house for Canadian observations has been conducted by Peter M. Millman at Ottawa. Figure 1-2 shows a group of visual observers under Millman's supervision.

FIG. 1-2. Eight visual observers, with a recorder in the center, plot meteors during the combined visual-radio program conducted by the Dominion Observatory and the National Research Council, Ottawa. (*Courtesy of P. M. Millman.*)

Rather than use a star chart during their observations, the British observers, under the influence of Prentice, have evolved a technique whereby they write down or call off to a recorder the position of the trail in relation to the star background, and the information is plotted later. Greater accuracy is obtained in this way, but one must possess a very intimate knowledge of the names and positions of all stars down to at least the third magnitude,* which can be acquired only with years of practice. Variations in the methods have also been used; for example, wire graticules have been placed in front of the observer's field of view to provide a frame of reference.

For many years, only visual data were available for computations of radiant positions, hourly rates, and magnitude distributions. Observations with binoculars and telescopes extended the limit of detectability from the fifth magnitude, which is about the faintest that can be seen by the unaided eye, to the twelfth or thirteenth magnitude. A great deal of patience is required in telescopic work since a long time may pass without seeing any meteors because of the small field of view. Only rough estimates of velocity could be obtained in these visual methods, owing to the large timing errors involved. Öpik (1934) designed an ingenious rocking-mirror device to improve the accuracy of visual velocity measurements. The observer watched the sky as reflected in the moving mirror, and when a meteor occurred, the trail appeared to have a number of kinks or whorls in it, because of the mirror's motion, from which the velocity could be deduced.

For most purposes the modern photographic and radio techniques provide data that are far more accurate than can be obtained from any of the visual methods. This should not imply that there is no longer a place for visual work. In magnitude relations, in particular, the visual records continue to be highly important, and both the photographic and the radio magnitude scales are referred to the visual one. The eye can detect meteors three or four magnitudes fainter than those which can be photographed by typical small cameras employed in direct and spectroscopic photography. The Super-Schmidt meteor cameras have reduced this differential to about one magnitude, but there are few such instruments available. The sensitivity of radio gear used in meteor work is usually well in excess of that of the naked eye—in fact, radio equipments can be designed to compete very favorably with powerful optical telescopes in this regard—but radio gives information about the trail ionization only, and it is often desirable to have simultaneous evidence about the visible aspects of individual meteors. Even where the visual observations serve no other purpose, they are essential in photographic work to establish the instant at which a meteor occurs during a lengthy time exposure.

* See Sec. 2-2 for a definition of magnitude.

Since the 1890s a great deal of information about meteors has been garnered from photographic plates which were exposed for other reasons. For example, the Harvard photographic patrol program was originally set up to take routine time exposures of the night sky, thus providing a long-term record which could be scanned for particular purposes, such as the orbital studies of comets and asteroids and the detection of variable stars.   From as far back as 1896, meteors have appeared on the Harvard patrol plates.   So useful were the data obtained that two modifications of the regular patrol program were introduced in the thirties by Whipple (1938) which enhanced the value of the records in meteor work.   One was to place a rotating shutter in front of the lens; this chopped up the trail image into segments from which the angular velocity could be measured.   The second was to mount two cameras 38 km apart, each directed to the same sky area; this enabled the path parameters to be completely determined, using the star images as reference data.   The pioneering experiments with this technique were actually carried out many years before by Elkin of Yale.   Between 1893 and 1909 he recorded about 130 meteor trails, using a bicycle-wheel shutter in front of his cameras.   Unfortunately, Elkin's baselines were only 3.3 and 5.0 km long, which were much too short for accurate height measurements. Dr. W. J. Fisher of Harvard further improved the design of rotating-shutter cameras, though the fruits of his work were harvested by others. Several independent groups in England, Czechoslovakia, Canada, and Russia used the rotating-shutter method prior to 1939 with varying degrees of success.   None of these groups appear to have embarked on sustained or major systematic programs.   Harvard has maintained its preeminence in this area up to the present, followed by the Canadian work (Millman, 1959a) and the Russian researches (Katasev, 1957). Jodrell Bank is a comparatively recent entrant in the field (Davis, Greenhow, and Hall, 1959a).

While he was at Harvard in the thirties, Peter M. Millman initiated a comprehensive program on meteor spectrography, the first to be undertaken anywhere (Millman, 1932, 1935).   Up to that time the historical records showed a total of only eight spectra, dating back as far as 1897. Visual spectroscopy had been attempted earlier, and, in fact, the astronomer Herschel is reputed to have observed a meteor spectrum in 1864 while looking at the spectrum of Capella.   However, the direct visual method is both frustrating and unrewarding and has been discarded in favor of the photographic plate.   Glass prisms were used in front of the camera lens in the early days, but the trend is now toward replica gratings.   Millman, who is the acknowledged world authority on meteor spectra, has continued his researches up to the present time.   His list of all meteor spectra available up to the end of 1958 (Millman, 1959c) comprises 318 specimens, including a significant representation from Czecho-slovakia and the U.S.S.R.   Of this number Millman himself has obtained over one hundred spectra on programs under his direction, and the over-all Canadian contribution to this list is nearly half of the total.

Shortly after World War II, James G. Baker of Harvard undertook the design of the Super-Schmidt meteor camera specifically for meteor photography.   Six of these cameras have been produced by the Perkin-Elmer Corporation; four are employed on various Harvard programs both in Massachusetts and New Mexico, and two were obtained by the Dominion Observatory in Canada and installed at stations in northern

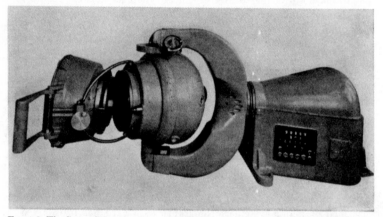

FIG. 1-3. The Super-Schmidt meteor camera in its equatorial yoke.   The drive mecha-nism is housed in the base at the right-hand side.   The camera is shown opened for a film change.   (*Dominion Observatory photograph.*)

Alberta.   Figure 1-3 shows the instrument, which stands 8 ft high when mounted on its pedestal.   The ratio of the focal length to aperture of this camera is 0.65, and the field of view is about 55°; hence very sig-nificant improvements in both sensitivity and coverage have been obtained over the more conventional types.   A Schmidt camera of some-what similar design has been built in England and is being used at the Jodrell Bank Experimental Station.

Photoelectric instruments designed for purposes such as the measure-ment of auroral activity, the light of the night sky, or the light curves of variable stars, have often recorded the passage of meteors, but only incidentally to their main functions.   In 1949, photoelectric equipment was designed and built at Ottawa specifically for the detection of meteors (McKinley and McKinley, 1951).   Although this instrument was moder-ately successful, it has not been used extensively, mainly because in its original form it was not sensitive to meteors fainter than the second magnitude. As far as we are aware, Astavin-Razumin (1958), in Russia, has developed the only other photoelectric equipment designed exclusively for meteor work, though remarks in the literature suggest that the possibilities have certainly been considered elsewhere.

1-5. Radio observations prior to 1939. In contrast to the visual, photographic, spectrographic, and photoelectric observations, which may be described as *passive* techniques because the detected energy is solely that which is radiated by the meteor, the radio methods are entirely *active;* that is, the primary energy is produced on the ground by means of a radio-frequency generator or transmitter, and a small fraction of this energy is scattered from the electrons created in the meteor trail back to a radio receiver on the ground. It should be made clear from the outset that the radio equipment does not pick up an echo from the meteoroid itself. Some energy is scattered back from the small moving particle, but it is usually too weak by several orders of magnitude to be detected. True, a very powerful radar system should be able to "see" a large meteoroid a hundred or more miles away, but the body would have to be of the order of a meter in diameter—a very rare object and one which would probably fall to earth as a meteorite. On the other hand, even a very small meteoric particle, less than the size of a pinhead, can create a long trail of ionization behind it when it strikes the atmosphere about 100 km above us. The total sum of the radio waves scattered back from all parts of this column of ionization, which may be tens of kilometers long at a given moment, will add up to a substantial echo even if very moderate transmitter powers are employed. A relatively small meteoroid thus leaves a radar target in its wake which not only is very much larger than that offered by the cross-sectional area of the particle alone but which may remain suspended in space for several seconds or even minutes after the particle has disappeared into dust and atoms. Figure 1-4 is a photographic record of the cathode-ray display of a meteor radar set and shows a range-time presentation of three meteor echoes.

Although the above introductory remarks anticipate the developments in later chapters, they have been inserted here to afford the reader an advantage over the radio pioneers and to permit him to appreciate more fully their early efforts to comprehend the effects of meteors on radio-wave propagation. Radio science was itself just beginning to be established as a valuable field of fundamental research when Appleton and Barnett (1925), in England, and Breit and Tuve (1926), in the United States, published their studies of reflections of radio waves from ionized layers in the upper atmosphere. The pulse technique of Breit and Tuve is the basis of modern radar, which, in a variety of forms, has provided us with much of our present knowledge of meteors.

Around 1929–1930, a number of investigators of ionospheric phenomena remarked on some unusual nighttime radio echoes from the E region, which is located approximately 100 km above the earth's surface. The observations suggested that the density of ionization was suddenly enhanced for a short period of time. Solar radiation had previously been shown to account for the normal increase in E-region ionization by day, but it seemed unlikely that the sun could cause these anomalous effects during the night. Appleton (1930), in England, concluded that some

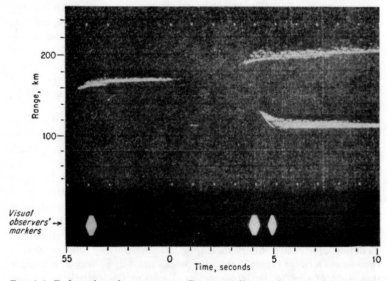

FIG. 1-4. Radar echoes from meteors. Range, or distance from the radar station, is the ordinate, and time is the abscissa. The lower right-hand echo is due to a meteor which has been detected as it approached the station; the other two echoes were detected as those meteors receded from the station. The diamond-shaped markers at the bottom were actuated by visual observers who saw the meteors in the sky.

unidentified ionizing agency must be acting on the dark side of the earth also, and Heising (1928) said that the effects seemed to be caused by great masses of electrons tossed suddenly into the atmosphere.

Perhaps the first man to go on record as attributing the phenomenon to meteors was Nagaoka (1929) of Japan, although his proposed mechanism was quite the opposite of that which we now believe to be the case. He thought that the ionization created by the meteor would be negligible in comparison with the ionization already existing in the E region, and that the effect of the meteoric particle would be to sweep away the electrons in its path, thus reducing the electron density and causing a local discontinuity in the refractive index of the ionosphere. However,

Skellett (1931, 1935), in the United States, is credited with the realization that the meteor adds rather than subtracts ionization.   He and his colleagues at the Bell Telephone Laboratories, Schafer and Goodall (1932), were able to demonstrate that meteors were directly associated with some of the anomalous ionospheric echoes.   Their work during the 1931 and 1932 returns of the Leonid shower, weak as these displays were by comparison with the famous spectacles of the nineteenth century, showed beyond any doubt that the transient echoes in the E region were correlated with the passage of bright meteors.

In the early thirties these discoveries were followed up all over the world: by Mitra, Syam, and Ghose (1934) in India; by Minohara and Ito (1933) in Japan; and by Appleton, Naismith, and Ingram (1937) during their observations on the 1932–1933 Polar Year Expedition. Eckersley (1932, 1937), in England, was able to measure the heights at which the echoes occurred and to determine their durations and daily variations in numbers, but he does not appear to have enlarged on the probable association of the echoes with meteors.   It remained for Skellett (1938) to reassert his earlier stand.   This was supported by contemporary measurements made by Appleton and Piddington (1938) on the size and density of the ionized clouds causing the echoes.   Their results implied that the clouds had relatively small linear dimensions, less than 30 m, and that they occurred between the heights of 80 and 160 km with a maximum concentration at 115 km.   It was noted by many observers that occasional radio contacts between two ground stations could be obtained over longer distances and on considerably higher radio frequencies than one would expect the normal ionosphere to be capable of supporting.   These effects were attributed to the creation of local clouds of ionization in the lower ionosphere, known as E-sporadic clouds, and Pierce (1938) of Harvard pointed out that meteoric ionization could account for some types of these clouds.

By the end of 1939, it had been established that meteors were certainly a factor to be considered in some aspects of radio propagation.   However, the majority of the observations had been carried out from the viewpoint of the radio scientist, whose primary aim was the study of ionization in the upper atmosphere and its influence on the propagation of radio waves. There were few, if any, indications that radio had yet been recognized as a powerful tool with which new knowledge about the century-old science of meteors might be wrested from nature.   In particular there does not appear to have been much active collaboration between radio men and meteor astronomers working in the well-established visual and photographic fields.   An exception to this statement might be made in the case of Harvard, where Pierce and Whipple, while following independent researches, were in a position to compare notes closely.

1-6. Radio observations since 1939. Although the outbreak of World War II naturally postponed plans for fundamental radio researches, meteors certainly made their presence felt in wartime radar operations. The equipment used in England at the beginning of the war to provide long-range warning of the approach of aircraft operated on relatively long radio wavelengths, in the range $\lambda = 7$ to 15 m. During the early days of radar, the operators of these aircraft-warning sets were occasionally misled by false targets produced by bright meteors. With experience, though, the echoes could usually be recognized as meteoric targets and discounted for military purposes. Later on, from January, 1945, to July, 1946, it was possible to use the early-warning radars in a systematic meteor-observing program (Eastwood and Mercer, 1948). British Army gun-laying radars, working on wavelengths in the neighborhood of 4 or 5 m, also detected the trails left by the celestial invaders; this was particularly noticeable during the V-2 rocket raids on London in 1944. The Army chain was kept in operation for a few months after the close of hostilities, particularly to investigate the meteor echoes in more detail. Hey and Stewart (1947) carried out a very comprehensive analysis of the Army radar data in a paper which may properly be regarded as the most significant advance up to that time in our understanding of radio echoes from meteors.

In the United States, during 1943–1944, continuous records were made by engineers of the Federal Communications Commission of the signals received from several high-power frequency-modulated transmitting stations which were operating on carrier frequencies in the neighborhood of 45 Mc/sec. Allen (1948) reports that short bursts of signal strength were observed, enduring a few tenths of a second to several seconds, which in some instances were directly correlated with visual observations of bright meteors. The daily variation of these burst rates was found to show a maximum about 0600 hours local time and a minimum around 1800 hours. The annual distribution of the burst rates given by Allen covers an entire year, and it is strikingly similar to meteor distributions obtained ten years later on surveys employing more sophisticated methods. This work might be regarded as the pioneering research in the field of forward-scatter transmissions via meteors. Short passages of speech or music were heard with clarity during the bursts, even though the distance between transmitter and receiver was as great as 1,370 miles in some of the tests. However, the forward-scatter technique lay dormant until the 1950s, when the practical possibilities of meteor communications were recognized. In the meantime, most of our information about radio meteors has come from backscatter observations, wherein the transmitter and receiver are located at or near the same site.

The first organized program of combined visual and radar observations was carried out in Japan in 1944. Huruhata (1949) and his associates at the University of Tokyo used a 25-Mc/sec radar during the Perseid, Orionid, and Geminid showers and were able to demonstrate a positive correlation between some of the echoes and simultaneously observed visual meteors. The observational data for their published relation between radar echo duration and visual meteor magnitude antedate similar measurements made in Europe and North America.

A novel aspect of the meteoric reflections was described by two Indian radio engineers, Chamanlal and Venkatareman (1941). They found that, when listening to a radio receiver tuned to an unmodulated short-wave transmitter, audible whistles could be heard which were short-lived and usually descending in pitch. This "radio Doppler effect" was correctly interpreted as a heterodyne beat between the transmitted wave and the wave reflected from a moving target. However, they assumed that the descending pitch of the beat note was due entirely to rapid retardation of the meteor whereas, as Appleton and Naismith (1947) have pointed out, the effect should properly be construed as due to the change in apparent radial velocity that is observed when the meteor is moving with a relatively constant linear velocity across the observer's line of sight. The current radio methods of measuring meteor velocities are based on this Doppler effect.

Even as the great Leonid spectacle of 1833 first generated intense scientific interest in meteors, a similar twentieth-century event spurred on the radio scientists. This event, for which the stage had been set by the great technological advances of World War II, was the Giacobinid shower on the night of Oct. 9–10, 1946. The Giacobinid meteors are associated with the Giacobini-Zinner comet (Comet 1900 III), which has a period of about 6.5 years. It was first discovered by Giacobini in 1900 and found again by Zinner in 1913. In 1933 the earth crossed the cometary orbit about eighty days after the comet, and a meteor shower was seen which, if not as spectacular as the 1833 or 1866 Leonids, was certainly the most brilliant of this century, with visual rates running as high as 5,000 hr^{-1} during the few minutes of peak activity. In 1939 the earth was 136 days ahead of the comet and no shower was seen. In 1946, though, the earth was only 15 days behind the comet, and the predicted shower lived fully up to expectations. The comet's orbit was perturbed slightly by Jupiter before the 1959 return and very few Giacobinids were seen in that year.

The 1946 event was covered in Europe and North America by groups of scientists employing conventional visual and photographic methods, augmented by independent radio programs organized by several teams using mainly wartime radars adapted for the purpose. In the United States, the Army operated 21 radars on frequencies of 100, 600, 1,200,

3,000, and 10,000 Mc/sec (Stewart, Ference, Slattery, and Zahl, 1947), and it was found that meteor echoes were seen with the 100-Mc/sec equipments only, which were modified SCR-270 radars—a type familiar to many World War II servicemen. The National Bureau of Standards also used an SCR-270 set (Bateman, McNish, and Pineo, 1946). In both experiments a very substantial maximum in the echo rates was noted between 2200 and 2300 hours local time on Oct. 9. A record obtained by Pierce (1947) with a 3.5-Mc/sec pulsed ionospheric sounder showed that the meteors were coming into the atmosphere in such great numbers that a temporary ionosphere, with a minimum height of 90 km, was formed for a few hours. This was confirmed by observers at Stanford (Manning, Helliwell, Villard, and Evans, 1946), who reported that the meteor-echo bursts from an unmodulated 29-Mc/sec transmitter were so numerous that they overlapped, producing a nearly continuous signal several times stronger than the direct ground wave between transmitter and receiver.

At the Radio Research Station near London, England, Appleton and Naismith (1947) used pulsed equipment working on 27 Mc/sec to examine in detail the activity of the 1946 Giacobinids, which reached a very sharp peak between 0300 and 0400 hours local time on Oct. 10, coincidentally with the time of maximum in North America. Hey and Stewart (1947) observed a similar peak with a 64-Mc/sec radar. It is worthy of note that Hey and Stewart detected a few Giacobinid echoes with a second radar operating on 212 Mc/sec. This was the highest radio frequency at which meteor echoes had been obtained up to that time, and indeed for several years thereafter the literature makes no mention of other successful meteor work at frequencies of 200 Mc/sec or higher. Perhaps the most significant feature of the observations made by Hey and his colleagues on the Giacobinids was their records of some of the brighter meteor echoes in which the change of range of the echo with time was clearly delineated. From 22 such moving "head-echo" records they were able to deduce a mean velocity of 22.9 km/sec for the Giacobinids (Hey, Parsons, and Stewart, 1947). These velocity measurements were the first ever made by radio methods. Hey and Stewart had a number of other "firsts" to their credit, including the original discovery of two daytime radiants active during June 6 to 13, 1945. Meteor science suffered a loss when Hey left his brilliant pioneering work on meteors to follow other avenues of radio astronomy.

Shortly after the war A. C. B. Lovell established the Jodrell Bank Experimental Station of the University of Manchester, located not far from the city of Manchester, in order to pursue radio astronomy studies. In those early days meteor research was the mainstay of the program, and the contributions of Lovell and his many coworkers in this field have been eminent. In later years they have expanded into galactic and extragalactic researches—the Jodrell Bank 250-ft telescope is world-famous, of course—but they have never abandoned their first love. The Jodrell Bank meteor team was already well organized by the time of the 1946 Giacobinid shower (see Prentice, Lovell, and Banwell, 1947). Their observations of the shower showed a peak rate of 168 echoes *per minute*, obtained with a 4.2-m radar for which the normal rate was five or six meteors per hour under nonshower conditions (Lovell, Banwell, and Clegg, 1947). Lovell (1954) has compared the activity of the 1946

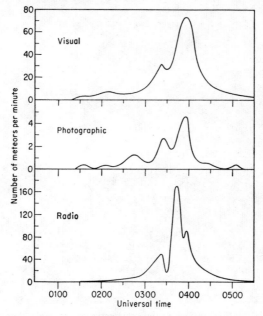

FIG. 1-5. The activity of the Giacobinid meteor shower of Oct. 9–10, 1946, as observed by three different methods. (*Lovell*, 1954.)

Giacobinid shower as observed by the visual method (Wylie, 1947), the photographic method (Jacchia, Kopal, and Millman, 1950), and the radio method using the Jodrell Bank data (see Fig. 1-5). At the maximum the visual meteors were appearing at the rate of 4,000 hr^{-1}, and the radar rate was nearly 10,000 hr^{-1}; but this great activity was sustained for only a few minutes, indicating that the individual meteor orbits had not yet spread very far from the cometary orbit.

Fedynski (1955) has reported that radio studies of meteors were first begun in the U.S.S.R. under Levin at the time of the 1946 Giacobinid shower. Not much information is readily available here on the Russian radio work (but see, for example, Fielko, 1957), though it appears evident that they are endeavoring to complement in this field the long history of valuable contributions to meteor science established by Russian astronomers using visual and photographic methods (Astapovich, 1958).

In Canada, radio observations of meteors were started at the National Research Council, Ottawa, during the summer of 1947. From the beginning a very close cooperation has been maintained with the Dominion

FIG. 1-6. Aerial view of Springhill Meteor Observatory of the National Research Council, located near Ottawa. The main building, with photographic apparatus on the roof, is right of center. The visual-observer's platform is at the upper right. Ground reflector mats for the radar antennas are visible at the bottom and upper left.

Observatory at Ottawa, which was already well known for its work in visual, photographic, and spectroscopic studies of meteors. From time to time other groups of optical and radio workers have joined forces to correlate radio with visual observations but not with the sustained purpose and effort of the combined research program at Ottawa. In 1957 the Springhill Meteor Observatory (Fig. 1-6) was established by the NRC about twenty miles south of Ottawa for scientific meteor research. Radio, visual, photographic, and spectroscopic methods are all employed (Park, 1958). Two striking examples of meteor echoes are shown in

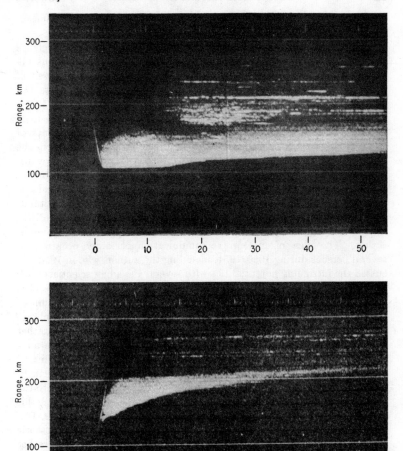

FIG. 1-7. Two unusual meteor echoes obtained with the low-power radar at Springhill Meteor Observatory. The head echo in the upper record (the thin slanting line at the beginning of the echo) indicates that the meteor was approaching the station. In the lower record the meteor was receding from the station. In both cases enduring echoes appeared after the head echoes, with delays up to several seconds.

Fig. 1-7. These were recorded by the meteor-patrol radar of the Spring-hill Meteor Observatory.

In 1952 another Ottawa team, headed by Forsyth of the Defence Research Board, began the study of forward-scatter transmissions via meteor trails. Because of the possible military implications a veil of security was drawn about some aspects of this work for several years, but this was removed in 1957 (Forsyth, Vogan, Hansen, and Hines, 1957). The idea of separating the transmitter and receiver by distances up to several hundred miles was not new, of course. The experiments of Allen (1948) have already been mentioned; the Stanford workers in the early 1950s had carried out many valuable investigations on forward-scatter (Villard, Peterson, Manning, and Eshleman, 1953; Eshleman and Manning, 1954); and from 1953 on, the National Bureau of Standards has been engaged in this particular area. Pineo of the Bureau of Standards is credited by Montgomery and Sugar (1957) with suggesting in 1951 that meteor signals might be used for intermittent high-speed communication. The idea of meteoric communication certainly occurred to several persons during 1950–1951, including the author, who in 1950 discussed the intriguing potentialities with several Canadian scientists after an examination of some of the Ottawa forward-scatter radar records obtained in 1949. Security restrictions precluded any public communication at that time, and even in 1954 a published paper showing photographic records and results of the 1949 tests had to be couched in rather guarded terms (McKinley, 1954b). No one seems to have done anything practical about implementing these proposals until Forsyth and his coworkers at Ottawa demonstrated in 1954 (still under the security cloak) a practical closed-loop communications system that utilized to the full the transient bursts of meteoric ionization. The principles of his method will be discussed in detail in later chapters. In essence, this system transmits intelligence when, and only when, a suitable meteoric reflector is available, and refrains from wasting words during the rather longer intervals when no acceptable reflectors exist. Besides this practical embodiment, the team at the Defence Research Board have made many valuable contributions to the pure science of meteors.

Australia entered the field of meteor astronomy for the first time in 1952, when a group at the University of Adelaide set up radio gear to measure the wind drifts of ionized meteor trails (Robertson, Libby, and Elford, 1953). This work has been followed by systematic radio surveys of meteor activity, conducted chiefly by Weiss (1955a, 1957b) at Adelaide. Radio research got under way in New Zealand in 1953 when Ellyett (1955), himself a graduate of the Jodrell Bank school, established a number of projects on radio observation of meteors and closely allied phenomena, at Canterbury University College, Christchurch. Before this time few sustained meteor programs of any kind had been carried out in the Southern Hemisphere, one notable exception being the lengthy series of careful visual observations conducted by McIntosh (1938) in New Zealand.

Since the middle fifties, interest in meteors has become even more widespread, particularly in radio research and applications, and many new groups have been formed. A part of this interest has been engendered by the potential military significance of meteors in connection with the detection and tracking of intercontinental ballistic missiles, but it is reassuring to note that the basic scientific results are usually made freely available. More powerful radio systems are pushing back the limits of detectability, and more precise measuring techniques are improving the observational data. Radio researches are being more closely integrated both with the older visual and photographic methods and with the newer opportunities afforded by rockets and satellites. Laboratory experiments, somewhat neglected in the past, will be essential in providing quantitative answers to some of the knotty questions posed by our observational studies of meteors. The new science of astroballistics is concerned with the motion of a solid through a gas at such speeds that melting and vaporizing of the surface of the solid takes place. Meteors and spaceships alike come under this science, which will necessarily combine many aspects of astronomy, aerodynamics, physical chemistry, and ballistics in ways that have not been attempted before (Whipple, 1959).

CHAPTER 2

Some Elements of Astronomy and Radio

2-1. Modern meteor science is polytechnical. In most branches of radio astronomy it has happened that radio scientists and engineers have taken the initiative, in the pioneering stages at least, and this has been particularly evident in radio studies of meteors. Apart from a few very notable exceptions, astronomers with an established background of visual or photographic experience in meteors have seemed hesitant to add the radio observing techniques to their repertoires, possibly because the gadgetry involved may have appeared intimidatingly complex and unfamiliar. On the other hand, it has not been uncommon that radio engineers have moved into the meteor field with confident assurance but without the essential initial grounding in classical meteor astronomy which would have enabled them to view their own work in the proper perspective—a background which, it is fair to say, most of them have eventually acquired. Several excellent review articles have been written specifically about the radio aspects of meteors by distinguished radio scientists (e.g., Kaiser, 1953; Van Bladel, 1955; Manning and Eshleman, 1959). It is natural that these particular reviews, by definition, have focused on the new radio techniques, but the uninitiated reader, who may not have had the opportunity to learn about the past history and current progress in the optical methods, could quite easily be left with the impression that the radio methods have taken over entirely—an impression which those authors would be the first to disclaim and deplore.

The progress of the past decade demonstrates that the optical methods (which as a class embrace the visual, photographic, and spectrographic techniques) and the radio methods are fully complementary to each other and that both are equally essential to future advances. Furthermore, the true meteor scientist can no longer afford to be typed as a narrow specialist: in addition to his training in both astronomy and radio he must have a working knowledge of the physics of the upper atmosphere, the chemistry of atomic and molecular reactions in rarified gases, and the ballistics of supersonic projectiles.

This book will have achieved one of the author's aims if it succeeds in impressing this viewpoint on the scientific layman and the radio engineer. It may be helpful to such readers to have a few basic elements of meteor astronomy outlined briefly. The professional astronomer could not be expected to view this elementary treatment with anything better than an amused tolerance, but, on the other hand, he may appreciate the condensed summary, in the latter sections of this chapter, of some principles of radio which the radio engineer in his turn will take for granted. Since most of this material is available in many excellent classical textbooks on radio and on astronomy, the emphasis here will be on statement and summary rather than on development and proof. It should be made clear that we are not attempting to write a general introduction to either radio or astronomy. A selection has been made of a limited number only of subjects which appear to warrant special attention. The reader will find fuller discussions of some of the astronomical points in Olivier (1925), Porter (1952), and Lovell (1954). Lovell also includes some elementary radio theory. A good background in the principles of radar may be obtained from the Radiation Laboratory Series (MIT), particularly Vol. 1 of the series, edited by Ridenour (1947).

The mks system of units is used generally but not slavishly throughout this book. There are times when it is more convenient or more conventional to express a quantity in metric units other than the basic mks ones. Familiar symbols are retained for many, though not all, physical quantities. This inevitably results in some duplication, which the context should resolve without difficulty.

2-2. Meteor magnitude. The visual observer compares the brilliance of the meteor with that of stars in its vicinity. The comparison is largely subjective and depends on many factors, such as the speed and color of the meteor, but trained observers can usually agree remarkably well on their assessments of visual meteor luminosities. The comparison stellar magnitude scale, which was established over a hundred years ago, may be expressed by the relation

$$M_1 - M_2 = 2.5(\log_{10} L_2 - \log_{10} L_1) \qquad (2-1)$$

where M_1 and M_2 are the magnitudes associated with stars, or meteors, having luminosities given by L_1 and L_2, respectively. An arbitrary zero magnitude has been selected which corresponds reasonably closely to the magnitude of the well-known star Vega in the constellation Lyra. Fainter stars have larger positive magnitudes while the brighter ones have negative magnitudes. The limit of detectability for the average human eye is around the sixth magnitude. Table 2-1 lists the magnitudes of some well-known celestial objects.

One standard candle at a distance of 1 m will appear as -14.2 magnitude on this scale, or 1 ft-c = -16.8 magnitude. From Eq. (2-1) it

Table 2-1. Some Representative Magnitudes

Object	Magnitude at maximum brilliance of object
Sun	−26.7
Full moon	−12.6
Venus	−4.4
Mars	−2.8
Jupiter	−2.5
Sirius	−1.6
Vega	+0.14
Polaris	+2.1

follows that the illumination from a zero-magnitude meteor will be 2×10^{-7} ft-c.

Öpik (1955a) has derived a useful relation between the absolute visual magnitude M_v, defined in the following paragraph, and I, the luminous power in watts radiated by the meteor,

$$M_v = 6.8 - 2.5 \log_{10} I \qquad (2-2)$$

Here, the radiated power I refers to that portion of the total radiation which can be detected by the human eye. The sensitivity curve of the eye extends roughly from 4,000 to 7,000 A (A = angstrom = 10^{-8} cm). The maximum occurs at about 5,600 A. A zero-magnitude meteor, for example, radiates visible energy at the rate of 500 watts, which, however, is but a small fraction of the kinetic power generated.

The absolute visual magnitude M_v of a meteor is defined as the magnitude it would have if it were placed in the zenith at a standard height of 100 km. It is convenient here to adopt 100 km as the unit of length; similarly, we shall have occasion to use 10^4 km^2 as the unit of area. Two corrections to the apparent visual magnitude of a meteor are necessary to convert it to absolute magnitude. The first is the usual inverse square law of attenuation of luminosity with the distance R to the meteor. The second correction is due to atmospheric absorption of the light. Since this absorption occurs almost entirely in the lower troposphere, it is independent of the meteor's height and is a function only of the meteor's zenith distance Z, which is the angle between the observer's vertical and his line of sight to the meteor. In Fig. 2-1 the distance correction is found by using R and curve A, *solid line*, and the absorption correction from sec Z and curve B, *dashed line*. The equation of curve A is simply $M = 5 \log_{10} R$, which follows from Eq. (2-1) and the inverse square law. The absorption correction has been taken from the *Handbuch der Astrophysik*. The use of the same abscissa scale for both R and sec Z is merely a convenience. In general, the abscissa values will not coincide exactly for a given meteor unless one assumes a flat earth and a meteor height $H = 100$ km, whence R (in 100-km units) = sec Z. To a first approximation, though, the ordinates of the two curves may be added to yield the total correction, if either R or Z alone is known. For example, a meteor which appears to be third magnitude when observed at a distance of 400 km would be about four magnitudes brighter if it were in the zenith; hence its absolute magnitude is -1. One word of caution: the atmospheric correction should be applied if, for example, a meteor far from the zenith is compared either directly with a star of known magnitude near the zenith or indirectly by comparison with a nearby star whose apparent brilliance is in turn referred to a known star overhead. The atmospheric correction should *not* be made if the meteor is compared only with a nearby star of known magnitude at the same zenith distance,

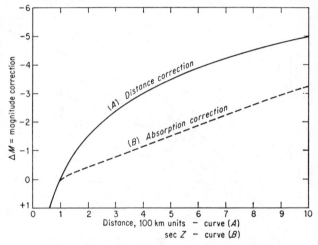

FIG. 2-1. Magnitude corrections to be added to observed magnitude to yield absolute magnitude.

as the absorption will affect both equally. In either case, of course, the distance correction should be applied. In practice, experienced observers seem to develop an absolute sense of magnitude; that is, they tend to express all meteor magnitudes in terms of known zenithal magnitudes. Hence both corrections are usually applicable.

The photographic intensity of a meteor may be compared with the intensities of star images on the same photographic plate, and a photographic meteor magnitude M_p may be derived directly, without reference to the visual magnitude M_v of the same meteor. These magnitudes are not identical, and the difference $M_p - M_v$ is defined as the *color index* of the meteor. For bright meteors photographed on blue-sensitive plates the color index is about -1.8 (Millman and Hoffleit, 1937). Recent Super-Schmidt studies (Jacchia, 1957) have suggested that the color index may be about −1 for fainter meteors, possibly because the peak sensitivity of the eye moves toward the blue for fainter light sources (Purkinje effect). Since the photographic magnitude is a more reliable and consistent measurement, it is used as the basic standard.

A radio magnitude relation can be defined in terms of ionization produced per unit length of the meteor path, without any reference to visual luminosity. However, it is more useful to correlate the visual and radio magnitude scales directly, which can be done by means of simultaneous radio and visual observations (Lindblad, 1956; Millman and McKinley,

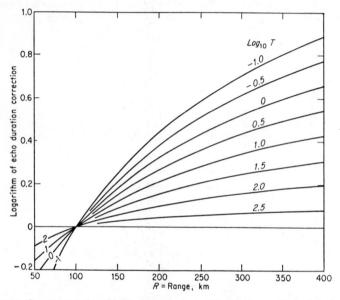

FIG. 2-2. Correction to be added to $\log_{10} T$, where T is the observed echo duration in seconds, to yield $\log_{10}$ (*absolute echo duration*).

1956). In reducing the observations, the apparent visual magnitude of each meteor is converted to an absolute magnitude (Fig. 2-1), and the observed echo duration is corrected to an absolute duration, that is, to the duration the echo would have had if the range had been reduced to 100 km. The absolute echo duration can be specified thus only as the average of a large number of observations, because the duration depends on the shape of the echo curve as well as on the peak echo amplitude, and there are wide variations in the individual curves. Any correction for atmospheric absorption is small in the radio case and may usually be neglected. The duration-correction curves of Fig. 2-2 were based on observations made with a radar of 200-kw peak power, operating on 9.2 m and using as an antenna a single horizontal dipole mounted a quarter-wave above a reflecting ground screen (McKinley, 1953a). The attenuation with range was assumed to vary as R^{-3}, and a mean antenna pattern was adopted from conventional antenna theory (see Sec. 2-9). The curves are relatively independent of the transmitter power or the radio wavelength, but they would have to be recalculated if a different type of antenna were used. The simple dipole antenna is widely employed as it offers a reasonably satisfactory approximation to the all-round coverage required in this and in many other investigations. As an example of the use of Fig. 2-2, a typical echo with an observed duration $T = 10$ sec at $R = 350$ km will have an absolute duration of antilog (1.4) = 25 sec, on the average.

The observational data yield an approximately straight line between the absolute magnitude and the logarithm of absolute echo duration. It will be shown in Sec. 8-10 that, to a first approximation, there is a theoretically linear relation between echo duration and the ionization q produced per meter of the meteor path for meteors brighter than magnitude 5 and fainter than magnitude -2. In Sec. 8-13 the following approximate radio magnitude relation is deduced, which is reasonably valid for meteors in this magnitude range moving at 40 km/sec,

$$M_r = 40 - 2.5 \log_{10} q \tag{2-3}$$

For faster or slower meteors a small magnitude correction may be necessary (cf. Sec. 8-13). Equation (2-3) should apply fairly well over the range $-2 \leq M_r \leq 5$. For $M_r < -2$, the observational evidence indicates that the linear relation between duration and ionization may not hold.

From Eq. (2-1) it will be noted that a 100:1 ratio in luminosity corresponds to a differential of exactly 5 magnitudes. On the decibel scale the radio engineer would express this same luminosity (or power) ratio as $10 \log_{10} 100 = 20$ db; hence one magnitude might be said to be equivalent to 4 db. This correlation of the astronomical and the electrical power scales is of academic interest only. Confusion could easily arise if it were applied literally because, for example, a 4-db increase in echo-signal strength by no means implies an increase in brightness of precisely 1 magnitude.

2-3. Right ascension and declination. The earth's axis may be extended to intersect an imaginary sphere of infinite radius—the celestial sphere—in two points known as the north and south celestial poles (see Fig. 2-3). The plane of the earth's equator will cut the celestial sphere along the celestial equator. The distant stars have fixed coordinates on the celestial sphere. The *declination* (Dec.) of a point on the celestial sphere is measured along the great circle (hour circle) through the point and the poles, in degrees away from the equator, the sign being plus if the point is north of the equator and minus if it is south.   The *right ascension* (R.A.) of the point is measured in either hours or degrees (1 hr = 15°) eastward along the celestial equator, from a reference point termed the *vernal equinox* to the hour circle passing through the point in question.

The *ecliptic* is defined as the sun's apparent annual path on the celestial sphere.   The *vernal equinox*, ♈, is the sun's position on Mar. 21, when it crosses the celestial equator going north (see Fig. 2-3); or, to be more

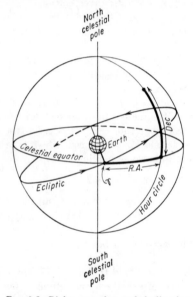

FIG. 2-3. Right ascension and declination.

exact, it is the point of intersection of the celestial equator and the ecliptic.   Alternatively, one can shift from a geocentric viewpoint to a heliocentric one.   On Mar. 21 the radius vector of the earth's orbit, when extended, meets the celestial sphere at the autumnal equinox, a point diametrically opposite to the vernal equinox.

The longitude of the sun, $\lambda\odot$, is measured in degrees eastward along the ecliptic from the vernal equinox ($\lambda\odot = 0°$) to the sun's position.   It will be apparent that the plane of the ecliptic is identical with the plane of the earth's orbit.

The right ascension and declination coordinate system described above is the most widely used because it is independent of the observer's position on the earth.   Two other systems are occasionally employed: (1) *hour angle and declination*—this differs from right ascension and declination in one respect; the hour angle of the point is found by subtracting its right ascension (in hours) from the sidereal or star time; (2) *azimuth and altitude* —azimuth is measured in the observer's horizontal plane in the clockwise direction as viewed from above, either the north or the south points being taken as the zero reference, and altitude is measured perpendicularly from the horizon to the zenith.

Universal Time (UT) is mean solar time of the meridian of Greenwich, otherwise known as Greenwich Civil or Greenwich Standard Time (GCT), and is reckoned on a 24-hr basis commencing at midnight. Local standard time is often used in observing programs; for example, Eastern Standard Time (EST) is 75th-meridian time and is five hours later than UT.

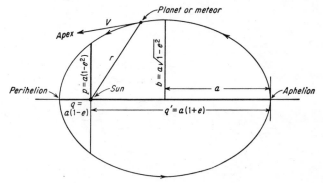

Fig. 2-4. The geometry of the ellipse.

2-4. Orbital elements and meteor velocities. Kepler's first law states that a body moving under the influence of the sun's attraction will trace out a plane curve known as a conic section, with the sun at one focus. The curve will be an ellipse, parabola, or hyperbola, depending on whether the velocity V at a given distance from the sun is less than, equal to, or in excess of, a certain critical value known as the parabolic velocity for that distance. Figure 2-4 shows some of the geometrical elements of an ellipse; a is the semimajor axis, b the semiminor axis, and p the semilatus rectum. The perihelion distance is $q = a(1 - e)$, and the aphelion distance is $q' = a(1 + e)$, where e is the eccentricity. For a circle, $e = 0$ and the two foci coincide. As e approaches unity the ellipse becomes more and more elongated, since $b = a(1 - e^2)^{1/2}$. We have a parabola when $e = 1$: the aphelion point recedes to infinity, and $q = p/2$. For hyperbolic orbits, $e > 1$ and a becomes negative.

The earth's orbit is very nearly circular ($e = 0.016727$), with a mean orbital or heliocentric velocity of 29.77 km/sec. The astronomical unit (au) is defined as the mean distance of the earth from the sun, approximately 149,500,000 km. The semimajor axes of orbits of other bodies moving about the sun are usually expressed in terms of astronomical units since the ratios of the axes can usually be measured much more accurately than the astronomical unit itself can be determined.

Our chief interest will naturally be in meteors whose orbits intersect the earth's orbit, since we cannot observe them otherwise. In Fig. 2-5 the plane of the meteor orbit is tilted at an *inclination i* to the plane of the ecliptic. If $i < 90°$, the motion of the meteor is said to be *direct*, that is, in the same direction as the planets; and if $i > 90°$, the motion is termed *retrograde*. The *descending node*, ☋, is the point on the ecliptic plane where the meteor passes from north to south; in this diagram it happens

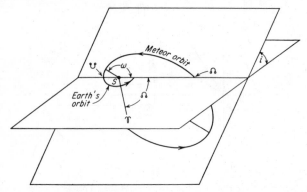

Fig. 2-5. The elements of a meteor orbit.

to be the point of intersection with the earth's orbit. The *ascending node*, ☊, is the point at which the meteor passes from south to north of the ecliptic; it could equally well be the point of intersection of the meteor orbit. The symbol for the ascending node, ☊, also represents the longitude of this node, that is, the angle from the vernal equinox to the ascending node measured along the ecliptic in the counterclockwise direction as viewed from the north. The angle ω is known as the *argument of perihelion* and is the angle from the ascending node to the perihelion, measured in the orbital plane and in the direction of motion of the body. If $\omega = 90°$, the meteor orbit will cut the earth's orbit at both nodes, regardless of the value of i. On the other hand, if i is small and the meteor stream quite broad, some meteors may intersect the earth's orbit both while approaching and while receding from the sun, independently of ω. Some writers use the symbol π for the *longitude of perihelion*, defined by $\pi = ☊ + \omega$.

The five quantities a, e, i, Ω, and ω will define the meteor orbit completely, but we must have a time specified as well if we are to locate the meteor in its orbit at any instant: the time usually given is that of perihelion passage. A useful, though not independent, parameter is P, the period of revolution of the meteor. Another of Kepler's laws states that P^2 (in years) $= a^3$ (in au). The direction of the velocity vector at any given instant is known as the *apex* (see Fig. 2-4). In particular, the *apex of the earth's way* is the point on the celestial sphere toward which the earth is moving at any moment.

Newton's law of gravitation states that the attractive force between two bodies is proportional to the product of their masses divided by the square of the distance between them. In the case of a meteor, comet, or asteroid, where the mass of the smaller body is entirely negligible in comparison with the larger or central body, the following equation may be derived from energy considerations:

$$V^2 = \mathbf{GM} \left(\frac{2}{r} - \frac{1}{a} \right) \tag{2-4}$$

where V is the orbital velocity of the smaller body when the two bodies are a distance r apart, $\mathbf{M}$ is the mass of the larger body, and the gravitational constant is $\mathbf{G} = 6.67 \times 10^{-11}$ (newton) $(m^2)/kg^2$. If the distances are expressed in astronomical units and the velocity in km/sec, and if, for the solar system, we put $\mathbf{M} = 1.987 \times 10^{30}$ kg, Eq. (2-4) reduces to

$$V^2 = 886 \left(\frac{2}{r} - \frac{1}{a} \right) \tag{2-5}$$

For a circular orbit, $a = r$ and $V^2 \sim 1/r$, while for a parabola a is infinite and $V^2 \sim 2/r$. Thus, at the same distance from the central body, the parabolic velocity is $\sqrt{2}$ times the circular velocity.

The earth's orbit about the sun is nearly but not quite circular. Assuming an eccentricity of $e = 0.016727$, one can calculate from Eq. (2-5) that the annual variation in the earth's orbital velocity is ± 0.5 km/sec. Depending on the time of year, the parabolic heliocentric velocity at the earth's distance from the sun will therefore vary from about 41.4 km/sec to 42.8 km/sec.

The geocentric velocity V_G of the meteor at the earth's distance from the sun will be the vector sum of the meteor's heliocentric velocity V_H and the earth's orbital velocity V_E. There are three corrections to be applied to V_G in order to arrive at V_o, the velocity observed in the earth's atmosphere, and these corrections will be considered in turn.

First, the gravitational attraction of the earth will increase the velocity of the approaching particle. Suppose the particle to have started from infinity with zero velocity relative to the earth. On reaching the earth's surface, and in the absence of any other influence, it will attain the parabolic geocentric velocity given by $v^2 = 2GM_E/r_E = 125$ km^2/sec^2, where $\mathbf{M}_E = 5.98 \times 10^{24}$ kg and $r_E = 6.37 \times 10^6$ m. This velocity, $v = 11.2$ km/sec, is the minimum velocity for an object reaching the earth's surface from a great distance. It is identical to the "escape velocity," that is, the least velocity that a body must reach in order to break free from the earth's gravitational field. In general the meteor will already have an appreciable velocity relative to the earth, so that its orbit in the immediate vicinity of the earth will be a hyperbola about the earth's center. From Eq. (2-4), now applied to the earth-meteor system, we obtain the apparent velocity V_a, in the absence of any atmospheric deceleration,

$$V_a^2 = \frac{2GM_E}{r_E} + \frac{GM_E}{a_E} = v^2 + V_G^2$$

or
$$V_a^2 = 125 + V_G^2 \qquad (2\text{-}6)$$

The effect of this correction is greatest as V_G approaches zero, for example, in the case of a meteor just catching up with the earth. Furthermore, the apparent radiant will appear to be somewhat closer to the observer's zenith than will the true radiant. It may be shown that the inclination of the path to the observer's vertical will be reduced by an amount ΔZ (Olivier, 1925), where

$$\tan \frac{\Delta Z}{2} = \frac{V_a - V_G}{V_a + V_G} \tan \frac{Z}{2} \qquad (2\text{-}7)$$

For larger values of V_G this correction to the radiant position amounts to only a degree or two, but for small values of V_G it can be quite appreciable. The name *zenith attraction* is applied both to the velocity correction [Eq. (2-6)] and to the direction correction [Eq. (2-7)].

The second correction is due to the rotation of the earth on its axis and is known as the *diurnal aberration* correction. The linear velocity at the earth's equator is 0.464 km/sec, and at latitude L the velocity will be 0.464 cos L km/sec. This velocity is to be added vectorially to the meteor velocity. The increase in apparent velocity will be greatest for meteors with radiants low in the east. The correction is small—at latitude 45° it cannot exceed ± 0.32 km/sec, for example—and it may often be neglected. A small angular correction to the radiant position may also be computed from the same vector relationship.

The third correction is due to *deceleration* of the meteor in the upper atmosphere, and, unlike the previous two corrections, it depends on some physical measurements and assumptions that are not as accurate or as well based as one could desire. Whipple uses the symbol V_∞ for the velocity that the observer would measure if there were no atmosphere present to slow up the meteor. When V_a is corrected for diurnal aberration, we obtain V_∞. The quantity $V_\infty - V_o$ is a measure of the effect of deceleration; it may range from 0.5 km/sec for the faster meteors to 1.0 km/sec for the slower ones, these values being representative means.

In practice, of course, we start with the observed velocity V_o, the apparent radiant position, and the observed deceleration, and then we apply the various corrections in the reverse order to arrive at V_H and the true radiant position, from which data the meteor orbit may be computed. It may take several hours to determine an individual orbit by hand, using log tables and a desk calculator; hence the current practice is to program the data for a high-speed electronic computer whenever possible.

2-5. Elementary radio principles. In the broad sense, the word radio covers the generation, detection, and utilization of electromagnetic radiation over a spectrum of many octaves, ranging in frequency from a few cycles per second to about 100 kMc/sec (10^{11} cps), close to the infrared. Radar, coined from the phrase "*radio detection and ranging,*" is a special form of radio technique which can provide us with information about remote objects which may themselves be passive or noncooperative. The object is illuminated with radio-frequency energy, usually (but not necessarily) supplied by a man-made radio transmitter. A small fraction of the energy which falls on the distant target is reflected or scattered. A sensitive radio receiver and cathode-ray-tube display can be used to detect and analyze the scattered radiation in order to deduce certain characteristics of the target, such as its size, position, motion, and possibly its shape and composition. If the receiver is located in the immediate vicinity of the transmitter, the system is described as a *back-scatter*, or *monostatic*, radar, whereas if the receiver is separated from the transmitter by a distance comparable to or greater than the distance of the target from either station, the system is known as a *forward-scatter*, or *bistatic*, radar.

In the simplest radar the transmitter emits an unmodulated continuous wave (cw), often called the carrier wave. This wave may be defined analytically by the amplitude relation

$$A = A_0 \sin (2\pi f t + \phi) \tag{2-8}$$

Since the amplitude A_0, the frequency f, and the phase ϕ are all fixed, each wave looks exactly like all the others, and at first glance it would appear that little information could be garnered by a cw system. Certainly the range of the target cannot, in general, be measured, because of the lack of identifying or timing marks on the emitted waves. Nevertheless, the pure cw system has been used very effectively in meteor work because the target itself can "modulate" the scattered wave. The magnitude of the echo signal will naturally vary both with the range and with the effective scattering cross section of the target at any moment. Even more important, the phase of the returning wave relative to the outgoing wave will change with range, and if the target is moving, there will be a difference in frequency between the two waves which will provide a sensitive and accurate means of measuring the target velocity—the so-called "radio Doppler technique."

2-6. Amplitude modulation. The transmitted wave may be modulated in one or more of several ways in order to obtain more information. In *amplitude modulation* the amplitude factor is varied with time at a lower frequency than that of the carrier wave.

$$A = A_0 g(t) \sin (2\pi f t + \phi) \qquad (2\text{-}9)$$

For the wave emitted by an ordinary broadcasting station, the modulating function has the form $g(t) = 1 + \sum_i m_i \sin 2\pi p_i t$, where $m_i \sin 2\pi p_i t$ represents one Fourier component of the speech or music waveform. In broadcast practice the instantaneous total amplitude of the components is kept well below unity to avoid overmodulation and consequent distortion of the speech waveform.

In radar systems the modulating function is usually a rectangular wave of duration d sec (also commonly expressed in microseconds), which turns on the carrier suddenly to its maximum amplitude and retains this level for a short interval (this interval must contain at least a few cycles of the carrier frequency, and in practice it will probably encompass many cycles). The amplitude then drops rapidly to zero where it remains for a much longer interval. The time D between the start of one pulse and the start of the next is known as the pulse-recurrence period. The time of flight of these short-duration pulse packets to the target and back is a direct measure of the target range. A Fourier analysis of the rectangular modulating function shows that it may be expressed analytically as

$$g(t) = \frac{d}{D} + \sum_n \underbrace{\frac{2}{n\pi} \sin \left(\frac{n\pi d}{D} \right)}_{\text{amplitude}} \underbrace{\cos \left(2\pi \frac{n}{D} t \right)}_{\text{frequency}} \qquad (2\text{-}10)$$

The values of the amplitude coefficients of the first few terms in this summation are indicated in Fig. 2-6 for the particular case $d/D = \frac{1}{4}$. The frequency of the nth component is n/D cps, and the amplitude of this nth component will be equal to zero when $n = D/d$ (the amplitude will then be a minimum but not zero if D/d is not an exact integer).

When the rectangular function is applied to a carrier wave of frequency f, a series of sidebands will be produced with frequencies $f \pm n/D$, and the envelope of the sideband amplitudes will be the same curve as in Fig. 2-6, symmetrically disposed on either side of f. Theoretically, an infinite receiver bandwidth is needed to pass all these frequency components in order that the original pulse may be reproduced without distortion. However, the energy tapers off rapidly in the higher order components, so that a finite bandwidth can be selected which will not distort the pulse excessively. The choice of bandwidth depends on the system requirements. One may require either great accuracy in the measurement of range or maximum sensitivity for the detection of weak echoes. In the latter case the echo is competing with thermal noise,

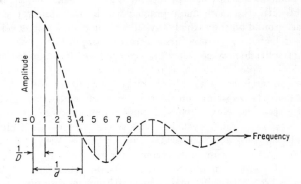

FIG. 2-6. The spectrum of the rectangular-wave modulating function

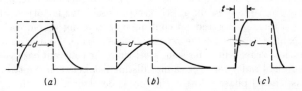

FIG. 2-7. Rectangular pulses before (dashed line) and after (solid line) passing through filters of various bandwidths. (a) $\Delta f = 1/d$; (b) $\Delta f < 1/d$; (c) $\Delta f > 1/d$.

natural terrestrial static, and noise from extraterrestrial sources which we shall consider in more detail in Sec. 2-8.

If the receiver bandwidth is made equal to the reciprocal of the pulse width, a rectangular pulse at the receiver input will emerge as a sloping pulse at the output, which approaches but does not quite reach its peak amplitude before decaying again (see Fig. 2-7a). If the bandwidth is narrower than $1/d$, the pulse falls well short of attaining its maximum amplitude (Fig. 2-7b), whereas a broader band allows the pulse to rise more quickly and to level off (Fig. 2-7c). The rise time of the detected pulse, not the pulse width, is important in precision range measurements because, from Fig. 2-7, it is apparent that the maximum timing error can be as great as this rise time, depending on whether the echo was very strong or was barely visible above the noise level.

In backscatter radar a timing error of t μsec is equivalent to a range error of $0.15t$ km. Where the emphasis is on accurate ranging the bandwidth should be greater than the reciprocal of the rise time of the transmitted pulse. The weakest echoes will be lost under these circumstances because of the increased noise power admitted by the broader receiver band. Some of this loss may be recovered in practice, since the broader the bandwidth, the more finely grained will be the appearance of the noise background on the cathode-ray-tube display, and a weak echo may often be detected by virtue of its contrasting size or shape even though its peak amplitude may be below the average level of the noise impulses. It should be noted that range resolution—the ability to distinguish between two targets close together in range—depends on the width of the transmitted pulse as well as on the rise and decay times.

Strictly speaking, this analysis of pulse-amplitude modulation applies to a *coherent-pulse* radar system. Such a system may be achieved in practice by allowing a master oscillator to run continuously at a constant frequency f. A power amplifier is coupled to the oscillator and keyed by the rectangular-wave modulator, with the result that the relative r-f phase [ϕ in Eq. (2-9)] will remain constant from pulse to pulse. In the ordinary or *incoherent-pulse* radar the modulation is applied to the oscillator, which feeds the antenna directly. The r-f phase will tend to vary randomly from pulse to pulse because the oscillator is turned off completely between pulses and no continuously running stable oscillations are available to maintain the reference phase. The Fourier analysis of the incoherent case will differ somewhat from the coherent case, although a conventional radar receiver cannot distinguish between the two. This is because the r-f phase is lost in the simple detector used in the ordinary receiver and the video output reproduces only the modulating function. In a coherent-pulse system the reference phase can be introduced appropriately into the detector in order to yield both the r-f phase and the amplitude of the returning echo signal. The coherent-pulse radar thus combines some features of the ordinary-pulse radar, which gives range information only, and of the cw system, which provides the instantaneous r-f phase of the echo.

2-7. Frequency and phase modulation. Instead of varying the amplitude parameter in Eq. (2-8) one may vary the frequency f or the phase angle ϕ. For frequency modulation (FM) by a sinusoidal wave of frequency p we may write

$$A = A_0 \sin \left(2\pi f + \frac{mf}{p} \sin (2\pi pt) + \phi \right) \qquad (2\text{-}11)$$

This yields a series of sidebands at frequencies $f \pm np$. The amplitude of the nth sideband is given by the Bessel function $J_n(mf/p)$. Phase modulation (PM) may be represented by the expression

$$A = A_0 \sin (2\pi f + m \sin 2\pi pt) \qquad (2\text{-}12)$$

which may also be expanded as a series of sidebands with Bessel amplitude coefficients, as in the FM case. The main difference in the two types of modulation is that the coefficient of the low-frequency modulation is inversely proportional to the modulating frequency in Eq. (2-11) and independent of it in Eq. (2-12).

Range information may be readily obtained from an FM radar if the modulating function is a triangular wave. There will be a constant difference in frequency between the outgoing wave and the wave returning from the target, and this frequency differential will vary directly with the distance to the target. A rectangular modulating function may also be used in either FM or PM. In theory at least, any one of the three methods, AM, FM, or PM, should be equal to any other for the transmission of intelligence. However, the state of the engineering art at a given period may favor one of the methods over the others for specific purposes. It has happened that most of the radio research on meteors has been carried out with ordinary incoherent-pulse radar, with pure cw next in popularity, followed by coherent-pulse methods. FM and PM appear to have been used rather rarely.

2-8. Cosmic and receiver noise. The faint echo returning from the meteoric target must compete with thermal noise generated in the receiver itself and with radio noise from the sun and the galactic system. In addition, every observer can testify to the occasions when the desired signals were drowned out by static from nearby terrestrial thunderstorms or by man-made electrical interference. The latter types of noise will not be considered further in this section, since it will be assumed that such emanations are temporary in character if they are neither controllable nor avoidable.

A resistor at a temperature T will deliver to an ideal noiseless receiver a thermal noise power $P = KT \Delta f$ watts, if the impedances are correctly matched. Here K = Boltzmann's constant = 1.38×10^{-23} joule/°C, and Δf is the over-all receiver bandwidth measured between the half-power points on the receiver response curve. By convention the room-temperature value is taken to be $T_0 = 290°$A (on the absolute or Kelvin scale), which makes $KT_0 = 4 \times 10^{-21}$ joule. No receiver is perfect, and the receiver-noise power P_r, which is generated chiefly at the input stage, may be expressed in terms of an equivalent temperature T_r or alternatively in terms of a receiver-noise figure F, as follows:

$$P_r = KT_r \Delta f = KT_0(F - 1) \Delta f \qquad \text{watts} \qquad (2\text{-}13)$$

For years the noise figure F has been employed to specify the performance of a receiver. The closer F approaches unity, or 0 db, the better the receiver. Recent developments in Masers and parametric amplifiers have produced receivers with noise figures so close to unity that the noise temperature is coming into use as a more significant indication of receiver performance. A noise figure of $F = 3$, or 4.8 db, is equivalent

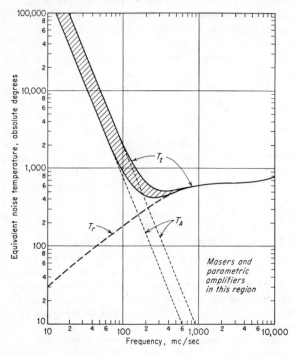

FIG. 2-8. Total noise temperature T_t of conventional receivers, as a function of radio frequency. T_A = cosmic noise temperature. The hatched area indicates the daily variation (*after Herbstreit, 1948*). T_r = noise temperature of well-designed conventional receivers (*after McCoy, 1958*).

to $T_r = 580°A$, which is representative of the best conventional receiver design at about 1000 Mc/sec. At 10 Mc/sec, T_r may be as low as 30°A ($F = 1.10$ or 0.4 db) with good engineering design (McCoy, 1958) (see the dashed curve of Fig. 2-8). The Masers and parametric amplifiers may approach noise temperatures of only a few degrees at 1,000 Mc/sec and above: their area of application is indicated in the lower right-hand corner of Fig. 2-8.

The noise power P_A picked up by the antenna from extraterrestrial sources may be written similarly as $P_A = KT_A \, \Delta f$ watts, where T_A is the equivalent noise temperature of a resistor replacing the antenna. At radio frequencies the cosmic radiation is not thermal in character; in fact, the noise power appears to vary as $f^{-2.3}$ over much of the frequency range. Equivalent noise temperatures may exceed a million degrees, but this should not be confused with the actual thermal temperature of the source, which may be much lower. The total noise power is

$$P_t = T_t K \, \Delta f = (T_A + T_r) K \, \Delta f \qquad \text{watts} \qquad (2\text{-}14)$$

Surveys of cosmic-noise temperatures in the h-f and vhf bands have been made, using a $\lambda/2$ dipole elevated a quarter-wave above ground (Herbstreit, 1948; Cottony and Johler, 1952). This is a popular arrangement in meteor work, except that a good reflector is usually placed on the ground under the antenna, which has the effect not only of increasing the upward antenna gain but also of shielding the antenna from thermal radiation from the earth. The dashed lines on Fig. 2-8 are based on Herbstreit's measurements, the hatched area indicating the diurnal variation in noise due to the uneven distribution of the main noise sources over the celestial sphere. The solid line of Fig. 2-8, obtained by adding the cosmic-noise temperature to the receiver temperature, shows the best performance one can expect with present conventional receivers, in the environment of extraterrestrial noise. Below 250 Mc/sec, and particularly in the band 20 to 100 Mc/sec where much meteor research has been done, it is clear that the cosmic noise predominates, and little if anything is to be gained by further receiver improvement. Above 250 Mc/sec, the low noise temperatures of Masers and parametric amplifiers can be utilized to advantage.

It follows from Eq. (2-14) that the over-all noise power is directly proportional to the bandwidth—this will be true also of contributions from thunderstorm static and some forms of broad-band man-made noise. On the other hand, in a pulsed radar system, the signal power of the sidebands falls off rapidly on either side of the carrier frequency, the envelope following a curve of the form $y = [(\sin x)/x]^2$ (cf. Fig. 2-6). If the receiver bandwidth is very wide, it is obvious that the noise power will override weak signals; on the other hand, the signal amplitude will be reduced if the bandwidth is very narrow (see Fig. 2-7b). It may be shown that the optimum signal-to-noise ratio is reached when $\Delta f \simeq 1/d$. This criterion is fairly broad, and as was indicated in Sec. 2-7, there are some practical advantages in using bandwidths that are wider than $1/d$.

2-9. Antenna gain. An isotropic antenna is one which radiates power uniformly in all directions, as in Fig. 2-9. The truly isotropic radiator does not exist, but it nevertheless provides the reference with which actual antennas may be compared. Any practical antenna is directive to some extent, and one often seeks to obtain a substantial gain in power in a given direction with an accompanying decrease in power radiated in other directions. The power density measured at a distance R from the isotropic radiator will be $P/4\pi R^2$ watts/m², if P is the power available

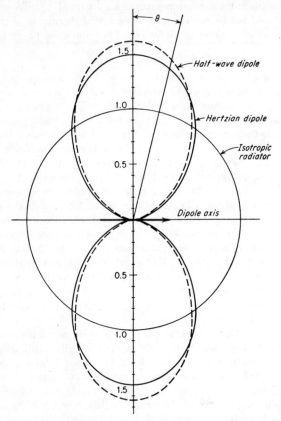

FIG. 2-9. Power radiation patterns of the isotropic radiator, the Hertzian dipole, and the practical half-wave dipole.

at the source. Any other antenna will have a power gain G_0 such that the power density in the direction of maximum radiation is $G_0 P/4\pi R^2$. In polar coordinates we may represent the power gain in any direction by $G = G_0(\theta,\phi)$, and since the total power radiated by either the isotropic or the actual antenna is to be the same, it follows that

$$\int_{-\pi/2}^{\pi/2} \int_0^{2\pi} G_0(\theta,\phi) \cos \theta \, d\theta \, d\phi = 4\pi \qquad (2\text{-}15)$$

The radiation pattern of the infinitesimally short Hertzian dipole is given by $G = G_0 \cos^2 \theta$; hence, from Eq. (2-15), we obtain $G_0 = 1.5$ for the maximum power gain of the Hertzian doublet over the isotropic radiator (see Fig. 2-9).   A practical dipole will usually be a half-wave in length, and for this case the gain function is

$$G = G_0 \frac{\cos^2 [(\pi/2) \sin \theta]}{\cos^2 \theta}$$

When this expression is inserted in Eq. (2-15), the gain of the half-wave dipole over the isotropic radiator is found to be $G_0 = 1.64$ (see Fig. 2-9).

Suppose the dipole is placed parallel to an infinite plane reflector at a distance d.   The dipole power pattern will now be modified by a factor $\sin^2 [(2\pi d/\lambda) \cos \theta]$.   A particular case often encountered in meteor work

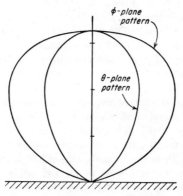

ϕ-plane pattern

θ-plane pattern

FIG. 2-10. Power patterns in the θ and ϕ planes of the horizontal half-wave dipole at a height of $\lambda/4$ above an infinite plane reflector.

is the horizontal half-wave dipole, raised a quarter-wave above a plane reflector.   The reflector increases the gain in the zenith direction by a factor of 3.4, whence $G_0 = 1.64 \times 3.4 = 5.6$ relative to the isotropic radiator (see Fig. 2-10).   In the θ plane the gain is

$$G_\theta = G_0 \sin^2 \left(\frac{\pi}{2} \cos \theta\right) \frac{\cos^2 [(\pi/2) \sin \theta]}{\cos^2 \theta}$$

and in the ϕ plane the gain is

$$G_\phi = G_0 \sin^2 \left(\frac{\pi}{2} \cos \phi\right)$$

From the zenith down to about 45° the power gains in the two planes differ by less than 3 db, and the antenna may be considered to be practically omnidirectional for many purposes.   However, at low elevations (large θ or ϕ) the differences can be quite significant. A pair of crossed dipoles, fed 90° apart in phase, will yield a much more uniform pattern at low elevations. Furthermore, if the crossed dipoles are raised somewhat more than $\lambda/4$ above the ground plane, the gain will be reduced in the zenith and increased at lower angles. A broad pattern of reasonably constant gain for all zenith angles between 0 and 60° can be obtained with a spacing of 0.4λ. This is of advantage in some meteor researches.

High-gain antennas can be built by using a number of half-wave dipoles. In the "billboard" array the dipoles are arranged in rows and columns with half-wave spacing, and all are excited in phase. A plane reflector is located a quarter-wave behind the dipoles. The Yagi antenna has only one directly driven dipole and uses several parasitically excited directors and reflectors to concentrate the radiation in one direction. Several Yagis may be combined for greater gains. If very large gains are required, some form of parabolical reflector is often employed with a single dipole at the focus. The paraboloid has the advantage, too, that only the dipole need be changed to accommodate a wide range of wavelengths. The gain of these antennas increases, and the beamwidth decreases, as the effective area of the antenna is increased. In terms of wavelength, $G_0 = 4\pi A/\lambda^2$ where the effective area A may be equal to or somewhat less than the actual area, depending on the power distribution over the area. A convenient rule-of-thumb formula for gain in terms of beamwidth is $G = 40,000/(ab)$, where a and b are the beamwidths in degrees of the antenna pattern measured to the half-power points in orthogonal planes through the main axis of the beam. For example, a beam 20 by 40° has a gain $G = 50$, or approximately 17 db over isotropic.

The antenna pattern will be the same whether the antenna is matched to a transmitter and radiating power or to a receiver and intercepting power. In the latter case the effective cross-sectional area is $A = G\lambda^2/4\pi$. The same antenna may be time-shared between the transmitter and receiver by means of a transmit-receive switch. This is often done in pulse radars employing fixed or steerable arrays.

2-10. Equivalent echoing area. When the wavelength is small in comparison with the target dimensions, we may use elementary geometrical optics to deduce, in a rather heuristic fashion, the equivalent echoing areas of some simple targets. Let the target be at a distance R from a source radiating 1 watt. The power flux per square meter at the target is $1/4\pi R^2$. By definition the echo power flux per square meter received back at the source is $(1/4\pi R^2)(\sigma/4\pi R^2)$. Here σ is the equivalent echoing area, defined as the area of a hypothetical body which, when it scatters the incident wave *isotropically*, will return the same echo flux as the real target—the scatter from the real target is nonisotropic, in general.

If the target is an infinite plane reflector, the received flux is $1/4\pi(2R)^2$, since the effect of the plane mirror reflector is merely to double the one-way distance.   Thus

$$\frac{\sigma}{16\pi^2 R^4} = \frac{1}{16\pi R^2} \qquad \text{or} \qquad \sigma_{\text{plane}} = \pi R^2 \qquad (2\text{-}16)$$

is the equivalent echoing area of a plane.   Note that the actual area on the plane, which is utilized in illuminating an area 1 m square back at the source, is just $\frac{1}{2}$ m $\times$ $\frac{1}{2}$ m $= \frac{1}{4}$ m².

For a cylinder of radius r the utilized target area has a linear dimension along the axis of $\frac{1}{2}$ m, the same as for the plane.   In the transverse direction the linear dimension is approximately $r\theta$, where $\theta \simeq 1/2R$ is one-half of the angle subtended at the center of the cylinder by a perpendicular length of 1 m back at the receiving area.   The effective area is $r/4R$, which is r/R of the effective area in the case of the plane.   The equivalent echoing area of the cylinder is therefore $(r/R)\sigma_{\text{plane}}$, or

$$\sigma_{\text{cylinder}} = \pi R r \qquad (2\text{-}17)$$

A sphere of radius r has an effective area of $(r\theta)^2 = r^2/4R^2$, which is r^2/R^2 of the plane area.   Thus, the equivalent echoing area of a sphere is

$$\sigma_{\text{sphere}} = \pi r^2 \qquad (2\text{-}18)$$

For an irregularly shaped body with two principal radii of curvature, r_1 and r_2, at the point where the line of sight is normal to the surface, we have $\sigma_{\text{irreg}} = \pi r_1 r_2$.   This case is intermediate between Eqs. (2-17) and (2-18).

CHAPTER 3

Visual and Photographic Techniques

The purpose of this chapter is twofold. First, it is intended to point out to the radio worker some ways in which the nonradio techniques can be of considerable assistance to his major program of radio observations, without demanding of him a highly specialized background or imposing on him an undue burden of expense. Second, whether or not he ever employs these tools himself, the radio scientist should have at least a nodding acquaintance with a representative sample of these methods, if for no other reason than to provide some background for an understanding of the visual and photographic results. These optical data form the solid core of observational evidence underlying modern meteor theory, and they will be discussed in some detail in later chapters. Without this explanation, the visual and photographic experts could rightly complain of the seemingly secondary roles here assigned to their fields.

In meteor studies, as in other areas of research where the old, sharp boundaries between classical fields of science are fast becoming blurred, the most rapid advances are likely to be made by an organization which can boast of many experts with diverse specialities, all working together on a comprehensive and interlocking program—always provided that the teamwork doctrine is never allowed to crush out the spark of individual genius. Almost inevitably the average working group will fall short of this ideal in some respects, but any specialist—in our case the radio scientist or engineer—cannot fail to profit from contacts with allied fields, particularly when it may be shown how easily and effectively he himself can learn and use some of the other man's techniques.

Another beneficial effect of this cross-pollination is that the electronic specialist may be stimulated into applying his new technology to the optical fields. Recent advances in photosensitive devices, such as the improved photomultiplier tube, the television image tube, and the infrared detector, should be exploited with a view to broadening and strengthening the optical researches. Some first steps have been taken in that direction (see, for example, Sec. 3-7 on photoelectric devices), but this potentially fruitful area has never been explored fully.

3-1. Naked-eye observations. For many years visual observation was the chief, if not the sole, means of gathering information about meteors, much of it accumulated through the efforts of amateurs. Even now, in the hands of experts, the visual technique can be made to yield data of considerable value in an area that is not thoroughly covered by the powerful instrumental attacks. Generally speaking, though, present-day visual observations are regarded in the professional ranks as ancillary to photographic and radio methods rather than competitive with them. In lieu of recapitulating the history of visual observing, which the reader will find well summarized by Olivier (1925) and Lovell (1954), we shall content ourselves with outlining briefly some particular ways in which the naked-eye observations can be of aid to radio and photographic work.

Time exposures are the rule in meteor photography because no one can predict when a meteor will occur. This means that, without other information, the error in timing the appearance of a meteor will be half the exposure time, which will create a proportional error in at least one element of the computed position or path of the meteor. A visual observer watching the sky in the field of view of the camera can therefore furnish an essential service if he does nothing more than time accurately the occurrences of the brighter meteors. He can easily supply other useful information, such as magnitude, train duration, and the general direction of motion, which will help in reducing the photographs.

In contrast to the photographic work, visual timing alone is not of the same intrinsic value to radar observations, since the times of the radio meteors can be read with great precision from the continuous film record of the cathode-ray-tube range display. However, other features of individual meteors are of interest to the radio worker, such as the magnitude, path position, and shower or nonshower identification. The necessary first step in establishing a one-to-one correspondence between visual and radio meteors is to compare the visual time with the radio record. The visual observer, on seeing a meteor, presses a button to illuminate a marker within the field of view of the display camera (see Fig. 3-1). The average timing error of a typical observer may lie between 0.5 and 1.0 sec: the radar record can usually be read to 0.1 sec without difficulty. A bright meteor is often associated with a long-duration echo, and conversely; but this connection is by no means inevitable. Furthermore, there is sometimes a real delay of several seconds in the appearance of the radar echo. Additional information is highly desirable and some of this can be provided if the visual observer plots the meteor path against the star background.

The plotting is done on a map on which a few of the brighter stars and well-known constellations have been marked. Various projections have been used to transfer the celestial sphere to a plane; the most useful from the viewpoint of meteor mapping appears to be the stereographic projection. The map shown in Fig. 3-2 is one of a set of four prepared by Millman for use near latitude 45°N. One of the set may be selected to suit any hour of any day of the year. As soon as the observer sees a meteor he presses his button, which flashes the film marker and also sounds a buzzer, and then he proceeds to plot the path of the meteor on his map. At the same time he calls out other pertinent information to the recorder, such as the magnitude of the meteor, whether it was

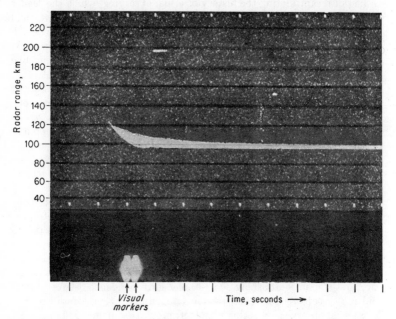

FIG. 3-1. Radar range-time record of a Perseid meteor, which was also seen by two visual observers—note diamond-shaped markers.

"shower" or "nonshower," the train duration if any, etc. The recorder notes the time as well, for comparison with the radar record, and he assigns a number to the meteor which the observer writes near the meteor path on his map. During a strong shower most of the observer's trails may appear to have originated in a common radiant point.

The coordinates of the plotted meteor paths may be readily converted to elevation angle h and azimuth angle by graphical reduction since an accuracy of a degree or two is adequate. A small mounted globe on which the paths can be drawn is an aid in this procedure. Range information only may be available from the radar; so the second stage in the correlation of the visual and radar meteors consists in computing one or more values of $H = R \sin h$ for each tentative radar-visual pair. If the H value lies within a reasonable height spread, say $80 < H < 110$ km, one may regard the association as fairly probable. A height-finding radar or a three-station range-triangulation system will yield the position of the meteor in space and sometimes the path orientation as well. From

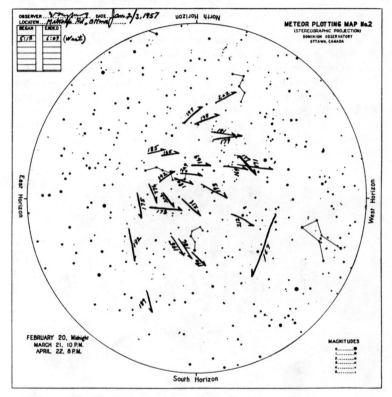

FIG. 3-2. Star map with meteor paths plotted. *(Courtesy of P. M. Millman.)*

these more extensive data the identity of the visual meteor with the radar meteor can usually be firmly established.

The mean errors of typical amateur observers working under professional supervision are listed in Table 3-1, based on Millman's reductions of the Ottawa data. Porter has estimated the errors shown in the second row of Table 3-1 to be representative of the more experienced British teams using a different and more difficult plotting method. The

Table 3-1. Mean Errors of Visual Meteor Observations

	Position of ends of trail— combined error	Angular direction of trail	Angular speed	Magnitude
Ottawa observers.........	±7°	±14°	No estimate	±0.42
British observers.........	±3°.1	±3°.1	21%	±0.56

positional errors of the Ottawa observers, although greater than those of the British workers, are quite acceptable for the purpose of visual-radio correlation. For the past few years one of the first considerations at Ottawa has been precision in the estimation of meteor magnitudes, a fact that accounts in part for the smaller error shown under this heading. An important visual-radio correlation, which has been investigated in the past but which could well bear further examination, is the relation between visual magnitude and radio echo duration. The connection between magnitude and echo amplitude is regarded as being less sig-

FIG. 3-3. Modern visual meteor observing at Springhill Meteor Observatory near Ottawa. Warm air is supplied to the individual compartments.

nificant, but nevertheless it should receive some attention. In either case, it is apparent that accurate estimation of magnitude and reasonably certain identification of the visual-radio pair are essential to reliable results.

If the visual observations are to be carried out consistently and extensively, or under winter conditions, it is recommended that some attention be paid to protecting the observers from the weather. The visual-observer's compound shown in Fig. 1-2 has seen many years of service at Ottawa. The canvas wall around the perimeter shields the eye from direct ground illumination and also wards off the chill wind. For sustained effort in subzero weather we recommend an arrangement of enclosed individual compartments similar to that depicted in Fig. 3-3, which is in current use at Ottawa. An oil furnace in the hut below the observers pumps warm air into each box.

3-2. The rocking-mirror method. Developed by Öpik (1934) and used fairly extensively on some of his visual programs, this method does not seem to have been adopted by others to any great extent. Nevertheless, it will be described here briefly both because it is simple and ingenious and because Öpik drew extensively on his rocking-mirror observations in formulating his conclusions on the orbital distribution of meteors. In one arrangement the observer looked down on a plane mirror which rested face up on three ball supports.
One of the supports was fixed and the other two, by means of a motor drive, were raised and lowered in simple harmonic motions, differing 90° in phase. The resultant conical motion at 10 rps caused the stars to appear as circles or ellipses of about 0°.5 in major diameter. Boothroyd devised a variation of the method in which the mirror rested on a single support and was given a conical motion of 30 rps by means of an eccentric shaft.

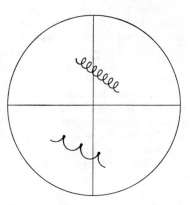

With either instrument, a meteor moving across the field of view would appear to the eye to trace out a curve resembling a cycloid (see Fig. 3-4).

FIG. 3-4. Sketch of meteor trails viewed in the rocking mirror.

The angular speed of the meteor may be deduced from the observed number of loops and the apparent length of trail. The observations may have some subjective limitations although Öpik believes that the observing conditions may be more favorable than direct viewing because of the two-dimensional appearance of the trail. The conversion to linear velocity demands a knowledge of the path position and orientation. The rocking mirror has also been used in conjunction with a small telescope to extend the visual range to fainter meteors.

Öpik (1953) has adapted the conical-motion principle to small-camera photography. Since a permanent record is available on the photographic plate for later analysis, any possibility of subjective error is eliminated. The intensity of the cycloidlike image on the photographic plate will vary according to its apparent speed, and at the nodes it will be greater than the average intensity which would be recorded by the same camera if it were stationary. Öpik states that this effect should double the number of recorded meteors.

3-3. Binoculars and telescopes. The limiting magnitude of stars which the average eye can detect when aided by a telescope of aperture a is given by the well-known formula $M = 9 + 5 \log_{10} a$, where a is in inches. The practical limit for the detection of telescopic meteors is about two magnitudes brighter than for stars; so we may write the limiting meteor magnitude as

$$M = 5 \log_{10} a \qquad (3\text{-}1)$$

where a is now expressed in millimeters. Thus the popular 50-mm binoculars should enable one to see eighth- or ninth-magnitude meteors, compared to the limit of fifth- to sixth-magnitude for the unaided eye. Fifteen-inch (380-mm) telescopes are not likely to be readily available to the radio worker, but if he had one he would be able to see twelfth to thirteenth-magnitude meteors—provided that he were blessed with the quality of patience in abundance! Owing to the very small field of view of most telescopes of this size, the actual yield is usually measured in terms of hours per meteor rather than meteors per hour. The smaller-diameter telescope of the "comet-seeker" type, which embraces a comparatively broad field of view, is better adapted to meteor work: typical rates with such a telescope, or with 50-mm binoculars, are about three or four meteors per hour.

3-4. Small-camera photography. During clear nights the radio worker will find that direct photography can provide a permanent and accurate record of the luminous effects of the brighter meteors, which should be of great assistance in interpreting the radio echoes. The cost is not inordinate—good-quality 35-mm cameras yield quite acceptable photos—and the technique is not difficult to learn. The limitation, of course, is that the average conventional camera will not record meteors fainter than zero or first magnitude. Photography is therefore not a complete substitute for visual observations, which should be carried on simultaneously in any case to enable the meteors to be timed accurately.

A good photograph is of particular value whenever a very bright meteor or fireball crosses the field of view and leaves behind a complex radio record of its passage.

The camera may be left in a fixed position so that the star images will be drawn out as short arcs on the plate during the time exposure, or it may be guided on a polar-axis mounting in order that the stars will form point images. In either case, the image of a meteor trail will record as a narrow line with little or no apparent curvature. From the stationary camera one may determine the position of the meteor trail in azimuth, elevation, declination, and also in right ascension if the exact time of the meteor is available. The guided polar axis camera will yield the right

FIG. 3-5. Millman's rotating-shutter mount in action. Several small cameras are mounted in position. (*Courtesy of S. A. Mott.*)

ascension and declination immediately, but the azimuth and elevation will remain ambiguous if no time is given. The stationary arrangement requires less equipment, of course, and furthermore is to be preferred to the guided one for several purposes, including that of photo-radio correlations. When good photographs are carefully measured and reduced by analytical methods, the positional errors of an individual trail can be quoted in minutes of arc, compared to a degree or two for the best radio method or ten degrees or more for a single visual plot. Rapid graphical methods (McCrosky, 1957) of deriving the information from the photographic plate are therefore quite satisfactory for comparison with the radio data.

A rotating shutter should be mounted in such a manner as to interrupt the light at some accurately determined rate in the range 10 to 60 times per second (see Fig. 3-5). The angular velocity of the meteor may thus be determined from the spacing of the breaks in the trail image (see Fig. 3-6), and if the position and orientation of the path can be determined, the linear velocity may be computed, in favorable cases to an accuracy of 0.1 per cent. Some train luminosity behind the meteor head may show

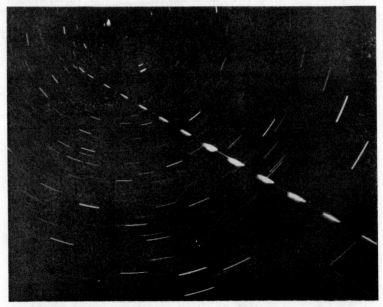

FIG. 3-6. A bright Perseid meteor photographed with the equipment shown in Fig. 3-5. Near maximum brightness, the shutter breaks (10 per second) are filled in with train luminosity. A second fainter meteor appears at the lower right. The star images have moved about the pole during the exposure. The Little Dipper appears just above the meteor trail. (*Courtesy of P. M. Millman.*)

in the shutter breaks, which would otherwise be obscured by the preceding and much brighter meteor head. A subsidiary advantage of the shutter is that the exposure time may be increased before skylight fogging becomes excessive. Off-to-on ratios of the shutter opening as high as 2:1 or 3:1 are sometimes used. An occulting shutter may be used to cut off the light for a few seconds once during each time exposure. This produces in the slowly trailing images of the stars a timed break which is a more accurate reference point for reduction purposes than are the end points of the star images. Low-wattage electric heaters located near the cameras will help to keep the lenses clear of mist and dew. A mounting for three aerial-reconnaissance cameras, with occulting and rotating shutters, is shown in Fig. 3-7.

If it is reasonable to assume that the meteor is a member of a shower for which the velocity and radiant are known, the height may be deduced from a single-station rotating-shutter photograph of the meteor trail against the star background. Otherwise, photographs of the same meteor must be obtained from two points on the earth's surface spaced from 20 to 50 km apart. Only two separate stations are needed for an

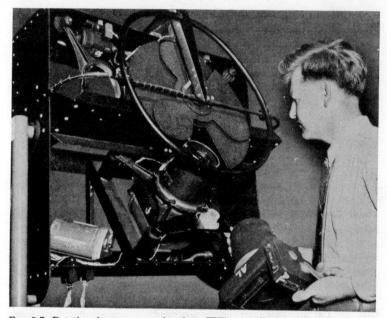

Fig. 3-7. Rotating-shutter mount for three Williamson F-24 aerial cameras. The three-bladed occulting shutter is closed once during each exposure to create a fiducial time break in the trailing star images. The two-bladed rotating shutter, which rotates at 6 rps, is next to the camera lenses. (*Webb*, 1950.)

unambiguous determination of the path in space because the distances may be found from the apparent displacement of the two meteor images with respect to the star background at infinity. The usual height error is about 0.1 km. The orientations of the camera axes need not be known accurately as long as one ensures that there is a reasonable overlap in the camera fields at the 95-km height level. A complete and fairly accurate determination of the spatial coordinates of any meteor may be made by combining the data from a single-station rotating-shutter photograph with the radar range. The ranges should be measured to one or more correlated points on the photographic and radio paths, e.g., to the point of nearest approach at the range R_0 or to two or more clearly defined bursts and flares. The main and auxiliary roles can be reversed, of course: information from a simple and inexpensive "range-only" radar set will greatly enhance the value of a single-station camera program.

The efficiency of the camera will vary with the lens aperture a, the focal length f, and the area A_s covered in the sky by the camera field. The quality of the image and the light loss in the optical system also affect the performance—as in many other applications the better the lens, the better the results. Time lost in changing plates should be considered in the over-all efficiency. This loss is negligible for a conventional film-roll camera since the exposures may be changed in a few seconds, an extremely brief period compared to the total exposure time, which may be from five minutes to one hour depending on the ambient light and sky conditions. On the other hand, the closed-open ratio x for a Super-Schmidt camera may be as high as 0.5, both because the exposures are necessarily short, due to the great light-gathering power of this instrument, and because the plate-changing process is somewhat complicated and time-consuming. An empirical formula for the efficiency E of a meteor camera may be written

$$E = k \frac{a^2 A_s}{(1 + x)f^n} \tag{3-2}$$

where the proportionality factor k includes the effects of lens quality and light loss, and the exponent n is probably near unity but may be as high as 2. The number of meteors photographed per hour is roughly proportional to E.

One may conveniently divide meteor cameras into three groups as follows:

A. Conventional small cameras with f/a between 4.0 and 8.0 and f between 100 and 500 mm. *Example:* studio cameras; their long focal lengths facilitate accurate measurement of the plates, although their efficiency is low.

B. Conventional cameras with f/a between 1.0 and 3.5 and f between 50 and 200 mm. *Examples:* miniature (35-mm) cameras and aerial-reconnaissance cameras.

C. Schmidt cameras with f/a between 0.5 and 1.0 and f between 100 and 300 mm. The most famous member of this group is the Perkin-Elmer Super-Schmidt designed by Baker (see Sec. 3-5), with $f/a = 0.65$ and $f = 200$ mm.

In very general terms the relative efficiencies of these three types, taking the Super-Schmidt as the representative of group C, are

$$A:B:C = 1:5:200$$

The sensitivity of any camera will tend to vary inversely with the velocity of the meteor; by contrast, the sensitivity of the eye is remarkably constant for a wide range of velocities.   On the average, though, one may say that group A cameras can record meteors down to 0 or -1 magnitude; group B down to 0 or $+1$ magnitude; and group C to $+3$ or $+4$ magnitudes.   Under good conditions the actual numbers of meteors recorded per 100 hr of exposure will be roughly 2, 10, and 400 for the respective groups.   One meteor photograph per night per miniature camera of good quality is a reasonable expectation,* and that photograph could be just the one needed to round out the analysis of a striking meteor echo.   The Perkin-Elmer Super-Schmidt meteor camera would be a powerful aid to radio research programs, but it is costly and not likely to be available for a purely ancillary role where its striking characteristics would not be fully utilized.   Figure 3-8 shows a meteor photographed with one of the Super-Schmidt cameras in Alberta (Halliday, 1957).

High speed is naturally the most important characteristic needed in films or plates used for meteor photography.   A blue-sensitive emulsion will be of advantage for some work because of the color-index effect (see Sec. 2-2).   Spectrophotography may be done with emulsions sensitive to selected wavelength regions or with panchromatic plates.   The latter are particularly useful in meteor-train photography.

3-5. Cameras with Schmidt optics.   The Super-Schmidt camera, designed by Dr. Baker of Harvard expressly for meteor photography, has no peer in this field.   Six were built by the Perkin-Elmer Corporation of Norwalk, Conn., in the early fifties, of which four have seen service in programs under the supervision of the Harvard College Observatory and two were acquired by the Dominion Observatory and installed at the Meanook-Newbrook Observatories in northern Alberta, Canada.   A cross-sectional sketch of the camera is shown in Fig. 3-9.   Figure 1-3 is a photograph of the complete instrument, comprising camera, equatorial mounting yoke, and drive system—the whole standing 8 ft high when mounted and weighing nearly three tons!   The aperture is 310 mm and the focal length is 203 mm.   Nominally, $f/a = 0.65$, though the effective f/a ratio is closer to 0.85.   The circular field of view is 55° in diameter.   Suction is used to hold the molded film against the spherical plate holder to a precision of 0.01 mm.   A two-vane shutter, with an off-to-on ratio of 3:1, is rotated just above the film surface at 30 rps.

Three Super-Schmidt cameras were built at the University of Bristol under the auspices of the Paul Instrument Fund of the Royal Society.   The British camera is similar in design to the Harvard instrument.   The

---

* Prof. L. A. Manning photographed 17 meteor trails during a one-minute exposure with an f 1.5 35-mm camera, at the peak of the 1946 Giacobinid shower.   This once-in-a-lifetime luck may not be matched for some time to come!

focal length is 206 mm, the effective f/a ratio is about 0.78, and the
circular field diameter is 56°. One of the cameras was constructed on
two-thirds the scale of the others, but its sensitivity was only a half-
magnitude less than the full-size models which have successfully photo-

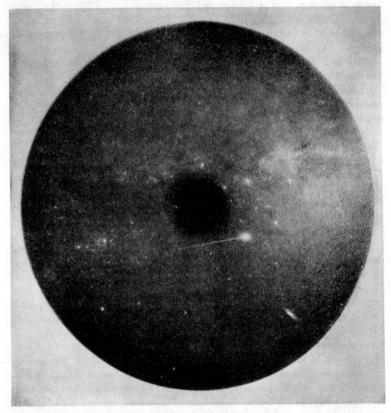

FIG. 3-8. Super-Schmidt photograph of a zero-magnitude meteor taken at Newbrook
Meteor Observatory, Alberta. The meteor moved from left to right, just below the
dark spot caused by the shutter shaft, and ended in a brilliant terminal burst. The
Great Nebula in Andromeda is visible at the lower right. (*Courtesy of I. Halliday,
Dominion Observatory.*)

graphed fourth magnitude meteors. Figure 3-10 shows one of the
British cameras, known as the Main Model, which is stationed in North
Wales and operated by the Jodrell Bank Experimental Station. A
bright meteor photographed with this camera may be seen in Fig. 3-11.

In addition to their role in direct photography of the moving meteor, the Super-Schmidts have proved to be very effective in recording the persistent, glowing train left by a bright meteor.   The camera is normally covered with a window-shade type of objective shutter.   When a bright meteor occurs, the shutter is opened in less than a tenth of a second, either by a photoelectric detector or by an attendant observer (Liller

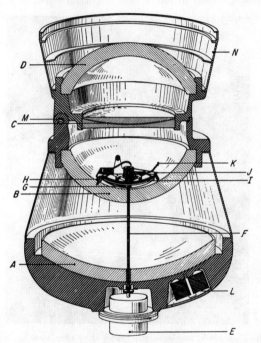

Scale: 0   3   6   9   12   3   6   9   24 inch

FIG. 3-9. Cross-sectional view of Super-Schmidt camera.   (*A*) Main mirror; (*B*) rear glass shell; (*C*) correcting plate; (*D*) front glass shell; (*E*) shutter motor; (*F*) shutter shaft; (*G*) rotating shutter; (*H*) focusing post; (*I*) film holder; (*J*) film holder hinge; (*K*) vacuum line; (*L*) counter weight; (*M*) hinge for opening camera; (*N*) dew cap. (*Dominion Observatory.*)

and Whipple, 1954).   Successive exposures of the train may then be made in rapid succession at intervals of about two seconds.   The camera axis is shifted by 0°.3 after each exposure to separate the train images. Two Super-Schmidt cameras have been employed in this way by the Harvard Meteor Expedition in New Mexico.   These train photographs give us detailed information about winds and turbulence in the upper atmosphere (see Sec. 5-8 and Fig. 5-19).

3-6. Meteor spectrophotography. Most of the conventional cameras may be converted to spectrographs by placing in front of the lens either a glass prism with an angle of about 30° or a transmission grating ruled with 80 to 400 lines/mm and designed to concentrate most of the light into the first-order spectrum. The grating has the advantage that the zero-order image will serve as a reference for the measurement of line wavelengths in the higher orders. This reference is not available with a prism. No slit is used in either case. The meteor-trail image has no

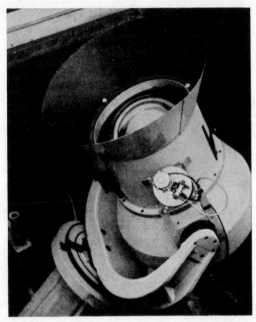

FIG. 3-10. The Main Model meniscus Super-Schmidt camera, installed in North Wales as part of the Jodrell Bank meteor program. (*Courtesy of A. C. B. Lovell.*)

appreciable thickness and the quality of the spectrum is excellent if the direction of the trail does not coincide too closely with that of the dispersion. The average sensitivity of a spectrographic camera will be about two magnitudes brighter than that of the same camera without the dispersive device, partly because of additional losses in the dispersive medium but mainly because the light is divided among several monochromatic lines. Figure 3-12 shows the spectrum of a Perseid meteor. Attempts have been made to operate the Super-Schmidts as spectrographs, using Fresnel-type prisms or mosaic transmission gratings, but they have not been very successful, owing to difficulties associated

FIG. 3-11. A Geminid meteor, magnitude −2, photographed with the Main Model Super-Schmidt on Dec. 14, 1947. The meteor traveled from left to right. The stellar images were partially trailed during the exposure for purposes of photometric comparison. The Andromeda Nebula can be seen just to the left of center, above the trail. (*Courtesy of A. C. B. Lovell.*)

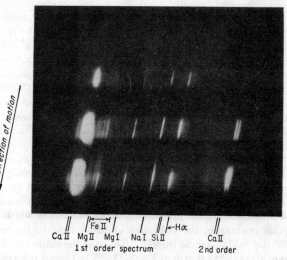

FIG. 3-12. Spectrum of a Perseid meteor. Neutral and ionized lines of several elements appear. The train spectrum is also visible in the dark spaces when the light from the bright meteor head is cut off by the rotating shutter. (*Courtesy of P. M. Millman.*)

with the unconventional optics and the very wide field of these cameras.

The measurement and interpretation of meteor spectra is a science—some say an art—which is understood and practised by only a few men in the world to-day. Unless he is willing to devote the time and effort necessary to acquire the requisite knowledge, the radio worker should not consider meteor spectrography as an aid to his main radio program. A direct photograph can furnish him with valuable and easily reducible information, but a spectrographic photo that is not very carefully analysed will add little to the radio story. A stronger case can be made out for the converse practice: an elementary radar system should be regarded as an important and useful handmaiden to the meteor spectroscopist.

3-7. Photoelectric observations.   Over a period of years the photocell has become established as an indispensable aid in stellar photometry and other astronomical and geophysical studies, and it may therefore be somewhat surprising to note how little attention it has received from meteor scientists. The high-speed response and the potential sensitivity of photoelectric devices offer several attractive possibilities for the trapping of the elusive and transient meteor. Only two photoelectric equipments, the one Russian and the other Canadian, seem to have been developed specifically for the observation of meteors. Astavin-Razumin (1958), at Moscow, has described some preliminary results that he obtained during 1955–1956 with a detector which consisted of three parallel photomultiplier tubes followed by a common amplifier. The recording device was a ballistic galvanometer, which provided some filtering action to damp out noise fluctuations caused by variation of light from the sky and by internal noise sources. A somewhat more complex photoelectric system was developed at Ottawa (McKinley and McKinley, 1951) in a form which permitted integration of its operation with that of a companion radar set or with visual observations. Despite some obvious shortcomings in the Canadian model, the basic technique was demonstrated in 1949 to be quite practical, and it is a matter of regret that several avenues of suggested improvements were not explored more thoroughly to make it a more potent tool. The following brief description of this equipment may provide a lead for future developments.

The individual photocell units of the Ottawa equipment consisted each of a 931-A photomultiplier tube mounted inside a box in which was cut a rectangular opening of the right size to admit light to the cell from a 30 by 36° sky field (using no lenses). To cover the entire sky, 19 of these units were arranged as shown in Fig. 3-13. The output from each photocell unit was sampled in time sequence by the electronic circuits sketched in block form in Fig. 3-14. Identical range sweeps, each 260 km long, were applied horizontally to two cathode-ray tubes located side by side.

The tubes were photographed by a camera in which 35-mm film moved in a vertical plane continuously past the open lens at 4 in./min (see Fig. 4-2). Seconds pulses and 20-km range markers were impressed on each sweep. The video output of the companion radar was applied to the radar cathode-ray tube as intensity modulation of the sweep, and the

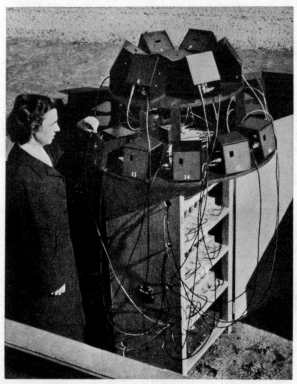

FIG. 3-13. A photoelectric meteor detector.   Nineteen photocells, covering the entire sky, are arranged on the circular tables.   The amplifiers and gating circuits are in the cabinet below.

gated output of the photocells was similarly impressed on the photocell cathode-ray tube.   The output of each photocell was sampled for 67 μsec (equivalent to 10 km of range) at 118 cps, the recurrence frequency of the radar pulses.

Figure 3-15 shows a typical record of a meteor detected by radar (top) and by photocell Nos. 6 and 12 (bottom), with the visual observer's marker appearing between the two records.

A few meteors as faint as third magnitude were recorded by the photo-

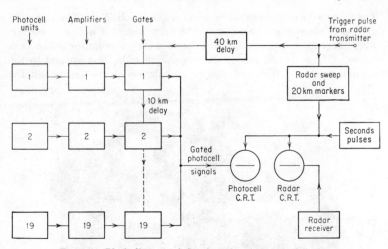

Fig. 3-14. Block diagram of the photoelectric meteor detector.

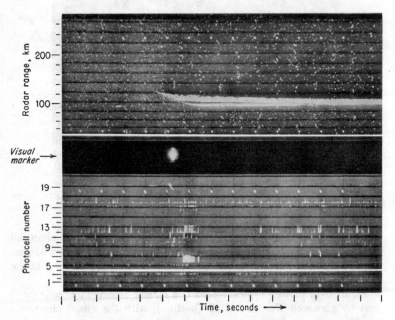

Fig. 3-15. A Geminid meteor observed by three methods: (*top*) radar-echo record; (*middle*) visual-observer's marker; (*bottom*) photoelectric record.

cell system, though the practical working limit appeared to be about the second magnitude. Most of the noise background in the photocell output was due to star scintillations and other random light variations. The sensitivity could therefore be improved by reducing the field of view until the internal photocell noise equalled the skylight fluctuations. Photomultiplier tubes are now commercially available with better noise characteristics than the 931-A; their introduction would permit still smaller apertures or suitable lens systems to be used with advantage. The 19-unit system yielded the approximate position of the meteor, and if more than one photocell was excited, the direction of motion was roughly indicated. A qualitative estimate of light intensity was also available.

The salient feature of the system was the high precision with which the photocell response to a meteor could be timed. When used as an aid to the timing of direct or spectroscopic photographs the photocell, with a timing error of 0.05 sec, greatly outperformed in this one respect the best efforts of experienced visual observers. Further development along this line seems to offer the most promising application of the photomultiplier detector.

One could arrange a large number of photocell units, each with narrow apertures, to cover a selected sky area with a sensitivity considerably better than that of the eye, but the resolution attainable with any practical number of cells would still be rather poor. An alternative suggestion is to use the television image tube, which will meet the requirement of high resolution. Certain types of these tubes which have been developed in recent years for very low light levels may well find a place in meteor research.

There are so many variables to be evaluated that an accurate prediction of the performance of television image tubes is difficult, but preliminary calculations suggest that the best of modern image tubes should exceed the sensitivity of the naked eye. For example, we may begin by assuming that the illumination level of a fifth-magnitude meteor is 2×10^{-9} ft-c, and that of a tenth-magnitude meteor is 2×10^{-11} ft-c (see Sec. 2-2). The photocathode surface of a typical image orthicon tube like the RCA type 6849 may be considered to be made up of a large number of individual elements. A lower limit for the size of an element will be set by the permissible spacing of the scanning lines. Five hundred scanning lines per 25 mm is a reasonable practice; hence the diameter of a "unit cell" may be taken as roughly 0.05 mm. If the objective lens has a diameter of 50 mm, the increase in illumination on the unit cell of the photocathode will be $(50/0.05)^2 = 10^6$. Thus the image of a fifth-magnitude meteor will be of the order of 10^{-3} ft-c in intensity, and that of a tenth-magnitude meteor will be 10^{-5} ft-c. The former value is well within the operating range of sensitive image orthicons and the latter figure is just on the fringe. Of course, there will be losses in the optical system, and the scanning losses, photocathode storage times, amplifier bandwidths, etc., will all need to be considered. Slow meteors will be favored over fast ones, perhaps by as much as two or three magnitudes. It should, however, be feasible to build a meteor-observing system, using commercially available components, which would be from one to three magnitudes more sensitive than the unaided human eye.

If the predicted increase in sensitivity is achieved in practice, a new and powerful technique will become available for observing both meteors and earth satellites. (One may visualize a group of devoted observers watching the picture tube in indoor comfort, with all the amenities customarily associated with viewing the late, late television show!) The value of the method will naturally be considerably enhanced if some kind of permanent record can be made for use later: this would still be true even if the anticipated sensitivity were not fully realized. The video output of the system may be stored on wideband video tape, for instance, and the tape played back at any desired speed. To avoid using miles of tape in a night's program, one could record on a closed loop of tape, say of 1-min duration, which is continually being erased and reused. After a meteor has been recorded, the tape could be stopped, either by an attendant observer or automatically if the meteor signal were strong enough, and that particular loop set aside while another went into service. No rotating shutter is needed in front of the lens because the meteor velocity can be determined from the frame rate. The frames of particular interest on the tape loop may be photographed frame by frame with a movie camera for a detailed slow-motion examination of the phenomenon.

At the 107th meeting of the American Astronomical Society, held in New York, December 27–31, 1960, John Spalding and Curtis L. Hemenway described some preliminary results obtained with a television system employing an f 1.1 lens and a GE-type Z5294 image orthicon tube. Meteors of the sixth magnitude, or perhaps fainter, were easily detectable. Meteor trains were observed as they were created after the meteor head. A prism placed before the lens yielded low-resolution spectra of meteors and trains. Further developments in this field will be awaited with interest.

CHAPTER 4

Radio Techniques

The early radio observations of meteoric ionization were mainly by-products of other research programs, such as ionospheric and propagation studies. Rough measurements of the ranges of the transient ionization could be obtained from the records of pulsed ionospheric sounders, and the Doppler whistles that were heard during reception of a distant h-f station definitely indicated a rapid motion of some reflecting agency. These observations suggested fairly strongly that meteors were the cause, but conclusive and quantitative evidence was lacking up to the early 1940s.

On any list of the most important technological advances made under forced draft during World War II one would certainly include the new and powerful radar systems for the detection and tracking of aircraft and ships. Very little effort was required to beat these swords of modern warfare into ploughshares with which to break virgin ground in the field of meteor research. Modified wartime radars were involved in many of the postwar radio researches and a few were still being used fifteen years later. In the main, though, current practice is to design and build equipments specifically for meteor research.

We shall begin here with a summary of the primary information that radio can provide, followed by a general discussion of the techniques by which these data may be obtained. Particular methods and representative equipments will then be described, some quite briefly and others more extensively, as their utility appears to warrant. It is neither feasible nor desirable in a book of this length and scope to attempt to go into the construction of a particular equipment in such detail that the reader could make himself a Chinese copy. Rather, it is felt that broad suggestions should suffice, with a block diagram here and there to guide the engineer in applying his stock in trade of radio knowledge and experience. This chapter will be mainly devoted to methods and apparatus employed in backscatter meteor researches. Techniques and equipments used for forward-scatter work and for practical meteor communications will be described in Chap. 9.

4-1. Primary observational data. The energy which develops in collisions between ablated atoms of the meteoroid and molecules or atoms of the upper atmosphere is sufficient to free electrons from the atoms. Positively charged ions are also produced, but these are too heavy and too sluggish in the field of the incident radio wave to contribute significantly to the scattered wave or echo signal. The electrons are the important elements, and the scattering phenomena may conveniently be divided into two major subdivisions, depending on whether the number of electrons produced per meter of path length is smaller or greater than a certain critical value. If smaller, the meteor trail is said to be *underdense*, the radio wave penetrates the column freely, and each electron acts as an individual scattering source. If greater, the trail is *overdense*, and the radio wave does not penetrate the column but is effectively reflected from that boundary surface inside which the electrons are dense enough to cause total reflection—a local miniature ionosphere, as it were. For either underdense or overdense trails, radio systems may be devised to provide the following primary observational data, although no single equipment is known to exist which could extract all the listed information with the optimum precision.

1. *Echo range.* The distance from the station to the meteoric target is known as the *echo range* and is a fundamental measurement easily made with pulse or FM backscatter radars. The total instrumental error in a range measurement is the sum of several kinds of inaccuracies, of which two are of major importance. The first is caused by a combination of pulse rise time and receiver bandwith (see Sec. 2-6); this error is independent of range. The second inaccuracy is caused by timing errors either in the speed of the range sweep or in the range-calibration markers; this error is roughly proportional to range. Without difficulty, one can build simple radar systems in which the over-all average range error is about 1 km, a quite acceptable error for many purposes. When necessary, a more precise ranging system may be incorporated which can increase the instrumental accuracy of absolute range measurement to better than 10 m if the transmitter-pulse rise time and the receiver bandwidth are suitably engineered (see Sec. 2-6). Of more general interest than extreme precision in the absolute measurement of range is range resolution, or the ability to discriminate between targets at slightly different ranges. A radar range resolution of 2 or 3 km is common, and the best practice narrows this to 50 or 100 m. If the meteor has produced a "head echo" over an appreciable path length, the rate of change of range is a measure of *meteor velocity*. In a few cases the rate of change of velocity, or the *deceleration*, can be found. The velocity errors may be as small as 1 per cent for good specimens, but the deceleration errors will seldom be less than 20 per cent.

2. *Echo phase.* This term is used to describe the phase of the received echo wave relative to the transmitter wave. A cw system can measure phase smoothly and continuously, and a coherent-pulse radar will sample the phase at frequent intervals. Looked at another way, the echo phase may be regarded as a very precise measurement of relative range. The error in phase angle may be only a few degrees, corresponding to a range error of a few centimeters. Unfortunately, the absolute range of the meteor cannot be determined by this Doppler, or diffraction, method. (A similar but more complicated technique used in tracking rockets, known as DOVAP,* does determine the absolute range by continuously integrating the phase angle from a known starting point.) However, the angular velocity of the meteor may be deduced from the phase variations as the meteor moves across the line of sight. The coherent methods (cw, or coherent-pulse radar) can fully utilize the echo-phase information all along the detectable trail as it is forming, but even a noncoherent radar can be used to measure velocity by virtue of the amplitude fluctuations which occur just after the meteor passes the point on its path nearest the station. In effect, the already-formed part of the meteor trail provides the reference phase in the latter case. Typical meteor diffraction records, reduced by simplified methods, will yield velocities with errors from 3 to 5 per cent. The best records, analysed by more painstaking methods, are subject to errors of less than 1 per cent. Because the path length over which the diffraction echo may be observed is usually short, deceleration measurements are difficult to make at a single station by this method.

After the meteor has run its course and disappeared into dust and atoms, the long trail of expanding ionization that is left behind will drift with the wind, and may also be twisted and bent. Slow variations in the echo phase will occur. Even without a reference phase at the ground station, interference effects may be observed between waves from different parts of the trail because these parts are moving at slightly different speeds relative to the observer. These slow variations, termed "body Doppler" by the Stanford group, have no connection with the high-speed fluctuations of the diffraction echo observed while the trail is being created.

3. *Echo amplitude, or echo power.* Either instantaneous or averaged measurements of the received signal strength may be expressed as field strengths in microvolts per meter. More usually they are given as power in watts. Amplitude-time records made with a calibrated linear receiver can be read with accuracies of a few per cent, provided that the echo has not saturated the receiver. Logarithmic receivers are occasionally used to extend the dynamic range over which signal strengths can be recorded; these receivers can be conveniently calibrated in decibels, with 1 db as a typical reading error. In other types of recording, such as the popular

* *DOppler Velocity And Position.*

range-time method wherein the signal modulates the intensity of a cathode-ray-tube range sweep, only a rough estimate of echo strength can be obtained, with errors ranging from 6 db upward.

4. *Echo decay time and echo duration.* Of even greater interest than the precise value of the absolute echo strength is the behavior of the echo amplitude with time. Underdense trail echoes rise rapidly to a peak after the meteor passes R_0 and then decay exponentially. This *echo decay time* T_{un} is measured from the time of maximum amplitude to the time when the amplitude (or the square root of the power) has fallen to a given arbitrary fraction of the peak, often specified as $1/\epsilon$ where ϵ is the base of natural logarithms. The echo decay time might more logically be called the echo time constant.

The rise of the echo is more gradual in the case of overdense trail echoes, and here the useful parameter is the *echo duration* T_{ov}. This is the duration of the echo above a given absolute reference level which may be chosen to be the receiver noise level. To avoid confusion it should be pointed out that these variations in echo amplitude are on a longer time scale than the phase and amplitude fluctuations associated with the moving meteor. The diffraction fluctuations have periods of the order of a few milliseconds, and these fluctuations are assumed to have been compressed together and smoothed out in the type of record used to determine echo decay time or echo duration. Typical echo decay times are of the order of 0.1 sec, while echo durations may extend from 0.1 sec to several minutes. Because of the highly individualistic behavior of meteor echoes, great precision is probably not warranted in measuring the decay times and durations. For example, a particular echo duration of 100 sec may easily be measured to an accuracy of 0.5 sec or less, but the true statistical spread of observed durations is many times this reading error.

5. *Echo polarization.* During the first few tenths of a second in the lifetime of an underdense trail, the echo amplitude may be found to vary with the orientation of the electric vector of the incident wave relative to the trail axis. When the electric vector is normal to the trail, the amplitude may be as much as twice that obtained when the vector is parallel to the path. The effect is due to resonance occurring between the incident wave and the natural frequency of plasma oscillations across the ionized column. The ratio of echo amplitude quickly falls to unity as the column expands. The phenomenon is of some importance in the evolution of the physical theory of meteoric ionization, but it has little practical effect on most types of meteor observing programs.

4-2. Secondary observational data. From the above primary observational data we may deduce a number of useful secondary data. Some of these derived characteristics have become so intimately associated with the meteor as to be regarded as primary parameters, but one should keep in mind that various interpretative processes have had to be employed, some of them properly subject to critical scrutiny and review. For example, the number of electrons q produced per meter of path length is certainly a basic characteristic of any meteor trail, but it may be deduced only by applying some idealized theoretical considerations. For underdense trails the theory indicates that q varies as the square root of the observed echo power P_r. For the basic model of the overdense trail, q is linearly dependent on the echo duration T, or alternatively, q varies as P_r^2. An individual specimen in the overdense category may yield quite different values of q depending on which theoretical relation is used. Three different answers for q may result for a meteor on the border line between underdense and overdense trails. This does not necessarily imply that the theory is wrong (although that possibility should never be overlooked—mistakes have appeared and have been corrected in the early theoretical developments). Rather, it means that the theory is intended to describe a simplified model of a well-behaved trail, created in a homogeneous atmosphere of known characteristics. This ideal trail model, even as an approximation, can only represent the average, and in meteor studies a selected specimen seems to deviate more widely from the group average than happens in many other areas of physical measurements. However, the theory can be both powerful and indispensable in analyzing many kinds of observational data if the results and predictions are correctly regarded as statistical averages and one recognizes and accepts the risk of error involved in attempting to apply the theory to an individual specimen.

Our knowledge of the atmospheric environment, too, is sketchy and deficient—so much so in some aspects that we may achieve fair success in combining meteor observations and theory to deduce certain properties of the upper air (Whipple, 1943; Evans, 1954). One example of this procedure is the calculation of the electron-diffusion coefficient D from the observed decay time T_{un} for meteors at known heights (Greenhow and Neufeld, 1955a). The rate of diffusion depends on the atmospheric pressure and therefore on the height; so once the diffusion-height scale is established, the decay time may be used conversely to find the height of the meteor. Another example appears in Whipple's (1938) early work on photographic meteors, where he was able to determine the relative atmospheric pressure throughout the range of meteor heights from the decelerations measured along the paths.

The *velocity* and *deceleration* of the meteor are derived data which have already been mentioned in the previous section. Other secondary data, largely geometrical in character, may be computed from the primary measurements: the *position* in space of the ionized cloud left by the brighter meteors may be triangulated from range measurements made at three spaced ground stations, or from a single-station range measurement combined with elevation and azimuth information obtainable with special direction-finding techniques. The position errors naturally depend on the instrumental accuracies: typical examples of either method commonly measure height and plan position with errors of the order of ± 1 km for meteors occurring within a range of 150 km and degenerating to errors of ± 5 km for meteors 300 km distant. Three-station observations of the head echo, or of the diffraction echo, can yield the *orientation* of the individual meteor path and hence the position of the *radiant*, with mean errors of 2 to 3°. The radiant of a strong shower may be determined statistically from the variation of echo rates with range and time, again with errors of the order of 2 to 3°.

It may be remarked that the observational errors quoted above for the various meteor parameters are, in general, an order of magnitude greater than the corresponding errors associated with the photographic methods discussed in Chap. 3. There are, however, several potent arguments to be advanced in support of the radio methods. First, they have been applied already to meteors as faint as tenth to fifteenth magnitude, and an extension to fainter meteors should be instrumentally feasible. Even the best photographic method is at present limited to third- or fourth-magnitude meteors, and any further extension is likely to be difficult and expensive. Second, radio works in all weather and by day or by night. Third, radio is a very sensitive detector of ionization, and quantitative measurements of q may be made on very faint meteors. Direct photography reveals little or nothing about the ionization, and although spectroscopy can tell us what elements are ionized in the bright meteors, it can assign a lower limit only to the total ionization produced because visible light does not necessarily accompany the ionization processes.

4-3. Pulse radar techniques. The echo power varies as λ^3 for the average meteor, the echo duration varies roughly as λ^2, and the hourly rates of radio meteors tend to increase as $\lambda^{3/2}$. All this would suggest that the longer the radio wavelength, the better for meteor research work. For many purposes this is indeed true, although several factors enter to set a practical upper limit to the wavelength. At wavelengths greater than about 10 m, interference from distant stations via ionospheric reflections is often troublesome, particularly in the daylight hours and during periods of sunspot maxima. Daytime absorption effects occurring below the normal E region can seriously affect wavelengths of 20 m or more. The increased duration of echoes on the longer wavelengths may result in an appreciable overlapping of the echoes on the range-time record. This is not necessarily a handicap, but in any case it may be alleviated by improving the range resolution of the radar system.

Some special applications, such as the delineation of radiants, demand narrow antenna beams that are steerable. Both the constructional difficulties and the costs of the required wide-aperture antennas will increase about as λ^3, so a compromise must be reached. Large steerable antennas are usually designed for wavelengths shorter than 5 m, while large fixed arrays can be built economically for wavelengths as long as 15 m. Meteor researches, using either single dipoles or more complex arrays, have been carried out on a variety of wavelengths extending from 100 to less than 1 m, but most of the important work has been done in the band 3 to 12 m.

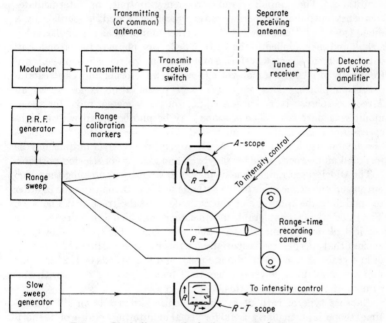

FIG. 4-1. Block diagram of a basic meteor radar system.

A block diagram of the basic elements of an elementary meteor radar system is shown in Fig. 4-1. The transmitter may be a self-excited oscillator employing a pair of conventional power triodes. The peak power output will be in the range 10 to 100 kw, with pulse widths from 3 to 100 μsec at prf's of 30 to 2,000 cps. The average plate power requirements are modest, of the order of a few watts up to a few hundred watts. A simple and effective modulator is the distributed-line type, made up of several sections of lumped inductance and capacitance to form the pulse together with a rotating spark wheel or a hydrogen thyratron to discharge the line. A synchronizing pulse from the modulator, or from its controlling prf generator, initiates the saw-tooth range sweep that is applied to the horizontal deflection plates of a cathode-ray tube.

Separate transmitting and receiving antennas are often used. However, if the antenna system is large and complicated, the additional complexity of a transmit-receive switch will be warranted to avoid duplication of the antenna structure and also to eliminate tracking problems if the antenna system is to be steerable. Meteor echoes picked up by the receiving antenna are amplified by a tuned receiver which is designed to have a bandpass appropriate to the pulse width and other operating conditions. The amplified radio-frequency output, or intermediate-frequency output if a superheterodyne receiver is used, is rectified by a diode (so-called "linear detector"), further amplified as a unipolar video signal, and then applied to the vertical deflection plates of the cathode-ray tube. Current-sweep waveforms and electromagnetic deflection coils are frequently used in place of voltage-sweep waveforms and electrostatic deflection plates. This *amplitude-range* presentation is known as an A-scope display. It is an essential part of every meteor radar for visual monitoring purposes. The A scope may be photographed with a high-speed movie camera if one is interested in recording the rapid fluctuations of echo amplitude with time. Alternatively, the receiver output may be recorded on magnetic tape for playback and analysis of selected portions.

The widely used range-time display is created by impressing the video output on one of the grids or the cathode of the cathode-ray tube in order to modulate the intensity of the cathode-ray-tube trace (see Fig. 4-1). The trace may be photographed by a camera in which film is drawn in the vertical plane continuously past the open lens. Figure 4-2 shows one camera that was designed especially for this purpose. Hundred-foot rolls of fine-grain 35-mm movie film are used, and film speeds of 1, 2, or 4 in./min are available. Several range-time meteor records made with this camera appear throughout this book.

Another type of cathode-ray-tube display, known as an RT (range-time) scope, is particularly useful for visual monitoring because of its short-term memory. The intensity-modulated range sweep is applied vertically to a cathode-ray tube which has a long-delay screen, e.g., the double-phosphor P7 type. At the same time a saw-tooth sweep with a period of the order of 1 min is applied to translate the range sweep slowly in the horizontal direction across the tube, with a rapid return. This slow-speed sweep may be generated by a motor-driven potentiometer. The viewer thus obtains continuously a range-time picture that extends 1 min back into the past at any moment.

Range-calibration markers are needed for accurate distance measurement. These may conveniently be spaced 20 km apart, say, if the overall sweep length is from 300 to 400 km. A simple calibrator unit consists of an oscillator of appropriate frequency which may be started with each synchronizing pulse and stopped at the end of the range sweep. The oscillator sine waves are squared and differentiated to produce narrow pulses which may be applied either to the vertical plates of the A scope or to the intensity control of the range-time cathode-ray tube. If very precise range measurements are desired, a continuously running quartz-crystal oscillator may be used, in which case the synchronizing pulse is usually derived from the crystal oscillator and employed to trigger both the modulator pulse and the range sweep.

FRONT VIEW

COVER OFF

FIG. 4-2. Two views of a camera designed to photograph an intensity-modulated cathode-ray tube. The time axis on the record is provided by the continuous motion of the film past the open lens.

Time markers may be added to the range sweep as well. Electric seconds pulses are first obtained from a clock, each pulse lasting for about 0.5 sec. These impulses are used to gate two very short pulses which are synchronized with the start of the sweep but delayed by, say, 30 and 230 km, respectively. When the gated pulses are applied to the intensity control of the cathode-ray tube the photographic record will show two rows of seconds markers. Two rows of dots are to be preferred to one row because the film transport speed is not entirely negligible compared to the sweep speed, with the result that the range axis slants slightly on the record.

As a rule, the higher the pulse-recurrence frequency, the better, because the information rate is directly geared to the prf. In order to obtain an unambiguous measurement of range, the reciprocal of the prf cannot exceed $2R_{max}/c$, where R_{max} is the maximum range to be measured and c is the velocity of propagation. The recovery time of the sweep and deflection circuits will further limit the maximum prf. Occasionally it is desirable to use much higher prf's than this criterion permits. The resulting range ambiguity may be removed if the prf is modulated at a subfrequency which is itself low enough to satisfy this requirement, e.g., either by double-pulsing every nth pulse or by deleting the nth pulse altogether. As a practical consideration, one should try to avoid the use of prf's which are commensurable with the power-line frequency. Electric impulse noises produced in short bursts by motors, leaky insulators, and other sources connected to the mains are usually synchronized with the line frequency. If the radar prf is generated by a multivibrator that is not locked to the line frequency, any false echoes which may be caused by this type of interference will drift along the range sweep. Thus the interference will be spread more or less uniformly over the entire range-time record instead of appearing as a confusing and spurious echo at a fixed range. If the recurrence frequency is relatively high, very long range echoes may occasionally appear on the second or third sweeps at apparently short ranges. Such echoes may be easily recognized if the prf is deliberately "jittered," e.g., if it is generated by an unstable multivibrator or a rotating spark wheel.

Almost infinite variety seems possible in the design of meteor radars. Perhaps the lowest output power that has been employed for meteor research is the 100-watt-peak (0.2-watt-average) power used at Ottawa as part of a high-low power test (McKinley, 1951c). This transmitter was a type 12AU7 receiving tube coupled to a single dipole. Despite the very low power, the meteor echo rates ran as high as 25 hr^{-1}. At the other extreme one may cite the radar developed by the Bureau of Standards (Bowles, 1958) with a peak power of 5 megawatts (5×10^6 watts) and an average power of 40 kw, on a frequency of 41 Mc/sec. This superpower equipment, when used with a single dipole antenna, should be capable of detecting 3,000 to 4,000 meteor echoes per hour, assuming the echo rate to vary as $P^{1/2}\lambda^{3/2}$.

4-4. A low-power meteor-patrol radar. This radar system was designed by M. J. Neale of the NRC, Ottawa, especially to provide a continuous record of meteor activity throughout the International Geophysical Year (see Fig. 4-3). Conservative constructional principles, together with some monitoring and calibrating devices not usually built into a meteor radar, are largely responsible for its reliable performance. Installed at Springhill Meteor Observatory in July, 1957, the system operated so satisfactorily that it has been maintained as a meteor-patrol radar ever since the end of the IGY. The continuous 24-hr record is a valuable complement to the activities of specialized or high-power radars which are used only intermittently.

FIG. 4-3. NRC meteor-patrol radar installation. From left to right the five cabinets contain: test and monitoring equipment, range-time recording unit, monitor scope and timing apparatus, modulator and power supplies, transmitting oscillator.

The operating characteristics may be summarized briefly as follows:

Carrier frequency	32.7 Mc/sec
R-f power output	20-kw peak, 30 watts average
Pulse width	12 μsec
Pulse-recurrence frequency	117 cps
Radiation pattern	Substantially omnidirectional in azimuth; extending from the zenith to $Z = 70°$
Recording	Range-time type, on 35-mm film

The block diagram of the system is shown in Fig. 4-4. Separate but identical receiving and transmitting antennas are used, both to avoid potential trouble with a transmit-receive switch and to simplify the checking of performance. Each antenna consists of a pair of crossed horizontal dipoles fed 90° apart in phase to give a circularly polarized wave. The dipoles are supported 0.4λ above a coarse-wire-mesh ground mat (Fig. 4-5).

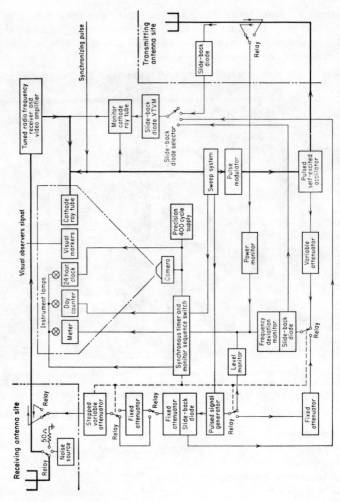

Fig. 4-4. Block diagram of NRC meteor-patrol radar. Heavy lines connect the major units of the system.

78

Fig. 4-5. Omnidirectional antenna and ground reflector used in the NRC meteor-patrol radar.

Signals from the receiving antenna (see Fig. 4-4) are amplified and detected by the receiver, which has an over-all bandpass of 500 kc/sec. Because of the wide bandwidth it is convenient and practical to use several tuned r-f stages with a linear detector and video amplifier: this eliminates any problems of image frequency signals and local oscillator drifts which

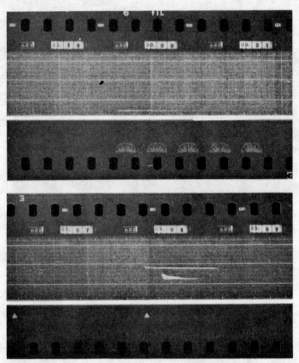

FIG. 4-6. Two samples of the records made by the meteor-patrol radar. *Top* shows the automatic calibrating sequence. The stepped test signal appears 10 sec after the hour at 50 km range and disappears into the noise. In order, the meter images show transmitter output, test-signal reference level, transmitter frequency, and test generator frequency (the fifth image is an unused spare). *Bottom* shows some meteor echoes, together with the triangular visual marker. 20-km range markers appear as black lines and 100-km markers as white lines.

could arise with a superheterodyne receiver. The range-time cathode-ray tube is photographed simultaneously with the illuminated day and hour indicators, the visual-observer's marker, and a monitoring meter (see Fig. 4-6). The range sweep is normally triggered at a prf of about 117 cps from an internal oscillator, but it may also be triggered from an external source, e.g., from a high-power radar which is used occasionally.

To avoid mutual interference in the latter case, the firing of the patrol radar is delayed by a time equivalent to 700-km range relative to the high-power pulse. The pulse modulator is a type 5C22 hydrogen thyratron switch used to discharge a pulse-forming line. The positive pulse from the modulator is applied directly to the plates of a pair of 5868 triodes working in push-pull as a self-excited oscillator.

A 400-cps tuning-fork oscillator provides a timing accuracy of ± 1 sec/day. Suitably amplified, the power from this source drives the camera and the 24-hr time indicator. In the event of failure of the 110-volt a-c mains, the fork and timing system are maintained by a battery-operated standby supply in order to maintain continuity of timing, although no attempt is made to operate the transmitter or other parts of the system during the relatively infrequent line breakdowns. The timing system incorporates a series of cams and switches to furnish impulses at intervals of 1 sec, 10 sec, 1 min, 1 hr, and 1 day. Cams are also provided to blank out the 29th, 58th, and 59th second impulses and to actuate light flashes for photographing the indicators and the monitoring meter.

Every hour a completely automatic monitoring sequence is carried out. During this period, a low-level pulsed signal is fed to the receiver through attenuators and a directional coupler: this test signal is delayed to appear at a range of 50 km on the record. At 10-sec intervals the signal level is decreased from 2 to 0.4 μv in 2-db steps. At the same time the monitoring meter is switched to indicate successively the transmitter power output, the unattenuated test-signal level, and any deviations in the frequencies of both the test-signal generator and the transmitter (see Fig. 4-6, *top*, for a typical calibration record).

Additional monitoring may be done manually. The output of a slide-back diode voltmeter, viewed on the monitor A scope, may be measured to check peak r-f level at the transmitter output and at various other points in the system. Checks may be made on the degree of mismatch of either antenna. Another feature is that either a 50-ohm matched load or a 50-ohm stabilized noise source may be switched in place of the receiving antenna when an absolute calibration of receiver-noise temperature is required.

4-5. Continuous-wave and other coherent-phase techniques. The Stanford scientists (Manning, Villard, and Peterson, 1949) were the first to record cw echoes from meteors. They used crystal-controlled transmitters which emitted pure, unmodulated carriers on either 23 or 31 Mc/sec. The output power in each case was of the order of 1 kw, radiated by a $\lambda/2$ dipole spaced $\lambda/4$ above a reflecting ground plane. A similar antenna was used at the receiving site, which was located in a small valley 6.5 km distant from the transmitter. It is essential in the cw technique that the magnitude of the direct ground wave at the receiving position should be well below the saturation level of the receiver. This is accomplished by the spatial separation, by taking advantage of natural terrain screening, and by orienting the two dipoles for minimum pickup of the direct signal. Alternatively, an auxiliary, highly directive array may be used at the receiving site to obtain from the transmitter a strong reference signal which may be applied to the receiver in the proper amplitude and phase to reduce to a reasonable level the direct signal picked up by the single dipole. The Ottawa cw observations (McKinley, 1951b) were carried out with a similar system working on 30.02 Mc/sec, where the transmitter and receiver were separated by 7.5 km. In a more sophisticated cw system the reference wave may be introduced toward the output end of the receiver, e.g., in a balanced or quadrature detector (Manning, Villard, and Peterson, 1952).

One must have the ranges of the meteor echoes if one is to translate the echo-phase fluctuations into quantitative meteor velocities or wind drifts, according to their nature. Both Stanford and Ottawa in the early days used auxiliary radars for this purpose. The correlations between the radar and the cw records were based mainly on coincidences in time, although secondary characteristics, such as a general agreement in echo intensities, were of use sometimes in resolving doubtful correlations.

Stanford was the first to use the coherent-pulse method to obtain the range as well as the phase of the meteor echo (Manning, Villard, and Peterson, 1952). Figure 4-7 is a block diagram of a similar coherent-pulse system developed by Greenhow (1954) at Jodrell Bank. In Greenhow's arrangement, the output from a 6.05 Mc/sec master crystal oscillator is pulse-modulated at a low level (20 μsec pulses at a prf of 150 cps), multiplied to 36.3 Mc/sec, amplified to a peak level of 100 kw, and then radiated from the transmitting antenna. The receiver local oscillator frequency is 37.3 Mc/sec, obtained from the 6th harmonic of a 6.217 Mc/sec crystal oscillator; hence the intermediate frequency is · centered on 1.0 Mc/sec. The beat frequency of 0.167 Mc/sec between the two crystal oscillators is also multiplied six times to give a frequency of 1.0 Mc/sec which maintains a constant phase relationship to the transmitted wave and therefore serves as a stable reference phase. One output of the receiver is an ordinary amplitude detector which may be observed on a conventional cathode-ray-tube display for purposes of measuring echo range and amplitude. Each of the other two outputs is a phase detector in which the output amplitude varies as the difference in phase between the two inputs. Number 2 phase detector has a 90° phase retardation introduced in the reference-signal output. The low-frequency beat between the signal from a moving target and the reference wave in No. 1 phase detector will therefore lead or lag the beat in No. 2 phase detector, depending on whether the target is approaching or receding. This relation will be reversed if the local oscillator frequency is chosen to be lower than the carrier frequency.

Greenhow used the coherent-pulse method for the determination of wind velocities, by observing the relatively slow phase variations caused by the drifting of the ionized clouds with the upper-air winds. The technique is also applicable to observations of diffraction–echo-phase variations from which the meteor velocity may be computed, although it will be necessary to increase the prf to 1,000 cps or more because beat

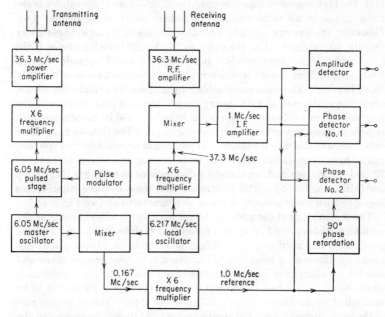

FIG. 4-7. Block diagram of a coherent-pulse radar system, with quadrature detector outputs (*after Greenhow*, 1954).

frequency components up to several hundred cycles per second will be involved in this case.

In order to measure range Robertson, Liddy, and Elford (1953), at Adelaide, superposed a 10-μsec pulse on their 27-Mc/sec cw carrier by raising the output power momentarily from 250 watts to 4 kw at 0.01 sec intervals. The Adelaide system was also phase-modulated with a 50-cps saw-tooth waveform. That is, the transmitter phase was suddenly retarded 90° and then allowed to drift linearly back to zero. The resultant "spikes" on the received waveform were used chiefly to determine whether the echo signal was higher or lower in frequency than the carrier

(approaching or receding target).   With a little additional circuitry, it
should be possible to extract range information from the phase-modulation
technique without having to resort to pulse-amplitude modulation.

4-6. Height and position measurements.   The position of a target in
space may be found by simple triangulation of the radar ranges to the
target as observed at three spaced ground stations.   In the meteor case we
must ensure that the echo at each station is from the same part of the
meteor trail.   For most of the underdense trails this will not be so—in
fact, the high degree of aspect sensitivity which these trails exhibit is the
basis of nearly all radio methods of radiant determination (Sec. 4-9).
However, the average overdense trail tends to lose its aspect sensitivity
rapidly, particularly when observed on.the longer wavelengths or if the
echo lasts at least a few seconds.   In the distribution of ionization along a
trail, irregularities can occur which may be ascribed to a number of causes
(see Chap. 8).   These are responsible for the one or more enduring echoes,
occurring at discrete and stationary ranges, that are characteristic of the
brighter meteors.   Such echoes appear to be localized in one or more small
regions in space, regardless of the viewing angle.   The Ottawa group have
determined in this way the height and position of several hundred meteors,
using three independent radar stations operating on frequencies between
32 and 36 Mc/sec and separated by distances of 36 to 57 km (McKinley
and Millman, 1949b).   The correlation was done by time coincidences
together with a comparison of the echo characteristics (see Fig. 4-8).

The zenith angle of the meteoric target may be found by comparing the
echo amplitudes picked up by two antennas which have different antenna
patterns in the vertical plane.   Clegg and Davidson (1950) placed one
receiving dipole at a height of $\lambda/2$ above a reflecting ground plane and
another at a height of $3\lambda/4$.   The power pattern of the lower antenna is
single-lobed with a null in the zenith, since the dipole pattern is to be
multiplied by the factor $\sin^2 (\pi \cos Z)$ (see Sec. 2-9).   The maximum gain
of the lower antenna occurs at zenith angles of 45 to 55°, depending on the
azimuth.   The multiplying factor for the upper antenna pattern is
$\sin^2 [(3\pi/2) \cos Z]$; hence the upper antenna will have two lobes, with a
maximum in the zenith, a null at $Z = 48.2°$, and a secondary maximum
around $Z = 65°$.   Clegg and Davidson used, at a height of $5\lambda/8$, a
separate transmitting antenna which had a pattern overlapping that
of the two receiving antennas.   With suitable switching arrangements,
the receiving antennas might be used for transmitting as well.   In either
case, the transmitting and receiving antenna patterns must be multiplied
together to determine the resultant theoretical ratio of echo powers on the
upper and lower antenna systems.

Certain ambiguities arise in this method since there are two values of Z
for each observed power ratio.   Some of these can be resolved because one
of the Z values, when combined with the range, may lead to an improbable

value of height H.   With this particular arrangement of antennas, though, either value of H could be acceptable for zenith angles between 42 and 57°; consequently, this region is not usable.   Other combinations of antenna heights could be employed to remove the ambiguities, but at the expense of increased complexity.   Despite the difficulties and limitations, the method will yield quite accurate heights of meteors occurring in acceptable regions of the sky.   Furthermore, the technique may be applied to underdense trails as well since aspect sensitivity or the lack of it is unimportant in a single-station method.   On the other hand, the system will measure bearing angle accurately only if the antenna pattern is very narrow in the horizontal plane.   In order to obtain a reasonable yield of meteor echoes, wide horizontal beamwidths are usually used, e.g., a 90° beam with a vertical-plane reflector behind the dipoles or a 360° beam with no reflectors.

The spaced-antenna method that Robertson, Liddy, and Elford (1953) devised to determine the direction of arrival of the incoming wave depends on comparisons of echo phases rather than echo amplitudes.   Three dipoles, each connected to its own receiver, are arranged at the corners of a right-angled triangle, the two short sides each being one wavelength long. The dipoles all lie in a horizontal plane located $\lambda/4$ above a ground plane reflector.   A plane wave from an elevated and distant source will reach each dipole at slightly different times, in general.   That is, there will be a difference in r-f phase at the inputs of the receivers.   The direct ground wave from the transmitter (19.6 km distant) is also picked up by the receiving antennas, so that each receiver acts as a detector of the phase difference between the direct and reflected waves at its input.   The phase difference between the slow beat frequencies at the outputs of any pair of receivers corresponds to the phase difference between the r-f waves reaching the antennas.   The phase measurement, therefore, can be done at the Doppler beat frequency rather than at the carrier frequency, where special precautions would have to be taken to ensure equality of phase shift in all receivers.   The direction cosines of the line of sight to the target are deducible directly from these measurements.   The sign of each direction cosine may be found by determining which receiver output of the given pair leads the other in phase as the target moves.

Another type of direction finder was designed by the Stanford group (Manning, Villard, and Peterson, 1950); it yields the azimuth but not the elevation of the meteor.   Four vertical receiving antennas, spaced about a vertical reflector, each cover a single quadrant.   The outputs of the antennas are sinusoidally modulated by electronic means and then combined for amplification and detection in a single receiver.   The effect is to rotate the receiving beam electronically several revolutions per second. If successive echo pulses are displayed on an A scope, for which the sweep is a saw-tooth wave of the same frequency as the modulating wave, the envelope of the pulses will be a sine wave. The phase of this envelope relative to the modulating frequency is directly equivalent to the azimuthal angle of the incoming signal. If the prf is chosen to be 16 times the modulating frequency, for example, then 16 compressed A scans will appear one after the other across the oscilloscope. Thus the separate envelopes due to echoes occurring simultaneously at different ranges can be resolved, although the degree of resolution might be improved by using range gates and multiple displays.

4-7. Velocity measurements—range-time method. Two radio methods have been developed to measure the velocity of the meteor. In the range-time method, if we assume the meteor to be following a straight-line path in space with constant velocity, the echo from the meteor head will appear on the ordinary radar range-time record as a segment of the hyperbola $R^2 = R_0^2 + V^2(t - t_0)^2 = R_0^2 + s^2$, where s is distance along the path relative to the point on the path that is nearest to the station, defined by R_0, or t_0 (see Fig. 8-1). By fitting calculated hyperbolas to the record, either graphically or analytically, one may determine V. The second method, known as the amplitude-time or diffraction method, records the rapid amplitude fluctuations that result from the echo-phase variations observed as the meteor moves across the line of sight. There are several versions of the latter technique in current use.

The range-time method was used by Hey and Stewart (1957) during the Giacobinid shower of 1946. Their work is of particular interest because it represents the first radio measurement of meteor velocity ever made. Later, McKinley and Millman (1949b) extended the technique, by means of three-station observations, to the determination of the meteor path in space and hence to the computation of the individual meteor orbit. In general the method is applicable only to the brighter meteors, from which a discrete moving echo may be obtained that is presumed to be associated with the actual meteor head. Echo records that extend over many kilometers of the meteor path have usually been necessary for accurate reductions, although the amount depends to some extent on the position on the hyperbola occupied by the observed segment. An echo detected over a 30-km path length will show a change in the range of 30 km if the meteor should happen to be coming directly at the observer. The same path length observed near the t_0 point will show a much smaller variation in echo range. The most striking echo records were created by bright meteors coming from radiants low in the sky—some of the observed paths were as long as 200 km. Meteors from radiants near the zenith have shorter ionized paths. The limitation of the method lay in the insufficient range resolution of the radar used and not in any scarcity of head echoes— ten head echoes per hour showing a range change of 5 km or so was common on the Ottawa records. A 30-km range change was needed for

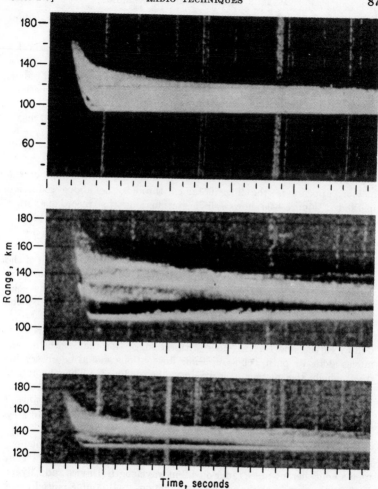

FIG. 4-8. Three-station records of a bright Perseid meteor: *(top)* Ottawa; *(center)* Arnprior; *(bottom)* Carleton Place.   The transient head echo is visible as a thin line at the left-hand side.   The enduring echo, which lasted for 549 sec at Ottawa, appears almost immediately after the head echo.

reasonably accurate work with the 1-km range resolution afforded by the Ottawa radar, and such echoes occurred at an average rate of about five per day.   A resolution of 0.1 km would permit the accurate reduction of 3-km head echoes.

Figure 4-8 shows range-time records of a very bright meteor, made at three spaced ground stations.   Here, the head echo is followed by enduring ionization which lasted for 9 min on the Ottawa record.

One may, by trial and error, fit a calculated hyperbola to the head-echo record to determine V.   If the t_0 point should not show on the photograph, various analytical methods are available to carry out the reduction.   For example, we may differentiate the equation for the hyperbola to obtain the expression $R \, dR/dt = V^2 t - V^2 t_0$, which is a straight-line relation between the quantity $R \, dR/dt$ and t of slope V^2.   Careful measurement of ΔR and Δt values will provide the data from which V may be found.   Alternatively, one may plot measured values of $s = (R^2 - R_0{}^2)^{1/2}$ against time to get a straight line of slope V.

It may happen that some curvature, denoting deceleration of the meteor, appears in the lines obtained through the above reduction methods.   Figure 4-9a shows a single-station range-time record of another bright meteor (in this instance no long-enduring ionization appeared after the passage of the meteor) which suffered a significant deceleration over its path (McKinley, 1951a).   The deceleration was measured by plotting $\Delta s/\Delta t$ values against t.   The measured velocity near the beginning of the observed path was 46.2 km/sec and near the end, 43.3 km/sec.   The mean deceleration was found to be -1.1 km/sec^2.   Figure 4-9b is the cw echo from the same meteor, from which the velocity may be found by the method to be described in the next section.

4-8. Velocity measurements—diffraction method.   Herlofson is credited by Ellyett and Davies (1948) with the suggestion that, as the meteor moves along its path, echo-amplitude fluctuations should be observable from which the meteor velocity may be deduced.   The theoretical analysis of this diffraction echo is given in Secs. 8-2 and 8-3.   The name Doppler-whistle echo has also been applied to the phenomenon because of the characteristic fall and rise in pitch of the audible beat note (in a cw system) as the meteor passes t_0.

Ellyett and Davies (1948), at Jodrell Bank, were the first to demonstrate the feasibility of measuring meteor velocities in this way.   They used a noncoherent-pulse radar on 4.2-m wavelength (Davies and Ellyett, 1949) with a prf in the range 500 to 1,000 cps, and double-pulsed every fourth pulse in order to measure range unambiguously.   Their receiver bandwidth was made wider than necessary in order to distinguish echoes clearly against the noise background.   Rather than record continuously, they used a signal discriminator and a trigger circuit whereby the sudden rise in echo amplitude as the meteor passed t_0 initiated two single-strobe A-scope sweeps.   One sweep, 7 msec long, provided the range measurement, and the other one, lasting for 0.1 sec, displayed the first 50 to 100 echo pulses following the initial pulse.   A single-frame movie camera photographed this amplitude-time record.   The radar amplitude-time records of Fig. 4-19 are illustrative of this method.   The upper limit of the fluctuation frequencies which may be observed by the pulse technique is about one-third of the prf, that is, about 300 cps.

The cw method, developed at Stanford in 1948 and used both there and

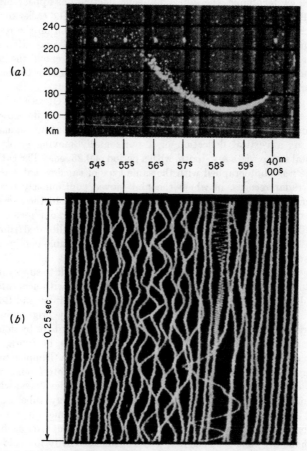

FIG. 4-9. (a) Radar range-time record of an unusual meteor head echo.   (b) Continuous-wave amplitude-time or diffraction-echo record of the same meteor.

at Ottawa, has already been mentioned in Sec. 4-5.   Two recording techniques were employed at Stanford.   In one experiment a Brush "penmotor" oscillograph, continuously running at a paper speed of 12.5 cm/ sec, enabled them to make a side-by-side comparison of the echoes received on two independent radio frequencies.   The resolution limit of the penmotor oscillograph was 120 cps, but the attainable resolution could be extended to 1,500 cps by employing ordinary magnetic-tape recorders. The magnetic tape was played back at slow speed to re-record selected meteor whistles on the paper tape.

In the cw technique, the diffraction-echo fluctuations appear prior to t_0 as well as after. The record before t_0 is often clearer and easier to measure since the slow-speed fluctuations due to wind action on the residual ion cloud tend to obscure the post-t_0 diffraction fluctuations. Hence, the recorder is usually allowed to run continuously to catch the small-amplitude signal prior to t_0. Trace-folding techniques help to conserve paper or film.

Two photographic recording techniques were used at Ottawa. In one, known colloquially as the "slow" Doppler because of its slow and economical film transport speed, the bipolar audio output signal was applied as a vertical deflection of a horizontally moving spot. The horizontal sweep was a saw-tooth, with a period of 0.25 sec. The cathode-ray tube was photographed with the same type of camera that was used for the radar records, in which the film moved continuously past the open lens at 4 in./min. Seconds pulses were applied to the saw-tooth sweep to facilitate direct comparison of the cw and radar records (see Fig. 4-10, top and bottom). The saw-tooth wave was calibrated from time to time with short timing pulses to allow for the inevitable nonlinearities in the sweep waveform.

A special 220-Mc/sec time-signal transmitter was built to supply all the radar and cw stations in the local observing network with accurate seconds pulses and with range and time calibrations (McKinley and Bourne, 1951). The nth minute of the hour was identified by brightening the radar trace (Fig. 4-10, top) at the nth second of the minute or by doubling the nth seconds pulse on the Doppler record (Fig. 4-10, bottom).

The upper limit of resolvable frequencies on the slow Doppler records was usually about 800 cps, although unusual noise or interference would lower the resolution. A fast Doppler system was also developed wherein the signal was applied horizontally to the cathode-ray tube with no vertical sweep. The film was then run through the camera in a vertical plane, back and forth eight times at a speed of 4 in./sec; after each pass, the cathode-ray-tube spot position was translated slightly to avoid overlap of the traces. The fast Doppler method produced some excellent records of meteor diffraction echoes, with a resolution limit of around 1,500 cps (see Fig. 4-11), but it was used sparingly because a standard 100-ft roll of 35-mm film lasted only 40 min, compared with 5 hr per roll for the slow Doppler and the radar films.

4-9. Radiant determinations—statistical. The amplitude of the average meteor echo reaches its peak just after the meteor passes the R_0

(or t_0) point on the trail (see Chap. 8).   This property is utilized in the statistical method for determining the common radiant point of a large number of meteors that are assumed to be members of the same shower. The radiant points of individual meteors are not measured.   Two varia-

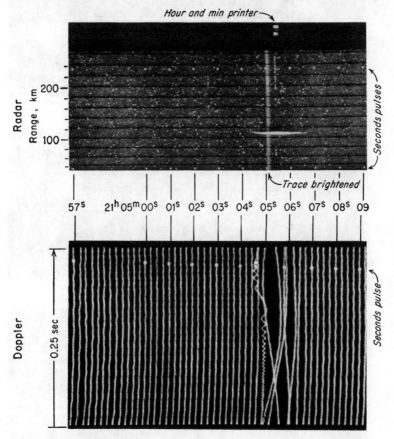

FIG. 4-10. A typical meteor echo observed (*top*) by radar, (*bottom*) by cw amplitude-time (slow Doppler) method.

tions of this technique, which depend on the same basic principle and differ mainly in detail, are on record, namely, the single-station two-beam method described by Clegg (1948) and the single-station omnidirectional-beam method (McKinley and Millman, 1949a; McKinley, 1954a).   The earliest radiant determination was in fact made in 1945 by Hey and Stewart (1947), using three independent narrow-beam radar stations

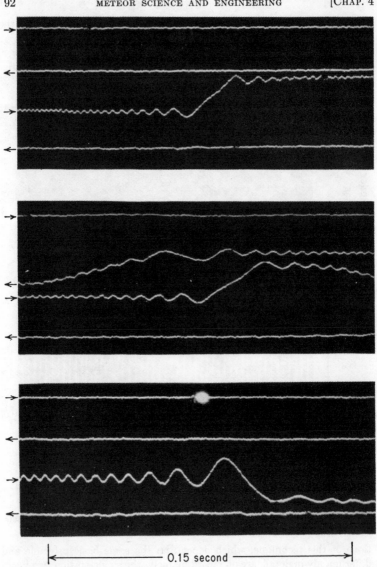

FIG. 4-11. Typical meteor diffraction-echo records obtained at Ottawa with the fast Doppler recording apparatus. The direction of travel of the film is indicated by the marginal arrows.

separated by distances of the order of 100 km. The beams intersected at a common point in the meteoric region. The position of the Delta Aquarid radiant was found without utilizing any range information by a comparison of the relative echo rate at each station. The method does not compete in accuracy or simplicity with the two mentioned above and will not be considered further here.

Two other observational methods have been developed which do yield the radiant points of individual meteors: these will be covered in Sec. 4-10. The first is the three-station method described by McKinley and Millman (1949b). From range-time records of strong head echoes the complete parameters of the meteor path may be found. The second method was implemented by Davies of Jodrell Bank (Gill and Davies, 1956); here the direction cosines of the meteor path are deduced from the differences in t_0 times observed at three receiving sites. Davies's method is undoubtedly the best of all, but the others will also be considered briefly, particularly because Clegg's method was used for many years by the Jodrell Bank workers and was the technique with which the daytime showers were discovered and delineated.

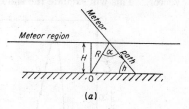

(a)

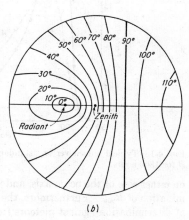

(b)

Fig. 4-12. (a) Geometry of meteor path relative to an observer at 0. (b) Curves of constant α, computed for the case $h = 45°$.

In essence, the statistical methods hinge on the fact that the strongest echo is received when the meteor has just passed the point of closest approach to the station, at the minimum range R_0. It is convenient to define the angle α between the meteor path and the line of sight drawn from the observer to a given point on the path as the *elongation from the radiant* of that point (see Fig. 4-12a). The perpendicular point on the path is $\alpha = 90°$, which corresponds to the R_0 or t_0 parameters mentioned before. Figure 4-12b shows a family of curves of constant α, plotted on a plane representing a thin-layer meteoric region, for a radiant elevation $h = 45°$. The curve of particular interest here is the straight line

$\alpha = 90°$. Theoretically, only those shower meteors that pass through or near this line will be detected. The minimum range is given by $R_{min} = H/\cos h$, where H is the height of the meteor. The elevation of the radiant may then be found from the observed R_{min} and the observed or assumed average height. The maximum range is geometrically limited only by the curvature of the earth, but other factors also enter to reduce the numbers of long-range echoes. Attenuation of echo power as R^{-3} will mean that the majority of the shower echoes will be grouped fairly closely near R_{min}. A high-gain antenna may be directed along the R_{min} vector. This will exclude the shower meteors occurring at longer ranges

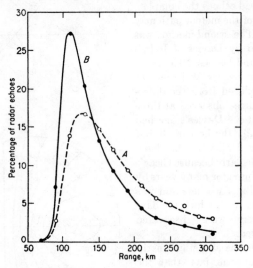

FIG. 4-13. Typical nonshower or "standard" range distributions: A for 0600 hours; B for 1800 hours.

on either side of the beam axis, and so will permit a more accurate determination of R_{min}. Furthermore, the narrow beam offers a useful measure of discrimination against meteors from radiants which may be active at the same time in other parts of the sky.

McKinley and Millman (1949a) used an antenna system that was substantially omnidirectional in azimuth. During a typical 24-hr period when no shower was present, they obtained hourly distributions of the meteor echoes with range; these served as "standard" distributions. In Fig. 4-13, A and B show two such distributions, A for a period centered on 0600 local time and B for a similar period around 1800 hours. The hourly range distributions of all echoes observed during the Geminid shower of 1947 are shown as solid curves in Fig. 4-14. By subtracting

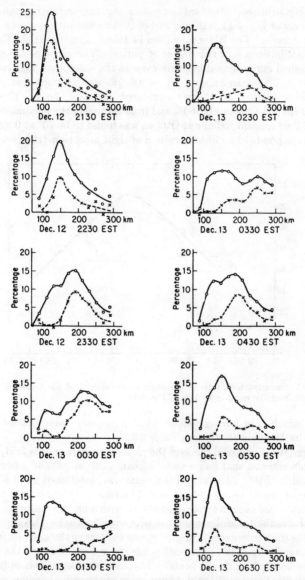

FIG. 4-14. Hourly range-distribution curves of meteor echoes obtained during the Geminid shower of 1947. *Solid line*, all echoes; *dashed line*, deduced distribution of Geminid echoes.

a suitably adjusted "standard" or nonshower distribution from the solid-line curves of Fig. 4-14, one may arrive at the distributions shown by the dashed curves. The latter may then be taken to represent the Geminid echo distributions to a fair degree of purity. The range of the peak of each dashed curve should be fairly close to the theoretical R_{min} value for that hour. A mean value of $H = 100$ km was assumed and the corresponding values of h were computed for each hour. These are plotted against time in Fig. 4-15, and from this curve the maximum elevation of the Geminid radiant at Ottawa was found to be 76° at 0208 EST. This corresponds to a radiant position at right ascension 112° declination

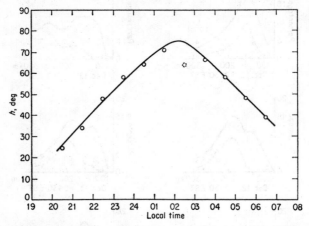

FIG. 4-15. Variation with time of the angle of elevation h of the Geminid radiant, computed from the radar-echo data of Fig. 4-14.

+31°, which is in fair agreement with the photographic radiant determined by Whipple (1947) (see Table 6-1).

Clegg (1948), who did much of the pioneering work in this field, used a steerable antenna that had a vertical beamwidth of 24° and a horizontal beamwidth of 16°. The axis of the beam was maintained at 12.5° elevation, but it could be directed to any azimuth. Continuous records of a new shower are not always easy to obtain with a narrow-beam apparatus since the radiant coordinates must be known to enable the antenna to track the shower meteors. However, one may leave the antenna fixed on one azimuth, say at 90° (due east), while the radiant rises and the shower meteors move through the beam. The time of onset of echoes from an active radiant will give the right ascension of the radiant. The antenna might then be rotated in azimuth, say to 180° (due south), and the declination of the radiant may be deduced from the difference in time of the onset of the echoes in the two beam positions. A more accurate determination of the radiant coordinates may be made if the range information is also utilized. Clegg (1948) has analyzed the problem in detail, including the effects of finite thickness of the meteoric region in the upper atmosphere and the antenna-pattern contours. Theoretical range-time contours may be computed for any preselected radiant point and setting of the antenna, and by trial one may determine the best fit with the observations.

A special radiant-survey apparatus, operating on 72 Mc/sec, was built at Jodrell Bank for the continuous and routine survey of radiant activity (Aspinall, Clegg, and Hawkins, 1951). Two permanent antennas were used, one directed on a bearing of 242° and the other on 292°. The beamwidths were each about 10 by 10°, elevated 8.5° above the horizon. The radar transmitter supplied both antennas simultaneously, and the received signals were fed via transmit-receive switches to a common receiver. The receiver input was switched at half the recurrence frequency to each antenna in turn, and at the same time the receiver output was switched alternately to two photographically recorded cathode-ray-tube displays. A set of typical examples of observed range-time plots obtained with this equipment is shown in Fig. 4-16. Theoretical range-time contours have been drawn on the charts to correspond to a radiant at right ascension 111.5°, declination 32.5° for the 1949 data, and at right ascension 112.2°, declination 32.5° for the 1950 data. The agreement with the known position of the Geminid radiant was excellent and established confidence in the technique when it was applied to the newly discovered daytime showers with previously unknown radiant points.

4-10. Radiant determinations—individual meteors. Three-station radar records of a meteor head echo may be reduced to yield the path position and orientation in space. The meteor velocity may be found from any or all of the three records. The path of the meteor which produced the records of Fig. 4-8 was determined by triangulation of ranges measured at the same instants at all three stations. This meteor had a radiant within 1° of the Perseid radiant and a velocity which varied from 60 km/sec at the beginning to 55 km/sec near the end of its path: one may therefore reasonably assume that it was a Perseid. Since it occurred in daylight, there were no visual observations.

From other three-station echo records, including those of some non-shower meteors, several meteor orbits have been computed in this manner (McKinley and Millman, 1949b). Per 50 hr of operation, the early Ottawa records yielded only about one example like Fig. 4-8 which was considered to be of adequate quality to permit the velocity to be measured to 1 per cent and the radiant position to 2° or so. The number of usable echoes can be greatly increased by raising the transmitter

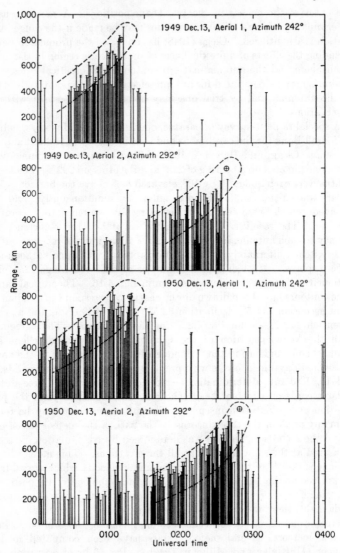

FIG. 4-16. Typical range-time plots obtained with the Jodrell Bank radiant-survey apparatus during the Geminid showers of 1949 and 1950. (*Lovell*, 1954.)

power (without changing the antenna gain, since an omnidirectional beam is highly desirable) and, more important, by increasing the range resolution to permit records of shorter path lengths to be accurately analysed. However, useful as the technique has been in the past and will probably be in the future for the detailed examination of individual bright-meteor phenomena, it will not compete, for orbital computations at least, with the ingenious method developed by Davies at Jodrell Bank.

Several years before Davies started his orbital work a general method for determining all the geometrical parameters of the meteor path from observations at three closely spaced stations was put forward by Manning (1948). The potentialities of Manning's proposal do not seem to have been fully explored in practice, but with recent improvements in observing techniques, it should be possible to devise a system which would

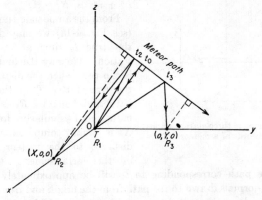

FIG. 4-17. Geometry of Davies's three-station system for determining meteor orbits.

yield complete and accurate data on single meteors. The geometry of Davies's experiment might be regarded as a particular case of Manning's general treatment; whether or not it was based on Manning's suggestion, the elegance and simplicity of Davies's analysis merits some detailed consideration here. For orbital computations, only the direction and velocity of the meteor are needed (although deceleration measurements would be highly desirable) and Davies's work is tailored strictly to these ends.

In Davies's method (Gill and Davies, 1956; Davies, 1957) a radar transmitter T and a receiver R_1 are located at the origin of a Cartesian coordinate system, as in Fig. 4-17. At the point $(X,0,0)$ is a second receiver R_2, and a third receiver R_3 may be placed at the point $(0,Y,0)$, for convenience and simplicity in the analysis—the third receiver does not have to lie on the Y axis in practice. The distances X and Y are about 3 to 4 km, so that specularly reflected echoes are likely to be received at all three stations from the same meteor trail, assuming that the trail may have a path length of 20 km or so. The diffraction-echo waveforms observed at R_2 and R_3 can be transmitted to the master station by telephone lines for timing comparisons. The equation of the meteor path in space is

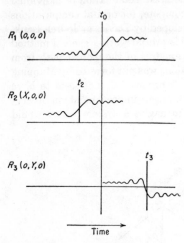

$$\frac{x - x_1}{L} = \frac{y - y_1}{M} = \frac{z - z_1}{N}$$

where x_1, y_1, z_1 are points on the meteor path, L, M, and N are the direction cosines of the line, and $L^2 + M^2 + N^2 = 1$.

From the amplitude-time records (see Fig. 4-18) we may determine the true t_0 time at the master station. We may also find t_2, which is the time when the distance from the transmitter T to the meteor path and back to R_2 is a minimum, and similarly for t_3. If X is small compared with the distance to the meteor, as it is in this arrangement, then the point on the path corresponding to t_2 will be approximately halfway between the normals drawn to the path from the origin and from $(X,0,0)$. The distance along the path between the normals is LX. The meteor velocity V can be measured from any of the records; hence, to a good approximation, we have

FIG. 4-18. Drawing of three-station amplitude-time cw records of a meteor diffraction echo.

$$L = \frac{2V(t_0 - t_2)}{X}$$

and similarly

$$M = \frac{2V(t_0 - t_3)}{Y}$$

and

$$N = -(1 - L^2 - M^2)^{\frac{1}{2}}$$

the negative square root being taken because all meteors are descending. In this manner the direction cosines of the meteor path may be computed; that is, the radiant point may be found. Note that the position in space of the path relative to the origin is not determined, nor is it needed for radiant and orbital calculation.

Davies used an ordinary noncoherent-pulse radar, which shows the diffraction fluctuations only after the meteor has passed the points cor-

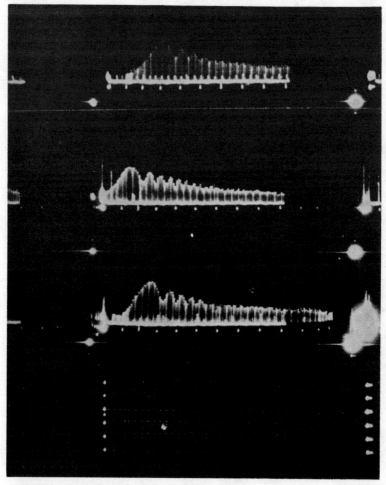

FIG. 4-19. Three-station amplitude-time radar records of a meteor echo observed at Jodrell Bank, from which the meteor velocity, radiant, and orbit may be computed. (*Courtesy of J. G. Davies.*)

responding to t_0, t_2, and t_3.   A typical set of his records is shown in Fig. 4-19.   A cw system or a coherent-pulse radar should be capable of providing greater accuracy in the time measurements, because the diffraction waveforms will effectively bracket the transit times.   However, Davies (1957) has produced more than 4,000 individual meteor orbits from his "one-sided" records, with an average precision of $\pm 3°$ in radiant position and ± 2 km/sec in meteor velocity.   The instrumental errors are smaller than these over-all errors, which include residual uncertainties in the correction for deceleration and in the allowance for wind shears.   Meteors as faint as the eighth magnitude give satisfactory results.   An analog computer was built to help with the film analysis and velocity measurement, and the reduced observational data were then fed into a high-speed digital computer for the orbital calculations.

It may help the reader if we draw some comparisons and distinctions among the three kinds of three-station techniques that have been mentioned in this chapter.   The Adelaide system uses base lines of the order of 4 to 5 m long, and the method, which essentially measures differential phases, gives the direction cosines of the line joining the group of receivers to the meteor but not the direction cosines of the meteor path.   Note that the 19.6-km separation between the Adelaide transmitter and the group of three receiving antennas was introduced chiefly to avoid saturation of the receivers by the cw ground wave, and it is not an intrinsic feature of the system.   The Jodrell Bank method employs base lines of the order of 4 to 5 km long and, by measuring time differentials, yields the direction cosines of the path but not the position of the meteor in space.   The Ottawa technique utilizes baselines of the order of 40 to 50 km long and, by measuring the absolute ranges, produces the direction cosines of both the line of sight and the meteor path.   Unfortunately, not many echoes are suitable for this method.

4-11. Wind measurements.   Mention has been made in earlier sections of this chapter of several equipments which have been designed to measure the effects of winds on the ionized cloud left after the passage of the meteor.   The earliest radio wind experiments with meteors appear to have been done at Stanford (Manning, Villard, and Peterson, 1950, 1954).   Their direction-finding system determined the azimuth of the target but not the elevation.   By observing the difference in frequency between the transmitted and received waves for each of a large number of meteors observed at various azimuths around the station, they were able to deduce the mean magnitude of the wind speed in the meteoric region.

The observed body-Doppler shift of the echo wave relative to the reference wave will be $\pm 2U_r/\lambda$ cps, where U_r is the radial component of the wind velocity relative to the station.   The plus sign applies to targets approaching the station.   Let us assume that the wind has a uniform velocity U directed along a given azimuth but inclined to the horizontal at a "dip angle" β.   It follows from elementary geometry that, for a meteor occurring at an azimuth angle θ relative to the wind direction,

$$U_r = U\left[1 - \left(\frac{H}{R}\right)^2\right]^{\frac{1}{2}} \cos\theta \cos\beta - U\frac{H}{R}\sin\beta \qquad (4\text{-}1)$$

where H is the height and R the range of the meteor. As a first approximation one may assume $\beta = 0$, i.e., a horizontal wind, when $\cos \beta = 1$ and the second term of Eq. (4-1) drops out. The average Doppler shift should therefore vary as $\cos \theta$. One may fit a cosine curve to the observations, as indicated in Fig. 4-20, and thereby determine θ, the direction of the mean wind velocity.

A small vertical displacement of the cosine curve (see Fig. 4-20) implies that the dip angle of the wind was not quite zero in this case. On the average, the Stanford data demonstrated that the winds were horizontal to within a few degrees. In particular they showed that at a frequency of 23 Mc/sec the drifting of the ionized clouds was not affected by the earth's magnetic field. Their rate of usable echoes was of the order of

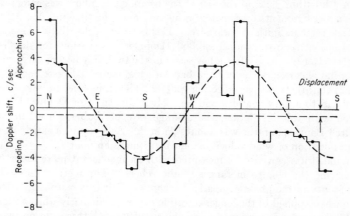

FIG. 4-20. Average body-Doppler frequency shift versus wind direction, obtained at Stanford on Sept. 11, 1949.

100 hr^{-1}, and one or two hours of observation served to specify average wind velocities to perhaps 20 per cent and directions to within 20°.

The direction-finding equipment employed by the Adelaide group (Robertson, Liddy, and Elford, 1953) differed radically from the Stanford gear (see Sec. 4-6), but they used essentially the same technique for computing the wind velocity from the observed Doppler frequency shifts. They also found that the winds were substantially horizontal (Elford and Robertson, 1953) and that the mean velocity of the wind increased with height.

At Ottawa, Rao (1958, 1959) developed a technique for finding the wind vector which effectively depended on measuring the rate of change with time of the observed body-Doppler frequency. He used the Ottawa three-station radar data to locate the position in space of the meteoric cloud and obtained the fading rates from the accompanying cw records. From the practical viewpoint the method, as actually applied, is subject to the same drawbacks as the Adelaide method, namely, that not very many suitable echoes per hour are available and the work of reduction is considerable.

The most sustained attack on the problem of determining wind velocities was that of Greenhow (1954), who used a coherent-pulse technique. He did not attempt to measure the azimuth angles of individual meteors randomly distributed across the sky but employed instead a narrow-beam antenna which could be pointed alternately in two directions at right angles for 10-min periods. The polar diagram of this antenna was stated to be such that an echo had a 50 per cent probability of lying on an azimuth within $\pm 12°$ of the axis of the beam. Greenhow was careful to make measurements on a meteor echo only over the time interval 0.2 to 1.0 sec after its initial appearance. This is because the diffraction-echo fluctuations tend to confuse the body-Doppler observations for the first 0.2 sec after t_0. Also, after a few seconds, the trail may become distorted by wind shears, or it may have had an irregular initial distribution of ionization: the multiple reflecting centers which thus tend to be created can lead to a very complex and unresolvable pattern of Doppler beats. Even with this restriction, the average rate of usable echoes on the Jodrell Bank apparatus was about 125 hr^{-1}. As a result, a satisfactory determination of wind velocity could be made in an hour.

Wind drifts can also be measured with an incoherent-pulse radar by observing the change in ranges of the echoes. The method lacks the sensitivity of the phase-comparison technique, but it is reasonably effective when applied to the longer-duration types, particularly when a high-resolution radar is employed (Greenhow, 1952b). A three-station radar system can track the progress of long-duration meteoric targets in three dimensions (McKinley, 1956). The value of these two range-measuring methods lies largely in the detailed examination that may be made of the effects of winds on individual meteor trails; suitable echoes do not occur often enough to warrant the converse use of the methods to measure winds on a routine basis.

CHAPTER 5

Observational Data on Meteors

A short compendium of the available observational material is usually considered to be an essential feature of a book on meteors, though one cannot pretend to do much more than scan the highlights. A considerable degree of selection and compression has to be applied to the large mass of published material. It should be pointed out that, despite the title, this chapter is not intended to be a bare recital of raw information, undigested and undiscussed. Recourse to the physical theory of the following chapters will be necessary from time to time in establishing some coherence of the experimental results, and occasionally it will be convenient to develop the appropriate argument on the spot. Furthermore, the presentation of observational evidence is not confined to this chapter alone: additional data has been introduced liberally throughout the book to support a theory or to illustrate an experimental technique. All of the observing methods mentioned in the earlier pages have contributed to the fund, though it seems fair to say that the most precise information to date has stemmed from photography. Radio, a late starter, is fast becoming a close competitor in many aspects; it is also filling a gap not covered at all by the older methods. Later chapters, which go into radio theory and practice in more detail, will logically contain some further observational material which would otherwise have been included here.

5-1. Meteor rates and magnitudes. At first glance it might appear that the determination of the rate of influx of meteors should be comparatively straightforward. However, each technique has its own restrictions, based on limiting magnitude, field of view, or meteor-path geometry; hence a somewhat different selection of the meteor population is made by each method. For measurements of relative variations in daily or annual rates, any one method is usually self-consistent, but the determination of absolute rates will depend on a number of correction factors, some of which are uncertain. We will now take the visual method as an example—different correction factors must be evaluated for the radio and the photographic observations.

Experience shows that a visual observer should detect each hour under standard conditions n_0 zero-magnitude meteors, $n_1 = rn_0$ meteors of first magnitude, and $n_2 = r^2 n_0$ meteors of second magnitude, and so on, where r is a constant in the range 2.5 to 4.0. The naked-eye limit is about fifth magnitude, and long before this limit is reached the observer will begin to miss meteors. His observed r will therefore differ from the true r as the meteor magnitudes become fainter. All visual observations tend to follow the trend shown in Fig. 5-1, *naked-eye visual*, where the total number observed down to various given absolute photographic magnitudes are shown as large dots. The leveling-off at about zero absolute photographic magnitude (corresponding roughly to 1.8 absolute visual magnitude) is apparent, although over the straight-line part of the

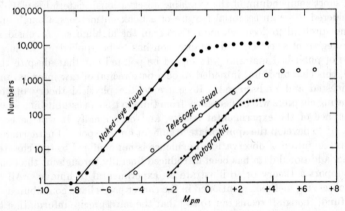

FIG. 5-1. The relative number of meteors N observed down to and including a given absolute-magnitude limit, versus absolute photographic magnitude at maximum brightness. *Naked-eye visual:* 10,287 meteors, Millman and Burland (*Millman*, 1957). *Telescopic visual:* 1,842 meteors, Kresáková and Kresák (1955). *Photographic:* 241 meteors, Hawkins and Upton (1958).

naked-eye curve one may assume a constant value of r. The observer's effective field of view for a bright meteor is much greater than for a faint one, and this is one of the major factors contributing to the fall-off in numbers with increasing magnitude.

If a group of six experienced watchers is adopted as a standard, the total count, summed over all magnitudes, made by any other number of observers should be multiplied by a factor f to equate it to the standard count. Figure 5-2 illustrates the variation of f with the number in the group, as adopted by Millman.

With respect to the fraction of meteors observable down to a given limiting magnitude, Öpik (1922) thought that a single observer should see all second-magnitude meteors in his normal field of view, 90 per cent of third magnitude, 50 per cent of fourth magnitude, and 8 per cent of fifth magnitude. On the other hand, Millman believed that his standard team of six observers should see all zero-magnitude meteors, but only 60 per cent of the first magnitude, 25 per cent of the second magnitude, 10 per cent of the third, 2 per cent of the fourth, and less than 0.5 per cent of the fifth-magnitude objects, visible over the entire sky. Other workers have evolved still different correction factors for this effect, for example,

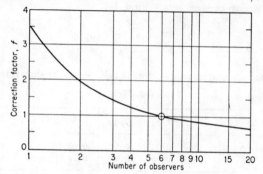

FIG. 5-2. The factor f to be applied to a meteor count made by an observing group of given size to adjust the count to the standard count for six observers.

Ceplecha (1950) and Kvíz (1958). If we adopt Millman's work we may assign a factor F as the amount by which the observed number should be multiplied to yield the true number. Table 5-1 lists Millman's relation between limiting apparent magnitude M_v and F.

Table 5-1. Factor F

M_v	0.5	1.5	2.5	3.5	4.5	5.5
F	1.0	1.5	2.5	5	12	30

We now return to the original problem, which may be defined as the determination of N_M, the number of meteors of absolute magnitude M and brighter entering the atmosphere over 10^4 km^2 of the earth's surface per hour. If we tentatively assume a constant ratio r for all magnitudes, we have $N_M = n_M r/(r - 1)$, the sum of a geometrical progression, where n_M is the number in a unit magnitude interval about M. The apparent magnitude of a meteor will be affected by its range and zenith angle (see Sec. 2-2). For a given zenith angle Z the relation between the true number N_M and the observed number $N_{M,ob}$ of apparent magnitude M_{ob} is

$$\frac{N_M}{N_{M,ob}} = \frac{n_M}{n_{M,ob}} = r^{(M-M_{ob})z} = r^{\Delta M z} \tag{5-1}$$

Values of ΔM_Z can be obtained from Fig. 2-1.   Note that ΔM_Z is negative because $M_{ob} > M$.

Consider an annular zone about the zenith, of area $A_Z \times 10^4$ km^2 and having a mean angular radius Z. $A_Z N_M$ meteors will arrive per hour over each annular area A_Z, and of this true number, the observer will actually see $A_Z N_M r^{\Delta M_Z}$.   The annular ring contributions may be summed over the whole of the observer's sky to yield the total number W seen by a specified group of observers.   First, let

$$\frac{1}{g} = \sum_{Z=0°}^{Z=90°} A_Z r^{\Delta M_Z} \tag{5-2}$$

Millman has computed values of g for selected r's as shown in Table 5-2

Table 5-2. Factor g

r	1.5	2.5	3.5	4.5	5.5
Naked-eye...........	0.04	0.16	0.25	0.32	0.37
Telescopic..........	0.05	0.14	0.19	0.22	0.23

If Q_M is the hourly rate for the standard team of six, then the total number W seen by any other group of observers will be

$$W = FfQ_M = \frac{N_M}{g} \tag{5-3}$$

by incorporating the correction factors mentioned earlier.

Let $\mathbf{N}_M$ be the total number of meteors of magnitude M and brighter encountered by the earth's atmosphere in a 24-hr period.   Since the effective surface area of the meteoric region is 5.26×10^8 km^2 (for a sphere $6,370 + 100$ km in radius) we have

$$\mathbf{N}_M = \frac{5.26 \times 10^8 \times 24}{10^4} N_M$$

$$= 1.26 \times 10^6 (gFfQ_M) \tag{5-4}$$

where Q_M is an average over the period.

Visual and telescopic data from many sources, covering meteors from magnitude -6 to $+7$, yield various r's in the range 2.3 to 4.0.   The best telescopic data in this respect are probably the work of Kresáková and Kresák (1955), shown plotted as open circles in Fig. 5-1.   Here, $r = 2.5$ for the straight-line part.   The Harvard Super-Schmidt photographic results (Fig. 5-1, *small dots*) yield $r = 3.44$, which agrees fairly closely with the Ottawa data for which $r = 3.7$.   Öpik (1958b) found an average value of $r = 3.3$ for all the meteors observed on the Arizona Expedition program.   Furthermore, Öpik was able to break this down according to the types of orbits followed by the meteors: for retrograde orbits he obtained $r = 2.80$, and for direct orbits near the plane of the ecliptic $r = 3.56$ and 3.66. From radio observations, the Jodrell Bank workers have concluded that the frequency of meteors increases by 2.5 per radio magnitude from zero to tenth magnitude, after the effects of strong showers such as the Perseids and Geminids have been removed from the data (Browne, Bullough, Evans, and Kaiser, 1956). Dr. J. S. Greenhow has been kind enough to give us, in advance of publication, some results of his recent work in this area. He concludes that the early radio estimates of r were low because of an inadequate allowance for the ceiling cutoff of echoes from faint meteors (Sec. 8-6) and that $r = 3.8$ may be a more realistic figure down to $M_v = 10$. Millman, in summing up, has adopted $r = 3.7$ over the range $M_v = -6$ to 1. The ratio may drop to as low as 2.5 at $M_v = 5$, but it is more likely to be somewhere between 2.5 and 3.7 down to $M_v = 10$. We know very little about the increase per magnitude for meteors fainter than $M_v = 10$.

We may now compute $\mathbf{N}_M$, the total daily numbers of visible meteors encountering the earth, from Eq. 5-4. Millman used $r = 3.7$ for $-6 \leq M_v \leq 1$ and reduced r gradually to 2.5 in the neighborhood of $M_v = 5$. As a fiducial point he has estimated that $\mathbf{N}_0 = 1 \times 10^6$; hence by summation he concludes that $\mathbf{N}_5 = 200 \times 10^6$. Hawkins and Upton (1958) are inclined to agree with Watson (1956) that $\mathbf{N}_5$ may be somewhat less, say about 75 to 90 million meteors. An uncertainty factor of 2 or 3 in the estimate is not unreasonable in view of the correction factors involved, some of which may differ by nearly an order of magnitude depending on the authority cited. Lack of understanding or agreement alone can cause significant discrepancies. For example, Millman defines the magnitude interval for a fifth-magnitude meteor as extending from 4.50 . . . to 5.49 . . . , whereas other writers may mean the interval 4.00 . . . to 5.00 . . . . This ambiguity can be perplexing where an author refers to "meteors brighter than fifth magnitude," when the context suggests that he may mean "meteors of fifth magnitude and brighter."

The relations between N_M, r, and M which were deduced in Eqs. (5-1) to (5-4) may be restated as a differential equation,

$$dN_M = \text{constant} \times r^M \, dM \qquad (5\text{-}5)$$

where dN_M is the number of meteors arriving between the magnitudes M and $M + dM$. This may be integrated from $M = -\infty$ to M to give

$$\log_{10} N_M = \log_{10} N_0 + M \log_{10} r \qquad (5\text{-}6)$$

where the constant of integration is the log of the numbers arriving with $M = 0$ and brighter. The problem is the same—to determine the values of N_0 and r from the observational data.

Hawkins and Upton (1958) concluded that $\log_{10} N_0 = -4.33$ for the per-hour total of all meteors of photographic magnitude zero and brighter striking 1 km²/hr. They made an approximate correction for the color index to arrive at $\log N_0 = -5.17$ for visual meteors. Hence

$$\log_{10} N_{M_v} \simeq -5.17 + 0.537 M_v \qquad (5\text{-}7)$$

for the meteoric flux per square kilometer per hour.

The number $\mathbf{N}_M$ encountered by the earth in a 24-hr period may be found by adding 10.10 ($= \log_{10} 5.26 \times 10^8 + \log_{10} 24$) to -5.17. With the new constant, 4.93, we find $\mathbf{N}_5 = 41 \times 10^6$. Since Hawkins and Upton (1958) state that $\mathbf{N}_5 = 91 \times 10^6$, it might be well to revise the constant upward to 5.27 to be consistent with their evaluation. The world-wide daily influx is then

$$\log_{10} \mathbf{N}_M \simeq 5.27 + 0.537 M \qquad (5\text{-}8)$$

This equation is assumed to apply over the range of observed photographic magnitudes.

We may express Millman's observations similarly, though the range $-10 \leq M_v \leq 10$ may be covered by three equations to provide a better fit with his data. One uses the equation appropriate to the M_v selected:

$$\log_{10} \mathbf{N}_M \simeq 6.0 + 0.57 M \qquad -10 \leq M_v \leq 0 \qquad (5\text{-}9a)$$
$$\log_{10} \mathbf{N}_M \simeq 6.0 + 0.50 M \qquad 0 \leq M_v \leq 3 \qquad (5\text{-}9b)$$
$$\log_{10} \mathbf{N}_M \simeq 6.3 + 0.40 M \qquad 3 \leq M_v \leq 10 \qquad (5\text{-}9c)$$

The numbers-magnitude relation given in Watson's (1956) Table 18 may be described analytically as

$$\log_{10} \mathbf{N}_M \simeq 5.88 + 0.40 M \qquad -3 \leq M_v \leq 10 \qquad (5\text{-}10)$$

Figure 5-3 shows, in graphical form, the three sets of observational data which were summarized by Eqs. (5-8) to (5-10), inclusive. There is no significant disagreement over the normal visual range. Any extension of the graphs outside the range $-10 \leq M_v \leq 10$ should be regarded as highly speculative. In the vicinity of $M_v = -10$, where Eq. (5-9a) suggests that the world daily total may be 1 or 2 meteors, we have entered the range of meteorite-dropping objects. At the other extreme, somewhere around the eighteenth magnitude perhaps, the sizes of the particles become so small that they are slowed down in the atmosphere without creating light or ionization. These micrometeorites cannot be detected by optical or radio methods.

If we adopt the radio-visual magnitude relation given by Eq. (2-3) and substitute for M in Eq. (5-7), we have

$$\log_{10} N_{M,r} \simeq 16 - 1.34 \log_{10} q \qquad (5\text{-}11)$$

for the number of radio meteors of visual magnitude M_v and brighter arriving per square kilometer per hour. Similar equations may be derived for $\mathbf{N}_{M,r}$ from Eqs. (5-8) to (5-10), inclusive. Equation (5-11) may be considered fairly satisfactory to about magnitude 5. Recent evidence suggests that the relation may be good even to $M = 10$, in contrast to earlier opinions that for magnitudes fainter than 5 the value of r dropped to around 2.5 and the coefficient of $\log_{10} q$ approached unity.

As we see from above, the visual data are very useful in evaluating the constants for the radio case, although one can establish an absolute radio

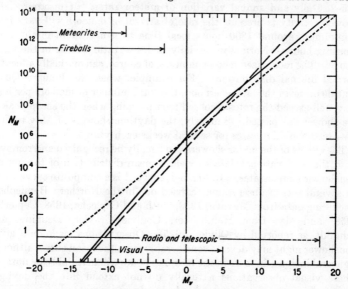

Fig. 5-3. The total number of meteors N_M incident upon the whole earth in a 24-hr period, observed down to and including a limiting absolute visual magnitude M_v. *Solid curve*, after Millman; *dashed curve*, after Hawkins and Upton; *dotted curve*, after Watson.

relation without the help of visual correlations. The basic problems are analogous, though not identical, to those which arose in the reduction of the optical data. To begin with, because of the strong aspect sensitivity of the fainter meteor trails, an estimate must be made of the fraction of the total meteor population which is detectable by radio. Kaiser (1953) and Weiss (1957c) have tackled this problem for the fainter meteors. Browne (1958) has carried out calculations with the aid of an electronic computer to determine the relation between the true and observed distributions for the brighter meteors. A bright meteor produces an overdense trail with less aspect sensitivity and longer duration; hence an increasingly larger fraction of the true number of a given magnitude will be detected as one goes to brighter magnitudes. The dependence of ionization on meteor velocity is a factor which must be assessed. The nature of this dependence has not been as well recognized as the analogous variation of the luminous efficiency with velocity, which is itself not known with certainty (see Sec. 7-3). The results of these independent reductions of the radio observations agree reasonably well with the optical-radio computations when the two scales are tied together through a common factor.

5-2. Daily and annual variation of meteor rates. If no appreciable shower activity is present, the rate of arrival of meteors will vary from a minimum around 1800 hours local time to a maximum in the early morning hours. Normally the daily high-low ratio will be in the range 3 to 5. The recognized meteor showers, of course, can markedly affect the normal diurnal distributions. For example, when the January Quadrantids occur in the late afternoon, the total number of meteors per hour may well exceed the rates recorded next morning when the sharp peak of the shower has passed. Similarly, the daytime showers of May to July elevate the midday rates for several weeks each year.

The effects of the major showers can usually be recognized and removed from the observational data to yield a mean distribution of the normal nonshower meteor rates. In Fig. 5-4, curve A is a composite curve based on several sets of observations carried out in the Northern Hemisphere (including data from Maveva, 1953, Guth and Ceplecha, 1958, Ceplecha, 1958, and also from Hoffmeister, Coulvier-Gravier, Denning, and Schmidt, as reported by Olivier, 1925). Observations made on a given nonshower night may deviate considerably from the mean curve, although a general increase in rates in the morning hours will invariably be noticed. These visual observations naturally do not extend into the daylight hours—this gap can be spanned only by the radio methods.

Curve B of Fig. 5-4 is based on backscatter radar observations made at Ottawa, comprising some 100,000 echoes observed on eight different days throughout one year. The limiting sensitivity of the radar equipment was about ninth magnitude. Curve C shows the mean daily variations of 5,800 nonshower meteor echoes obtained with the Ottawa backscatter cw equipment (McKinley, 1951b). Each of these meteors produced a good diffraction-echo record from which the velocity was determined. Because of the special selection, the average limiting magnitude for curve C was probably about 4 or 5. The forward-scatter observations made over an 860-km path by Vogan and Campbell (1957) are shown in Fig. 5-4, curve D. More than 210,000 forward-scatter echoes are included in these data obtained from continuous operation over a complete calendar year. Although Vogan and Campbell made no attempt to separate shower and nonshower meteors, the general trend of their curve is quite similar to the

others.   Their work is typical of the statistical results obtainable with
the forward-scatter technique.   Despite the difficulties and ambiguities
which are inherent in the more complicated geometry of the method, very
useful data can be obtained.   This is particularly true in the case of
strong showers where the radiant is known (Hines, 1955, 1958; Forsyth,
Hines, and Vogan, 1955).

Weiss (1957a), in Australia, has obtained monthly averages of the
daily rate distributions of nonshower meteors.   There are marked
changes in both the shapes of the curves and the maximum rates from

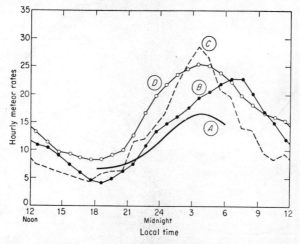

FIG. 5-4. The mean daily variation of meteor rates. *Curve A*, nonshower visual
observations, based on data from several sources (see text).   Use ordinate scale as
shown. *Curve B*, backscatter radar observations, 100,000 echoes.   Multiply ordinate
scale by 50.   (*NRC, Ottawa.*)   *Curve C*, backscatter cw observations, 5,800 echoes.
Use ordinate scale as shown.   (*NRC, Ottawa.*)   *Curve D*, forward-scatter cw observations, 210,000 echoes.   Multiply ordinate scale by 2.   (*Vogan and Campbell*, 1957.)

month to month.   As Weiss points out, though, one feature of interest
is that the diurnal curve for a given month tends to repeat itself in successive years, even to the point of duplicating some seemingly minor
irregularities.   This suggests that, despite the best efforts to remove the
effects of the known showers, many meteors from minor annual showers
still remain in the data.   It may be that a large number of the so-called
sporadic or nonshower meteors would be found to be members of weak
streams if one were able to resolve and identify them.   Hawkins (1956a)
has carried out a similar radar survey of sporadic radiants in the Northern
Hemisphere.   His diurnal rate curves also show significant changes from
month to month.   The effects of the daytime meteor activity in May,

June, and July show up more strongly in Hawkins's work than in the results published by Weiss.

The annual variation of visual meteor rates has been investigated by a number of distinguished meteor scientists. Perhaps the best set of recent records is that assembled by Murakami (1955) from observations made over a period of five years by the Oriental Astronomical Association. Murakami took care to eliminate the recognizable showers from his data

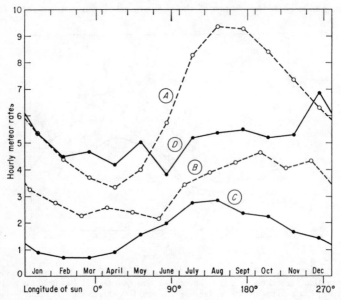

FIG. 5-5. The mean annual variation of meteor rates. *Curve A*, naked-eye visual observations. (*Murakami*, 1955.) *Curve B*, telescopic visual observations. (*Kresáková and Kresák*, 1955.) *Curve C*, forward-scatter radio observations. Multiply ordinate scale by 20. (*Vogan and Campbell*, 1957.) *Curve D*, backscatter radio observations. Multiply ordinate scale by 2. (*Weiss*, 1957a.)

as far as possible and achieved the graph of annual variation of nonshower meteor rates shown in Fig. 5-5, curve *A*. The salient feature of this curve is that the rates are low in the early months of the calendar year and high during the latter half. A similar annual rate variation for nonshower telescopic meteors (Fig. 5-5, curve *B*) has been published by Kresáková and Kresák (1955). This is based on several years work by many observers at the Skalnaté Pleso Observatory in Czechoslovakia. They used binoculars with an aperture of 100 mm, thus extending the detection limit to the tenth or eleventh magnitude. One may note the broad minimum during spring in the Northern Hemisphere and the maximum during the autumn months.

In passing, it may be remarked that the average rate of 3.5 meteors per hour observed in Czechoslovakia is typical of the rates reported by other workers using similar optical aids in observations down to the tenth or eleventh magnitude: for example, 4.0 hr^{-1}, Öpik (1930); 2.8 hr^{-1}, Astapovich (1935); 4.0 hr^{-1}, Williams (1939). The one startling exception is the series of observations carried out by T. C. Poulter of Stanford Research Institute during the second Byrd Antarctic Expedition, 1933–1935. Using 7 × 50 Zeiss Navy binoculars, Poulter's observers reported rates ranging from 30 to 1,000 meteors per hour! Poulter thought that the clear, cold Antarctic nights were at least partly responsible for these phenomenal rates—his correlation between rates and ambient temperature indicates that the colder it got, the more meteors they saw—but there may be other factors involved. In this connection a Stanford meteor radar was sent to the Antarctic during the IGY. Only the normal rates of meteor echoes were observed. This suggests, though it does not prove conclusively, that the earlier visual results may not have been entirely realistic. Further visual observations in the Antarctic will be needed to solve the puzzle satisfactorily.

The Canadian forward-scatter radio results are presented as curve C in Fig. 5-5. Although these forward-scatter data of Vogan and Campbell have not been purged of shower meteors, any contribution of such meteors to the over-all record does not appear to have masked the general agreement in form of this curve with the visual observations. Weiss (1957a), at Adelaide, has accumulated radio-echo information over a period of four years, which is summarized in curve D of Fig. 5-5. Again, the minimum occurs in the early part of the year and the maximum toward the end. In this case, though, the trend is rather unexpected because, as the following discussion will show, one might have anticipated that observations made in the Southern Hemisphere should show a maximum in March and a minimum in September.

5-3. Discussion of the daily and annual variations. The problem of accounting for the observed daily and annual variations of meteor activity was first investigated by Schiaparelli (1866) and pursued further by other scientists, notably von Niessl (1878) and Hoffmeister (1948). One may start with the simple assumptions that meteor radiants are uniformly distributed over the celestial sphere and that each radiant produces meteors at the same constant rate. Because the earth is moving in its orbit at 30 km/sec, we will encounter more meteors when we are on the "forward side" of the earth, around 0600 local time, than we will 12 hr later. The late afternoon meteors will have to catch up with the earth; hence there will be fewer of them and their resultant velocities will be lower.   This general argument may be stated in more technical language as follows.   The earth's velocity V_E is directed along the apex of the earth's way (see Sec. 2-4).   A meteor moving with a heliocentric velocity V_H from a radiant located at an angular distance b away from the apex will have a resultant geocentric velocity V_G given by

$$V_G{}^2 = V_H{}^2 + V_E{}^2 + 2V_H V_E \cos b \tag{5-12}$$

and the radiant will appear to be shifted to an angular distance c from the apex where

$$\sin c = \frac{V_H}{V_G} \sin b \tag{5-13}$$

This is discussed further in Sec. 6-3.

These equations show that the apparent radiants will be concentrated about the apex and that meteors with $b < 90°$ will appear to be speeded

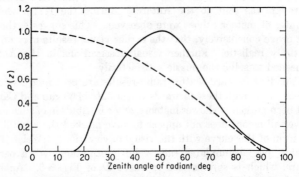

FIG. 5-6. The probability function $P(Z)$.   *Dashed curve*, the approximate visual probability function $P(Z) = \cos Z$; *solid curve*, an empirical radio probability function determined for a single-dipole radio system.

up while meteors with $b > 90°$ will appear to be retarded.   Both V_G and the apparent direction of the radiant will be altered slightly because of the earth's attraction.   Further corrections may be made to allow for this zenith attraction, as pointed out in Sec. 2-4, though they are not very important in the present qualitative discussion.

The actual numbers of meteors which may be seen by a visual observer or detected by a radio apparatus will depend on the zenith angles of the radiants.   To a first approximation the equivalent probability function for visual observing is $P(Z) = \cos Z$ (Öpik, 1955b), as shown by the dashed curve in Fig. 5-6.   It simply means that if the observer sees n meteors per hour from a radiant overhead, he would see $n \cos Z$ meteors per hour from the same radiant if it were at a zenith angle Z.   Similar probability functions for radio systems can either be computed from the equipment parameters or be deduced experimentally by observing the activity of a single strong radiant (assumed to be emitting meteors at a constant rate over a period of several hours).   In Fig. 5-6 the solid curve shows a radio $P(Z)$ determined experimentally for the single-dipole apparatus at Ottawa from observations on the Geminid radiant (McKinley, 1951b).   Here, the probability approaches zero for meteors coming from a radiant near the zenith because the R_0 distances to the perpendicular points on their paths are very great.   Even if the earth's curvature does not intercept the line of sight, the attenuation with range is severe. Other antenna systems will have different characteristic probability functions.

We now have enough background information to enable us to calculate the daily and annual rate variations to be expected from our simple model.   There are several ways of reaching a solution; a straightforward, though somewhat tedious, numerical integration method is quite useful. However, we shall desist from further quantitative analysis here, not because we wish "to leave it as an exercise for the student" (invidious phrase!) but because the answer, when compared with observations, tends to indicate what the meteor distribution is not, rather than to determine what it is.   For a hundred years meteor scientists have gone through the process amending the theoretical distributions in various ways in an endeavor to fit the observations.   When only visual data on meteor rates were available—and sometimes rather poor data at that— the analyst had a wide choice of theoretical models from which to select to prove whatever thesis he had in mind.   The choice narrowed considerably when accurate velocity measurements were produced by photographic and radio methods, thus tying down another and very important parameter.   Later on we shall describe briefly some of this more recent work at Jodrell Bank and Ottawa which did enable certain lines to be drawn, e.g., ruling out the possibility that a large percentage of the meteors in the visual range have an interstellar origin.   However, rates and velocities alone are not enough to delineate the true meteor distribution with completely satisfactory precision.   Only accurate measurements of the individual meteor orbits can really answer the question unequivocally, and such measurements are now beginning to be accumulated in statistically significant numbers.   When one has thus determined the real distribution of meteors in space and time, the usefulness of the model synthesis methods will fade away.   Strictly speaking, of course, even with complete and accurate observational data one can never do more than observe past history and trust with reasonable confidence that the pattern will repeat, at least in broad outline.   Recent work by Gallagher and Eshleman (1960) implies that this confidence may not extend to predicting the occurrence of streams of very faint meteors. Their preliminary radio results for meteors of tenth to fifteenth magnitude suggest that rate and radiant distributions of these objects do not repeat very consistently from year to year.

Let us return to the qualitative problems of explaining the daily rate variations. The morning maximum and evening minimum are a natural consequence of the earth's motion in its orbit, based on the uniform radiant model or, for that matter, on almost any model distribution which is assumed to be symmetrically disposed with respect to the ecliptic. The shapes of the diurnal curves vary with the model selected, and the maximum-minimum ratios will be different; but the morning maximum will always be characteristic because the earth's motion is the dominant factor. One would expect the greatest daily variation to be observed at the equator and the least at either pole. These deductions are borne out by the experimental evidence, in qualitative terms at least.

When we come to the annual variation, we find that none of the simple model distributions, which are assumed to be constant throughout the year, can be adapted to explain the observations. The apex of the earth's way is above the horizon of an observer in the Northern Hemisphere for more hours each day during September than it is during March. One would thus expect that the annual rates in the Northern Hemisphere would show a maximum around September and a minimum around March. That this is indeed the case is shown by Fig. 5-5, curves A, B, and C. On the other hand, in the Southern Hemisphere the apex is highest in March and lowest in September, so that the natural expectation is that the observed annual rates would be greatest around March and least around September. The Australian observations shown in curve D of Fig. 5-5 contradict this—in fact, they tend to agree with the Northern Hemisphere observations. Obviously, the simple models cannot explain this: there must be a real change in the density and distribution of radiants during the year.

Weiss fully realized the significance of his results. To bring out the point more clearly, he undertook to correct his data for the apex effect, as well as he could, in order to compare them with Northern Hemisphere data that had been similarly corrected. His observational information consisted of the hourly rates together with a knowledge of the directions of the meteor echoes. For purposes of the present discussion one need consider only the observed hourly rate variation. Weiss tried out two hypothetical radiant distributions; one was a concentration of radiants located near the ecliptic but spread uniformly around it, and the other was a more uniform distribution over the whole celestial sphere—in either case, a mean heliocentric meteor velocity must be assumed, and Weiss adopted typical speeds of 35 km/sec and 42 km/sec. In order to convert the hypothetical distributions into predicted hourly rates as seen by the radar, he had first to determine the probability function for the Adelaide antenna. This was a rather involved calculation because this particular antenna had some minor lobes whose effects could not be neglected (a single dipole, with no side lobes, would have much to recommend it for this work). The predicted rate variations could then be obtained by numerical integration methods.

In this manner Weiss was able to compare the theoretical and observed distributions. Perhaps the most significant result was obtained by correcting the observed echo rates (curve D of Fig. 5-5) for the effect of the earth's motion. There appeared to be little to choose between the

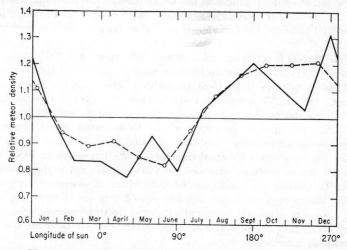

Fig. 5-7. The annual variation in the relative density of nonshower meteors, corrected for the effect of the earth's orbital motion. *Solid curve,* Southern Hemisphere radio observations. (*Weiss, 1957a.*) *Dashed curve,* Northern Hemisphere telescopic observations. (*Kresáková and Kresák, 1955.*)

ecliptical model and the uniform model in this analysis. Figure 5-7, *solid curve,* shows the corrected Adelaide data, based on the ecliptical model and plotted as the relative meteor density around the earth's orbit. Figure 5-7, *dashed curve,* is the telescopic data of Kresáková and Kresák, similarly corrected for the apex effect. The Northern and Southern Hemisphere observations may thus be compared directly, and the agreement is remarkable. Furthermore, the trend of the two curves in Fig. 5-7 shows beyond any doubt that the density of the so-called nonshower meteors is far from uniform throughout the year.

The Jodrell Bank radio results (Lovell, 1954, pp. 120–122) also demonstrated that the distribution must be highly irregular, although they indicated a maximum in June rather than in October.   Hoffmeister (*Die Meteore*, 1937, p. 60) compared visual observations made by himself and others in the Northern Hemisphere with a series made by McIntosh (1934) in New Zealand.   Both curves showed a definite trend toward higher rates in the latter part of the year, though the over-all agreement was not so good as that displayed in Fig. 5-7.   Öpik (1955b) pointed out that the visual data from the Arizona Meteor Expedition of 1931–1933 clearly indicated an asymmetrical annual distribution.   In synthesizing his model at that time, Öpik assumed that about 30 per cent of the meteors were interstellar.   There seems to be little point in arguing about these and other discrepancies in any detail because this particular attack on the problem of orbital distributions, based on observed rates or on rates and radiants, has been pushed about as far as it will go—perhaps too far.

5-4. Meteor magnitudes and masses.   We presented in Sec. 5-2 some typical observational relations between rates of arrival and optical magnitudes of meteors [Eqs. (5-8) to (5-10)].   The relations depend on directly measurable quantities, and provided that one can agree on the definitions and measuring techniques, there should be no basic impediment to acceptance of the results within the indicated margin of error. The connection between numbers and radio echo durations or decay times can be found with equal directness.   We happen in this case to have chosen to relate the observed radio magnitudes, not to the primary radio measurements, but to an indirectly deduced ionization value q. If the theory involved in this last step should turn out to be wrong, we can always revert to the basic radio data; so, to this extent at least, we may claim that the optical and radio rate-magnitude relations are in reasonably satisfactory shape.

This is much more than can be said for the determination of meteor masses and the mass-magnitude correlation.   In fact, our present knowledge of meteor masses is so vague and leans so heavily on certain theoretical developments which are the subject of some dispute, that we would hesitate to include meteor masses at all in this chapter were it not that mass is conventionally considered to be a fundamental and observable physical property.

The observational problem is further complicated by recent evidence that most meteoric bodies break up into many small particles as they strike the upper air.   Öpik and Whipple are among those who assume that in these cases the original meteoroid consisted of an aggregate of small solid particles—a porous object which might be described as a "dustball" or, more vividly, as a "stoneflake" (Öpik, 1958a).   Whipple concludes that the effective density of a dustball may be as low as 0.1 and that the mass scale would therefore require upward revision by one or two orders of magnitude. Others, notably Levin (1956), question this latter viewpoint. In searching the literature to find an acceptable value for the mass of a meteoroid which, when entering the atmosphere at a specified velocity, would produce a meteor of zero visual magnitude, we have encountered the following opinions:

1. Whipple (1952) gives $m = 1.25$ g, for $V = 40$ km/sec, for a solid meteoroid.

2. Whipple (1957) gives $m = 25$ g, for $V = 28$ km/sec, for a dustball.

3. Whipple and Hawkins (1958) give $m = 0.15$ g, for $V = 30$ km/sec, presumably for a solid meteoroid.

4. Levin (1956) gives $m = 0.055$ g, for $V = 40$ km/sec.

5. Watson (1956) adopts $m = 0.25$ g, velocity unspecified.

6. Öpik, in his book "Physics of Meteor Flight in the Atmosphere" (1958a), declines to be tied down explicitly. However, he provides a formula which can be used with certain assumptions to deduce a mass value. In his equation

$$\log_{10} m = 10.02 + \log_{10} L - \log_{10} \tau_I - 3 \log_{10} V - 0.4 M_v \quad (5\text{-}14)$$

L is the length of the visible meteor path and τ_I is the luminous efficiency, or the fraction of the kinetic energy that is converted into light. From Öpik's Table LI we may obtain $\log_{10} \tau_I = -3.35$ for a dustball, or $\log_{10} \tau_I = -2.68$ for a solid particle. Also, from his Table XVIII we may assume $L \simeq 36$ km for $V = 42$ km/sec and $M_v = -0.1$. These data would yield $m = 1.29$ g for a dustball and $m = 0.28$ g for a solid meteoroid.

These wide variations in the estimates of the mass of a zero-magnitude meteor make it difficult to draw up a definitive table of masses versus magnitudes. Several such tables have been published in the literature, and some of them have been widely quoted with a confidence which the authors themselves probably did not have when they prepared them. Perhaps the best approach here will be to state a set of assumptions and limitations, from which some conditional conclusions may be drawn.

Most authorities are agreed that, throughout the visual range at least, the luminosity of the meteor is directly proportional to its mass. Thus, from Eq. (2-2) or directly from Eq. (5-14), we have

$$m_M = k \times 10^{-0.40M} \quad (5\text{-}15)$$

Note that Eqs. (5-8) to (5-10) are of the form $\log_{10} N = \log_{10} K + pM$, where $p = \log_{10} r$. Differentiating, we obtain $dN/N = p \, dM \log_e 10$ for the number of meteors in the magnitude interval dM, at the magnitude M [cf. Eq. (5-5)]. We may substitute for N and set $dM = 1$, to obtain

$$\Delta N_M = 2.303 pK 10^{pM} \quad (5\text{-}16)$$

as the daily world rate per unit magnitude at magnitude M. If we multiply Eqs. (5-15) and (5-16) we obtain the mass per unit magnitude interval,

$$\Delta \mathbf{m}_M = (m \, \Delta \mathbf{N})_M = 2.303 pkK \times 10^{(p-0.40)M} \qquad (5\text{-}17)$$

We shall tentatively select three masses, 30 g, 1 g, and 0.03 g, respectively, as indicative of the uncertainty in our estimate of the mass of a zero-magnitude meteor. Appropriate values for p and K, taken from Eqs. (5-8) to (5-10), and for k from Eq. (5-15) may then be inserted in

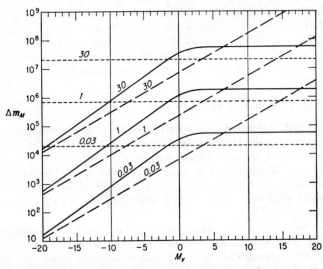

FIG. 5-8. The mass $\Delta \mathbf{m}_M$ in grams per unit magnitude interval, incident upon the whole earth in a 24-hr period. Three arbitrary values have been selected for the mass of a zero-magnitude meteor—30, 1, and 0.03 g. *Solid curves*, after Millman; *dashed curves*, after Hawkins and Upton; *dotted curves*, after Watson.

Eq. (5-17). The results are plotted in Fig. 5-8. It is quite apparent that there can be a wide spread in the estimated meteoric mass per unit magnitude, owing mainly but not entirely to the arbitrary selection of the fiducial mass. The spread due to the differences in the empirical numbers-magnitude relations (Fig. 5-3) is smaller, but still appreciable.

The situation becomes even more hazy when we attempt to estimate down to a given limiting magnitude the total mass $\mathbf{m}_M$ incident daily on the earth. Integration of Eq. (5-17) from $M = -\infty$ to M gives

$$\mathbf{m}_M = \frac{pkK \times 10^{(p-0.40)M}}{p - 0.40} \qquad (5\text{-}18)$$

provided $p > 0.40$. Watson's data cannot be used here: his law of constant mass per magnitude leads to an infinite mass as $M \rightarrow -\infty$. The empirical relations deduced from Eq. (5-18), using the observations of Millman or of Hawkins and Upton, do yield a finite mass for the influx of meteors brighter than a given limit, which at least is in qualitative accord with our experience. In particular, when the summation is carried out for Millman's data from $M_v = -\infty$ to $M_v = 10$, we find that $\mathbf{m}_{10} \simeq 2 \times 10^7$ g, or about 20 tons, on the assumption that $m = 1$ g for $M_v = 0$. There is considerable uncertainty about the rates and masses in the range of meteorite sizes, where the scarcity of events adds to the difficulty of accumulating reliable statistics. Here, we are not likely to fare much better than to accept Watson's (1956) guess, based on the frequency and residual masses of meteorite falls, that $\mathbf{m}_{-10}$ is of the order of 500 kg per day. When we consider the contributions from the very faint meteors, we see that all the relations predict an infinite total mass as $M \rightarrow \infty$, which we know cannot really be the case. In Sec. 5-5 we shall have a brief look at what little is known about the mass influx of minute particles which are too small to become incandescent meteors but which could be placed on our magnitude scale as fainter than the nineteenth or twentieth magnitudes, through extrapolation of the mass-magnitude relation.

Before leaving this section, we may note that two laws of numbers versus mass are readily deducible from Eq. (5-15) and the general observational relation $\log_{10} \mathbf{N} = \log_{10} K + pM$. First, by eliminating M, we have

$$\mathbf{N} \sim \mathbf{m}^{-2.5p} \tag{5-19}$$

In the particular case where $p = 0.4$, the total number of meteors of mass m and greater is inversely proportional to m. Differentiation of Eq. (5-19) yields the differential mass law

$$\Delta \mathbf{N} \sim \mathbf{m}^{-(2.5p+1)} = \mathbf{m}^{-s} \tag{5-20}$$

The exponent s should be deducible indirectly from radio observations; hence we may find r from $s = 1 + 2.5 \log_{10} r$. For nonshower meteors down to tenth magnitude, Kaiser (1953, 1954b) has suggested that $s \simeq 2.0$ and $r \simeq 2.5$, using experimental data furnished by McKinley (1951c), but Greenhow has recently criticized the calculations on the grounds that the effects of the "radio echo ceiling" were not properly taken into account.

Differences in the magnitude distributions within some of the strong showers as compared to the general background were noted by several observers some time ago, including McKinley and Millman (1949a), who reported that the maximum radio ratio of Geminids to non-Geminids was $1:1$, whereas the visual ratio was between $2:1$ and $3:1$. The sensitivity of their radar was about ninth or tenth magnitude, well below the naked-eye limit, and hence it follows that there is a smaller proportion of Geminids to non-Geminids at the tenth- than at the fifth-magnitude level. Further evidence was provided by the fact that the percentage of echoes with durations in excess of 1 sec doubled during the Geminid shower relative to the percentage observed during typical nonshower periods, thus indicating the presence of a greater proportion of large particles in the shower.

The subject was investigated more thoroughly by the workers at Jodrell Bank. They used several methods to obtain s values for various showers, one of which will be mentioned in Sec. 5-6. Table 5-3, based on a paper by Browne, Bullough, Evans, and Kaiser (1956), shows values of s and r computed from observed height distributions for three showers that have been well known for many years and for one new daytime shower, the Arietids, which was discovered at Jodrell Bank in 1947.

Table 5-3. Mass Distributions for Shower Meteors from Jodrell Bank Radio Observations

Shower	$0 \leq M_r \leq 2$		$M_r \simeq 3$		$5 \leq M_r \leq 7$		$M_r \simeq 7$	
	s	r	s	r	s	r	s	r
Quadrantids....	1.8	2.1	....	...	1.78	2.1		
Perseids........	2.0	2.5	2.0	...	1.59	1.7	1.38	1.4
Geminids.......	2.3	3.3	2.24	3.1	1.62	1.8	1.45	1.5
Arietids........	1.8	2.1	....	...	2.7	4.8		

The decrease in the r values for the Perseids and Geminids as we go to fainter magnitudes demonstrates that these showers contain relatively few small particles. For both these showers the greatest mass per magnitude interval seems to occur around $M_r \simeq 3$. On the other hand, the high value for r for the faint Arietids implies that this shower is rich in small particles, although relatively few are in the naked-eye range. The radio rates, down to seventh or eighth magnitude, of this daytime shower are about the same as those of the Geminids and Perseids, but the Arietids would probably not approach the other two showers in visual brilliance were it possible to view the Arietids at night.

As we mentioned earlier, it now seems probably that the reduction methods used in obtaining the data given in Table 5-3 may not have taken adequate account of the radio ceiling cutoff effect. A tentative reevaluation suggests that each of the r values given in Table 5-3 might well be increased about 50 per cent.

5-5. Micrometeorites and meteoric dust. Telescopic observations

(Olivier, 1950) and radio records (Gallagher, 1958) have been made of meteors estimated to be as faint as $M_v = 15$. The instrumental limits have not yet been reached, and efforts are being continued to improve the sensitivity of both the optical and the radio methods. It will be interesting to see if more sensitive apparatus will indeed detect fainter meteors or if, as Astapovich (1935) suggested some time ago, there are no true meteors fainter than about the nineteenth or twentieth magnitudes.

We do have evidence to indicate that very small particles are coming in abundance into our atmosphere without creating any appreciable light or ionization. Heat is created by collisions with air particles in direct proportion to the mass and, hence, to the volume of the meteoroid. Heat radiation from the meteoroid is proportional to its surface area. The ratio of surface area to volume increases as the size diminishes. There will be a limiting size for which the temperature does not exceed the ablation point and the particle is decelerated to its terminal "free-fall" velocity with little or no loss of mass. The free-fall velocity is quite slow—it may take a month for the particle to drift down to earth from the 100- to 120-km level where its flight was arrested. These micrometeorites are real meteorites in the sense that they are tangible, though very small, mineral specimens from extraterrestrial space, each having pursued its independent orbit about the sun. Fragments broken or melted off larger bodies as they strike the upper air can indeed be very small or even dustlike, but, strictly speaking, we do not apply the word micrometeorite to them. The relatively large objects which we conventionally describe as meteorites survive the atmosphere's fiery erosion because their initial masses are great enough to leave sizeable residues. On the other hand, micrometeorites land unharmed because their masses are so very small. In between these extremes, over a range of about 25 magnitudes ($-7 \leq M_v \leq 18$), are the ordinary meteors which evaporate almost completely as atoms in the upper atmosphere, leaving only small solid residues.

Three rather different approaches may be taken in attempting to determine the size, shape, mass, composition, and previous history of the micrometeorites. These are recovery of the particles when they reach the earth, indirect deduction from zodiacal light investigations, and direct observation of the particles in the upper atmosphere by means of rocket- or satellite-borne instruments.

The collection and analysis of micrometeorites and meteoric dust has been well summarized in a book by Buddhue (1950). These minute particles can be collected by exposing sticky surfaces at ground level or at aircraft heights. The identification of meteoric material among the unavoidable terrestrial contaminants is difficult and uncertain. It is assumed that iron particles with a relatively high nickel content are likely

to be nonterrestrial.   A microscopic examination of the collecting surfaces sometimes reveals small shiny spherules varying in diameter from
1 to 100 microns (1 micron = 1 μ = 10^{-4} cm).   Landsberg (1947)
reported unusually large numbers of these spherules to have fallen within
a few days to a month after the strong Giacobinid shower in 1946.
Recent work by Hodge and Wildt (1958) suggests one such object per
day may fall on every square centimeter of the earth's surface.   If the
mean diameter is taken to be 5 μ and the composition to be of stone, this
means that the total mass of spherules that is added to the earth daily
may be several hundred tons.   The suggestion has been made that the
spherules might be minute refrozen droplets which were melted from
larger meteorites as they passed through the upper air (Krinov and
Fonton, 1954).   If this were so, they would not be considered to be true
micrometeorites as we have defined the word.   From a study of nickel
oxide cores obtained by drilling the ocean bottom, Pettersson and Rotschi
(1950) have suggested that several thousand tons per day might not be an
unreasonable estimate of the total daily accumulation of meteoric dust in
all forms.   Hunter and Parkin (1960) found that the black magnetic
spherules in deep-sea sediments can be divided into two main types, one
of mean density 3, which is rich in magnesium, and the other of density 6,
which contains a nickel-iron alloy.   An exhaustive treatment of all
aspects of the interplanetary dust problems has led Öpik (1956b) to conclude that about 1,000 tons per day is a figure compatible with most of
the available evidence.

Allen (1946) and van de Hulst (1947) have each sought to explain the
zodiacal light in terms of diffraction of sunlight by myriads of micrometeorites in interplanetary space.   The hypothesis works out well if one
can assume space densities of meteoric material to be from 10^{-23} to
10^{-21} g/cm^3 near the earth's orbit, with individual particle sizes ranging
from 0.3 to 300 μ.   Little or nothing is known about the orbital characteristics of these particles—they could possess low elliptical velocities, or on
the other hand, a large fraction of them might be from interstellar space.
If they are assumed to follow the pattern of the ordinary meteors, van de
Hulst has calculated that the daily influx on the earth may be as high as
10,000 tons, which is comparable with the conclusions drawn from ocean-
bottom samples.   A more recent estimate by Beard (1959) puts the
particle flux near the earth at 10^{-2}/(m^2) (sec), which is of the same order
as reported by Dubin (1960) from Explorer I satellite observations.
This flux rate is about an order of magnitude less than the earlier estimate
made by Hodge and Wildt.

There are many variations of the rocket or satellite methods, but the
few results which have become available so far are not very conclusive.
If the rocket head is recoverable, one may examine exposed surfaces for

pitting or etching. Other measuring techniques which can be tele-
metered in flight include using microphones to pick up the sounds of
meteoric impacts (Dubin, 1960), breaking of wire grids, puncturing of
pressurized chambers, and creating ionization or light by impact with
either gas particles or solid surfaces (Berg and Meredith, 1956). After
contact with the upper atmosphere, the micrometeorites are moving
very slowly in comparison with their earlier velocities in space; hence the
volume density of the particles at the 120-km level and below should be
considerably higher than in interstellar space. The frequency of impact
sounds heard as a rocket passed through this region would therefore
depend chiefly on the rocket speed and the local volume density of the
particles. Satellite measurements well above the E region should provide
the best information about the sizes, velocities, and spatial distribution of
the micrometeorites.

5-6. Meteor heights. The height at which a meteor appears depends
on its mass, velocity, and path inclination as well as on the density of the
atmosphere. We shall adopt a standard atmosphere, which may be considered to be homogeneous and isothermal at least for small height differentials in the meteor region. The observational evidence will then be
examined to see if the effects of the various parameters of the meteoroid
are separable.

For this purpose the best data have come from the Harvard photographic programs (Whipple, 1943; Hawkins and Southworth, 1958).
Millman has made use of the published information, together with some
further results kindly communicated by L. G. Jacchia and others at
Harvard in advance of publication, to draw up the set of three graphs
shown in Fig. 5-9a, b, and c. Meteor height H has been plotted against
the computed no-atmosphere velocity V_∞. The observed velocity V_0
does not usually differ from V_∞ by more than 1 km/sec, so that the
resultant error is unlikely to be significant here, even if the derivation of
V_∞ from V_0 should turn out to rest on some weak assumptions.

As described in the caption, three different selections of the photographic material have been made in Fig. 5-9; they have fallen conveniently into three magnitude groups. In each graph of Fig. 5-9, the
vertical lines indicate the mean spread between the appearance and disappearance of the meteors in a given velocity class, and the solid dots
show the heights of maximum light output. The same dashed line has
been superimposed on each graph, differing only in its vertical displacement. This line is an empirical one. While it fits none of the graphs
perfectly at or near the height of maximum light, it is nevertheless a
reasonable compromise to fit all three. It is fortunate that the shape of
the line turns out to be relatively independent of magnitude, for otherwise the separation problem would be more involved. We may use this

curve (shown as a solid line in Fig. 5-9d) to correct the observed height of
a meteor moving with a given velocity to the height it would have had if
the velocity had been 40 km/sec.   For comparison, the theoretical variation of photographic height with velocity, obtained from Eq. (7-25) of
Sec. 7-5, is shown as the dashed line in Fig. 5-9d.

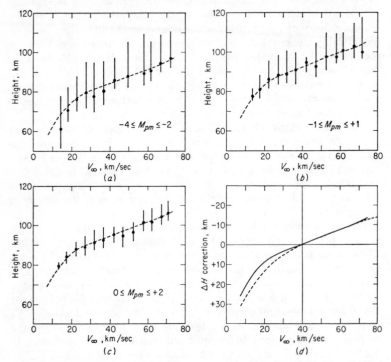

FIG. 5-9. Photographic meteor heights versus no-atmosphere velocity V_∞. Vertical
lines show the mean spreads between the appearance and disappearance of the light,
and the solid dots mark the point of maximum light. (a) 217 small-camera meteors,
from data by Whipple (1943), and by L. G. Jacchia ($-4 \leq M_{pm} \leq -2$); (b) 263
Super-Schmidt meteors, selected by Jacchia for deceleration measurements ($-1 \leq$
$M_{pm} \leq 1$); (c) 358 Super-Schmidt meteors, random selection from the Harvard data,
by Hawkins and Southworth (1958) ($0 \leq M_{pm} \leq 2$); (d) *solid-line*, empirical height-
velocity correction curve; *dashed-line*, theoretical curve (from Sec. 7-5).

Radio heights also increase with the meteor velocity, as illustrated in
Fig. 5-10.   The data were obtained by two different methods.   The
Jodrell Bank heights (Evans, 1955) are systematically higher than the
Ottawa heights by 2 to 3 km, although the slopes of the two fitted lines are
not greatly different.   The Jodrell Bank single-station equipment measured

the height at the t_0 point, whereas the Ottawa three-station system measured the height of the enduring ionization. The heights observed at Jodrell Bank were converted to "characteristic heights" before plotting; that is, they were corrected to the height of maximum ionization of the smallest meteor detectable by the system. This has the effect of raising slightly the mean height of a given velocity group. Furthermore, the minimum sensitivity of the Jodrell Bank equipment was estimated to be

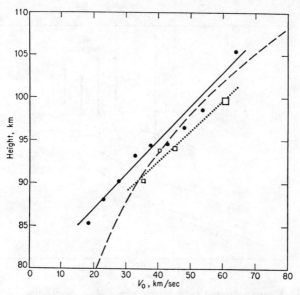

FIG. 5-10. Radio meteor heights versus observed velocity V_0. *Solid circles and solid line,* Jodrell Bank characteristic heights (*after Evans,* 1955); *open squares and dotted line,* Ottawa three-station heights; *dashed line,* theoretical height-velocity curve (from Sec. 7-5).

around the sixth or seventh magnitude, whereas the Ottawa meteors were somewhat brighter, on the average. The theoretical variation of radio height with velocity is shown in Fig. 5-10 as the dashed curve, assuming that $H = 93$ km at $V_0 = 40$ km/sec (see Sec. 7-5).

The Harvard photographic data and the Ottawa radio data displayed in Figs. 5-9 and 5-10, corrected to a velocity of 40 km/sec, have been replotted in Fig. 5-11 to show the variation of meteor height with magnitude. Smoothed curves have been drawn through the beginning and end points of the photographic paths and also through the points of maximum light. The small-camera observations are indicated by the dashed portion of these lines, and the Super-Schmidt results are shown by the dotted parts. For the maximum light and the end points, the small-camera and Super-Schmidt appear to overlap, but the envelope of the Super-Schmidt beginning heights diverges toward higher altitudes for brighter meteors. As one would expect, the brighter photographic meteors have the longer visible paths. The beginning heights would appear at first sight to be reasonably constant around $H = 100$ km. However, in the relatively short time that the Super-Schmidts have

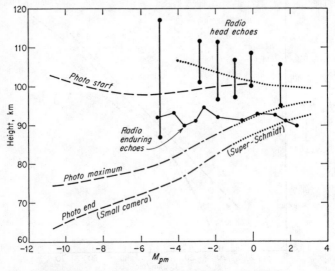

FIG. 5-11. Photographic and radio heights versus M_{pm}, the absolute photographic magnitude at maximum light. Data are from Figs. 5-9 and 5-10, corrected for the velocity effect. *Dashed and dotted lines*, beginning, maximum light, and end points for 808 photographic meteors. Dashed parts are for small cameras, dotted parts for Super-Schmidt cameras. *Solid line*, heights of 645 enduring radio echoes; *vertical lines*, height ranges of 76 head echoes.

been in operation, there have been few observations of meteors with $M_{pm} < -5$. To judge from the divergence of the Super-Schmidt graph, it would seem likely that the beginning height for $M_{pm} \simeq -10$ will turn out to be appreciably higher than that shown by the dashed line, when more very-bright-meteor statistics are accumulated by the Super-Schmidts. The maximum light and terminal points, though, should not change much with improved sensitivity. It is of particular interest to note that for meteors brighter than -5 the maximum light output occurs about three-quarters of the way along the visible path (this might be better than four-fifths if the Super-Schmidt results were extrapolated), whereas for the faint meteors the point of maximum light is about the middle. This has some bearing on the fragmentation question.

In Fig. 5-11 the velocity-corrected heights of the enduring radio echoes show very little variation from a mean of about 93 km over a range of nearly eight magnitudes. For bright meteors this height of enduring ionization is greater than the corresponding height of maximum light. At zero magnitude the heights are about equal, and for fainter meteors the visible light maxima are above the mean radio-echo height. The optical observations apply to the production of light in the immediate vicinity of the moving meteoroid, whereas the enduring echo is really a train phenomenon. One would expect that the duration of the echo would be limited at high altitudes by rapid diffusion and at low altitudes by turbulence, by recombination of the ions, or by attachment of the electrons to neutral molecules. The diffusion factor works in the opposite sense to the latter effects as the height increases; hence for maximum duration of either the visual train or the radio echo there will be an optimum height which will not be very sensitive to meteor magnitude. Very-long-duration echoes appear to occur at or near 93 km (McKinley, 1956), almost independently of the meteoric velocity.

The vertical lines on Fig. 5-11 are mean values for the height spreads of observed meteor head echoes, grouped at intervals of either one or two magnitudes. These particular echoes have not been corrected for the velocity effect. The same correction that was used for the enduring echoes and for the optical data might apply here, but we do not yet have enough information about the head echoes to be certain. The transient ionization causing the head echo seems to be closely connected with the moving meteoroid. In this respect the effects of the head echoes should more nearly parallel the optical phenomena than do those of the enduring echoes. However, the average height range of the head echoes appears to be considerably higher than that of the photographic meteors of equivalent magnitude; no ready explanation is apparent for this phenomenon.

We may determine the dependence of height upon path inclination, that is, upon cos Z, if we correct the observations first for the velocity effect (Fig. 5-9d) and next for the magnitude effect (Fig. 5-11). In doing this, Millman has divided the Harvard data into two parts which are conveniently delineated by the type of instrument used. For brighter meteors photographed with small cameras, the reduction was made to $V = 40$ km/sec and $M_{pm} = -5$, which lies about the middle of the small-camera range. Similarly, the Super-Schmidt meteors were corrected to $V = 40$ km/sec and $M_{pm} = 0$. Since two successive empirical corrections have been made, one should not place great reliance on the resultant graphs. These are shown in Fig. 5-12. There does appear to be an indisputable trend toward greater heights as the inclination of the path from the vertical increases. Speaking qualitatively, this is quite understandable, because a meteor that drops vertically from the zenith will encounter fewer air particles in moving from H_1 to H_2 than will one of identical mass and velocity that passes the same height levels while traveling along a highly inclined path. The latter meteor will produce more light per unit height differential (not per unit path length) and will therefore burn up at a greater height. Weiss (1959) found a diurnal variation of about 3 km in the heights of nonshower radio meteors. The maximum occurred near midnight and the minimum around noon. This

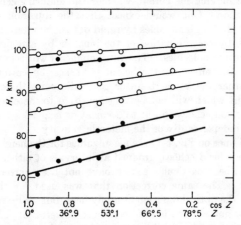

FIG. 5-12. Photographic meteor heights versus cos Z, or Z the zenith angle of the radiant. Data have been corrected for both velocity and magnitude effects. Beginning, maximum light, and end points are shown. *Open circles,* Super-Schmidt meteors, mean magnitude $M_{pm} = 0$; *solid dots,* small-camera meteors, mean magnitude $M_{pm} = -5$.

variation may be explained as a combination of zenith angle and velocity effects caused by the daily motion of the earth's apex. Qualitatively, this observed variation in height change does not appear to be incompatible with the empirical relations given in Figs. 5-10 and 5-12. A quantitative appraisal would involve some complex computations based on assumed radiant distributions. Weiss made an attempt in this direction but concluded that the available information was insufficient for precise comparisons. Daily changes in the air density could also cause an effect of this magnitude by raising or lowering the point of maximum light or ionization.

A typical frequency distribution of numbers versus height is shown in Fig. 5-13, based on 548 meteor observations made during the Ottawa three-station program. The computed heights referred to the long-duration part of the echoes. The data are heterogeneous in the sense that no corrections have been applied for velocity or magnitude, therefore the suggestion of fine structure in the outline may not be very significant, although the subsidiary peak near 106 km has appeared in other observations as well. The Stanford workers have observed more than one such subsidiary peak separated by height intervals of 6 to 7 km. When the minor irregularities are smoothed out the peak frequency in Fig. 5-13 is seen to occur at about 95 km.

A frequency-height distribution of meteors belonging to a shower (of known velocity) will not necessarily maximize at a height that is predictable from the radio height-velocity relations of Fig. 5-10. In each

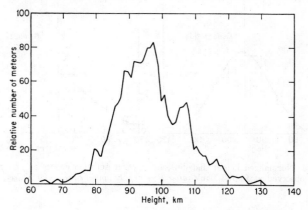

FIG. 5-13. Frequency-height distributions of 548 long-enduring echoes observed at Ottawa.

case the shape of the height distribution curve is characteristic of the particular shower. This is demonstrated by the Jodrell Bank observations (Browne, Bullough, Evans, and Kaiser, 1956) shown in Fig. 5-14. Kaiser (1954a,b), in an exhaustive theoretical analysis of the height distribution problem which we shall not attempt to reproduce here, has concluded that the shape of these curves depends chiefly on the atmospheric scale height H (see Appendix) and the exponent s in the differential mass law [Eq. (5-20)]. If either s or H is known, the other quantity may be evaluated directly by measuring ΔH, the root-mean-square value of the deviations of H from the mean height H_m. The narrower, more sharply peaked curves correspond to larger values of s and therefore of r. We are inclined to agree with Greenhow that this analysis may have failed to give adequate weight to the probable true height distribution. Figure

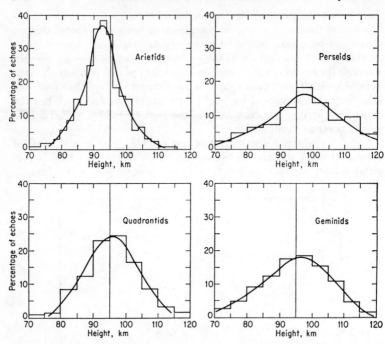

FIG. 5-14. Normalized height distributions of short-duration echoes of four meteor showers observed at Jodrell Bank (*after Browne, Bullough, Evans, and Kaiser, 1956*).

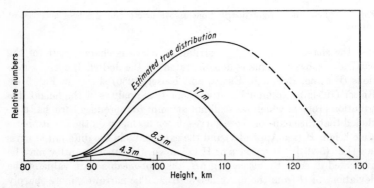

FIG. 5-15. The observed height distributions of underdense meteor echoes (mean magnitude = 6.5) at wavelengths of 4.3, 8.3, and 17 m, together with the estimated true distribution. (*Courtesy of J. S. Greenhow.*)

5-15 summarizes some of Greenhow's observations and includes his estimate of the true distribution which cannot be directly evaluated because of the underdense-type echo ceiling. The deduced s values will be increased if the estimated true distribution is adopted.

5-7. Meteor velocities. The Ottawa cw radio program, carried out in 1948 to 1950, yielded some 11,000 meteor velocities (McKinley, 1951b). The normalized distribution of all these velocities is shown in Fig. 5-16, *solid-line graph*. The mean velocity is 44.7 km/sec. Millman (1954c) has assembled the published Jodrell Bank records of their early velocity and radiant programs for comparison with the early Ottawa data (see

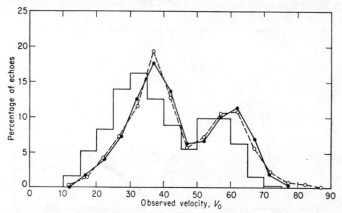

FIG. 5-16. Normalized distributions of observed radio velocities, V_0. *Solid-line graph*, 11,073 meteors, Ottawa meteor velocity programs; *dashed-line graph*, 1,838 meteors, Jodrell Bank meteor velocity and radiant programs; *histogram*, 2,000 meteors, Jodrell Bank meteor orbit program.

Fig. 5-16, *dashed-line graph*). The mean of this distribution is also 44.7 km/sec, and the agreement between the two graphs in practically all other respects is strikingly close. This coincidence in detail is interesting but largely fortuitous, because neither graph represents a continuous year-round average and the selected samples differ considerably. A fairly strong emphasis was placed on shower observations in both programs, but these were not necessarily the same showers or periods.

An additional set of velocity observations has been made available by Dr. J. G. Davies, prior to publication. These velocities, some 2,000 in number, were obtained in the Jodrell Bank meteor orbit survey which commenced in 1953. The normalized distribution of these velocities is displayed in Fig. 5-16 as the stepped histogram. The average velocity, 39.2 km/sec, is somewhat less than for the other two distributions but the general shape is similar. The two broad maxima present in all three distributions result from a complex interaction of several factors. For stations in middle latitudes of the earth, even a theoretically uniform radiant distribution will yield a double-humped type of velocity distribution, due to the apex and antapex effects together with the influence of the radio probability factor. Furthermore, there are small areas on the celestial sphere which are necessarily deficient in meteor radiants because the corresponding orbits pass so close to the sun that the meteoroids are vaporized: an allowance for this effect may accentuate the double hump. An ecliptical concentration of orbits (see Sec. 6-4 and Fig. 6-8) also emphasizes this feature.

An important point to note in Fig. 5-16 is that rather less than 1 per

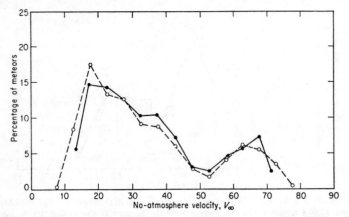

FIG. 5-17. Normalized distributions of no-atmosphere photographic velocities, V_∞. *Solid line*, 621 Super-Schmidt meteors (data from Fig. 5-9b and c by L. G. Jacchia, and by Hawkins and Southworth, 1958); *dashed line*, 2,433 Super-Schmidt meteors (rapid reduction method by R. F. McCrosky).

cent of the velocities exceed the nominal geocentric parabolic limit of 72 km/sec.* Of this small fraction fewer still are more than 10 km/sec above that limit, and in the Ottawa data and the more recent material at Jodrell Bank none exceed 80 km/sec. The probable error of an individual measurement was 5 per cent on the average; hence it is not possible to state with certainty that any of the meteors with $V_0 > 72$ km/sec really were travelling in hyperbolic orbits. This line of inquiry will be pursued further in Sec. 6-3; at the moment all one can say is that there

---

* The maximum geocentric velocity for a particle moving in a parabolic orbit, at the earth's distance from the sun, can be as high as 74 km/sec, depending on the time of year. We shall adopt 72 km/sec as a nominal mean for discussion purposes, particularly in considering the interstellar-meteor problem (cf. Sec. 6-3).

are not likely to be many hyperbolic velocities present in the data.

The Harvard photographic velocity data are summarized in Fig. 5-17. Here the selections of Super-Schmidt meteors with well-determined velocities (errors from 0.1 to 1 per cent), referred to separately in Fig. 5-9b and c, have been combined to yield the solid line graph. Less accurate velocity measurements (3 per cent errors) of 2,433 Super-Schmidt meteors have been made by R. F. McCrosky of the Smithsonian Institution using a rapid graphical reduction method; these are shown as the dashed curve in Fig. 5-17. The small-camera observations (Fig. 5-9a) are not shown here—they were rather heavily weighted with Geminids and Perseids. The mean velocity for the solid curve is 35.6 km/sec and for the dashed curve 34.3 km/sec. The double hump in the distributions is again apparent, as is the lack of velocities in excess of 80 km/sec.

A comparison of Figs. 5-16 and 5-17 shows that, over the range 15 to 60 km/sec, there is a greater proportion of high velocity meteors in the radio observations. Whipple (1955a) has deduced from these data that, up to velocities in the neighborhood of 50 to 60 km/sec, the ratio of the numbers of radio to photographic meteors increases about as the square of the velocity. This conclusion is of importance in assessing the relative efficiencies of the processes involved in the production of ionization and luminosity. Above $V = 60$ km/sec, the over-all rates of radio meteors are still well in excess of the photographic rates, but the ratio falls below that predicted by the V^2 relation. One reason for this relative decrease is probably the "underdense-type echo ceiling" for radio meteors (Sec. 8-6).

5-8. Meteor trains. Every visible meteor creates a train of excited and ionized atoms. These atoms are slowed down fairly quickly to ordinary thermal velocities and are left to glow in the wake of the meteor head. The intensity of the train luminosity is very much less than that of the meteor head, and it decays at a rate that is determined by environmental factors, including diffusion, recombination, and attachment. The eye cannot resolve the short-duration trains associated with faint meteors because these may last for only a very small fraction of a second and may extend for but a few meters behind the head.

Short-duration wakes, lasting for a few hundredths of a second, can be photographed in the rotating shutter breaks for some meteors as faint as the third or fourth visual magnitude. Millman (1950b) has even obtained a train spectrum in this manner, of a -4 magnitude meteor. The train spectrum showed a complete absence of ionized lines, although the radio echo persisted for 110 sec in this particular case, while the visible train faded after 11 sec.

Long-duration trains, lasting from a few seconds to many minutes, are commonly associated with bright meteors and fireballs. The first comprehensive analysis of visual trains was made by Trowbridge (1907), who pointed out that the trains tended to occur within a narrow height range which he placed between 80 and 85 km. He suggested that the observed train intensity at time t fitted a formula of the form

$$I_{(train)} = I_{0(train)} \frac{1}{(1 + kt)^2} \qquad (5\text{-}21)$$

where k is a decay constant, and $I_{0(train)}$ is the train intensity immediately after the passage of the meteor. Recent work by Hawkins and Howard

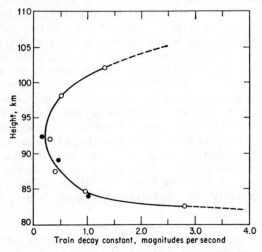

FIG. 5-18. Height variation of the decay constant for photographic meteor trains. *Open circles*, after Liller and Whipple (1954); *solid dots*, after Hawkins and Howard (1959).

(1959) showed that there is a linear relation between train magnitude and time. Therefore the intensity decreases exponentially with time, as follows:

$$I_{(train)} = I_{0(train)} \epsilon^{-kt} \qquad (5\text{-}22)$$

which is not greatly different in general form from Eq. (5-21). The decay constant k may be expressed in magnitudes per second. The observed variation of k with height is shown in Fig. 5-18. The flat minimum near $H = 93$ km implies that the longest train durations will be found near this height, regardless of the magnitude of the meteor itself.

The initial *trail width* (the apparent width of the luminosity at the meteor head) is difficult to determine, and estimates vary widely from several tens of meters down to a few centimeters. Hawkins and Whipple

(1958) have concluded from photographic evidence that meteors from zero to third magnitude have finite trail widths of the order of 1 m in diameter. The column quickly expands radially, of course, and after several seconds or even minutes the glowing train may be of the order of a kilometer in diameter, which can easily be seen or photographed.

Olivier (1942, 1947, 1957) has accumulated a large collection of visual-train observations, some 2,073 examples in all. The persistent observer may expect to see one train with a duration of 10 sec or more for each 1,000 meteors he enters in his log. Kresák (1948) expressed this in another way when he stated that in his own experience an observer would see on the average one enduring train per 150 hr of sky watching. The nighttime visual trains appear to occur most frequently near a height of 90 km, with a minor peak in the frequency at around 60 km. Daytime trains are lower still, from 45 down to 27 km. These trains are usually seen by sunlight reflected from the cloud of dust particles shed in the wake of the meteor rather than by radiated light. On the whole, the brighter the meteor, the longer the train duration. Millman and Robins (1935) have shown also that for a given magnitude the duration increases with the speed of the meteor.

Long-enduring trains not only show a general drifting motion but usually develop many kinks and bends fairly soon after formation, as in Fig. 5-19. The distortion of the train is due to crosscurrents or wind shears in the upper atmosphere. From a detailed study of 40 visual trains, Millman (1959b) has concluded that the winds may blow in opposite directions over as small a height differential as 6 km, with net velocities of the order of 50 m/sec. Results from five trains photographed with the Harvard Super-Schmidts (Liller and Whipple, 1954) indicated a similar height interval. Liller and Whipple found that the average horizontal wind speed was 68 m/sec and also that the mean maximum vertical wind shear was 50 m/(sec)(km) (see Fig. 5-20). Hughes (1959) determined from 48 train photographs that the height of maximum initial train intensity (not maximum train duration) corresponds closely to the height of maximum light produced by the meteor head. In some of the cases he noticed that two intensity maxima were present, spaced vertically by about 7 km. Greenhow and Neufeld (1956a) have studied the height variation of the upper-atmosphere winds with particular emphasis on the semidiurnal changes in the gradient of wind shear.

Meteor trains are characteristically associated with bright meteors or fireballs, which themselves are certainly worth a few remarks. A spectacular fireball may exhibit a wide range of colors; green-white or blue-white is common, and yellowish and reddish shades may appear. The head may be teardrop in shape and of quite appreciable size. Light bursts are often observed, and occasionally the trail will appear to split

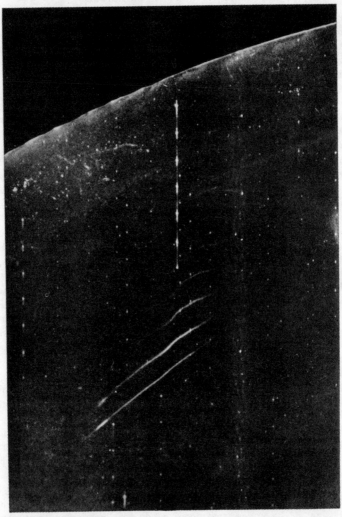

Fig. 5-19. Seven successive images of a meteor train taken in New Mexico in 1954 with a Super-Schmidt camera, showing the distortion caused by winds. The first time exposure (*bottom*) was 0.5 sec, and the sequentially displaced exposures were 2.0 sec each. The actual flight of the meteor, from right to left, has not been recorded. (*Courtesy of F. L. Whipple.*)

into two or more slightly diverging trails as the meteoroid breaks into fragments. Below about 50 km sounds may be heard, first the sharp crack of the shock wave created by the supersonic object and then a rumbling sound similar to thunder as the air fills in the hole that the body literally bores through the atmosphere. These sounds travel at a speed near 330 m/sec; hence several minutes may elapse between the passage of the meteor and the arrival of the sound. LaPaz (1958) has reported on a number of apparently well-authenticated cases of swishing or

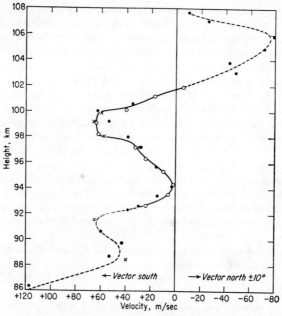

FIG. 5-20. Variation of train velocity with height, from a Super-Schmidt meteor train sequence, taken in Massachusetts, Aug. 13, 1950. (*Courtesy of F. L. Whipple.*)

whistling sounds which were heard simultaneously with the passage of the meteor. It seems that although a satisfactory explanation is lacking, all the accounts of these anomalous sounds cannot be dismissed as purely subjective effects.

5-9. Meteor spectra. Of the 318 meteor spectra in the world list compiled by Millman (1959c), three-quarters are from meteors of nine major showers, included in the list of Table 6-1. This is a natural consequence of the difficulty of securing spectrophotographs; the observer tends to concentrate on the more productive shower periods. The apparent meteor magnitudes for these spectra ranged from 1 to -10, and the mean M_{pm} was -5.

Where heights are available for these spectra, they have agreed in the main with the photographic heights of Fig. 5-11, though the Giacobinid spectra occurred 15 to 20 km higher than the average for $V = 23$ km/sec. The height of peak luminosity of the spectral lines for meteors of magnitude $M_{pm} = -7$ or fainter was close to 90 km, and for the brighter (and usually slower) fireballs the luminosity maxima were in the height range 50 to 70 km.

Meteor spectra are predominantly emission line types, and individual specimens may contain from 1 or 2 to more than 150 lines. Blends of crowded atomic lines are sometimes erroneously identified as band structure, though occasionally true molecular bands have been observed which are due to the atmospheric N_2 molecule (Cook and Millman, 1955). A certain amount of continuous thermal radiation is probably present in some cases. Meteor luminosity is essentially a low-excitation effect. The energies of the observed multiplets range from 2 to 14 ev (electron volts) with the majority being below 7 ev. The ionization potentials for the atoms observed in the first ionized state are from 6 to 8 ev.

Iron is present in almost every spectrum, and the D-lines of sodium and the b-lines of magnesium are frequently prominent in the orange-green region of the spectrum. Strong lines of ionized calcium and magnesium in the blue-violet are characteristic of fast meteors, as are also the red lines of ionized silicon. Lines of ionized calcium and of the atmospheric gases nitrogen and oxygen are found in the infrared spectra of high-velocity meteors.

Millman has developed a nomenclature for the classification of meteor spectra into four general types:

Type Y: high excitation. The H and K lines of Ca II* are strongest, in the blue-violet.

Type X: moderate excitation. Na I or Mg I is strongest, either in the orange-green or blue-violet.

Type Z: low excitation. Fe I or Cr I is strongest, either in the orange-green or blue-violet.

Type W: miscellaneous spectra which do not fit into the above classes.

Type Y is predominant in high-velocity shower meteors. Shower meteors in the range 30 to 50 km/sec are usually of Type X, though a few are of Type Y. Shower meteors with velocities from 20 to 30 km/sec are invariably of Type X or Z. Probably only half a dozen out of the total list of spectra are due to a nickel-iron type of meteoroid, presumed

* The symbol Ca I is one way of describing the neutral calcium atom; Ca II is the first ionized state, sometimes written Ca^+; Ca III or Ca^{++} means that two electrons have been removed; and so on.

to be of asteroidal origin. So far, 11 of the 14 elements common in meteorites (Urey and Craig, 1953) have also been found in meteor spectra. These are: Al I; Ca I, Ca II; (Co I); Cr I; Fe I, Fe II; Mg I, Mg II; Mn I; Na I; Ni I; (Si I), Si II; Sr II, where the bracketed elements indicate some doubt of the identification. Sulfur, potassium, and phosphorus, which are found in meteorites, have not been identified in meteor spectra. This may be because these elements are uncommon in cometary meteors or because their strong lines fall outside the observable spectrum. On the other hand, the atomic-hydrogen red line is prominent in the spectra of fast cometary meteors, and it may be due to a residue of Whipple's cometary ices (Sec. 6-5). Other meteor lines not commonly found in meteorites are nitrogen, undoubtedly due to the atmosphere, and a weak evidence of strontium. Many spectra show Si II quite strongly, though Si I has yet to be identified with absolute certainty since its strong lines blend with iron and other elements.

There is a general tendency for excitation and ionization to build up along the path of a fast meteor. This may appear to the eye as a progressive color change from red to blue. The occurrence of a burst or flare can change the character of the spectrum markedly. Oddly enough, the excitation levels during a burst appear to be lower, while the ionization levels are in many cases higher than during the preburst part of the path (Millman, 1935; Russell, 1960). Cook (1955) has given an excellent summary of this and other features of meteoric radiation.

The rotating-shutter technique makes it possible to study the spectrum of the meteor wake. Millman (1950b, 1953) and Halliday (1958a) have noted that low-excitation multiplets are particularly strong in the wake spectra. Of special interest is the presence in some wake spectra of the forbidden line of atomic oxygen, often called the auroral-green line, which was first identified in meteor spectra by Halliday (1958b). All meteors showing the auroral-green line are high-velocity ones, and in most cases the line appears at considerably greater heights than does the rest of the meteor spectrum. Furthermore, the fact that it lasts through the shutter breaks shows that its duration is well over 0.1 sec. Halliday suggests that the effective duration is about 1 sec, which is characteristic of the lifetime of the forbidden oxygen state. There may be a connection between the circumstances of the appearance of the line in meteor spectra and the occurrence of solar or auroral activity.

Long-enduring luminous trains have been observed visually, lasting for a few seconds up to several minutes, though unfortunately no spectrum has yet been obtained of a really persistent train. We lack satisfactory clues to the process by which this visible radiation can continue to be released so long after the passage of the meteor. It is possible that the required energy is latent in the atmosphere and is released by catalytic agents introduced by the meteor. Sodium and caesium ejected from rockets in the upper atmosphere give rise to analogous clouds of luminosity, and the processes may well be related.

The radio engineer may wonder why some meteor spectra show comparatively few ionized lines when, according to his radio apparatus, the meteors are obviously creating large amounts of ionization. For example, no lines of any ionized elements at all were found in spectra obtained during the spectacular Giacobinid shower though the radio echoes were most prolific. The answer, somewhat oversimplified, lies in the mechanics of the atom—an electron can be removed entirely but, unless a second valence electron is raised to an excited state and then drops back, no radiation may take place. Or, even if a second electron does become excited, the resultant radiation can well lie outside the frequency range of the observing apparatus, or be absorbed in the ozone layer. The spectrophotograph can therefore only set an extreme lower limit to the total ionization produced by the meteor.

CHAPTER 6

Astronomical Aspects of Meteors

Much of the basic material in this chapter is obviously of an observational nature and could therefore be considered a part or extension of the previous chapter. A division at this point seems logical, not merely to keep the chapter lengths within conventional bounds, but because the primarily observed data have been processed rather thoroughly in an endeavor to extract some cosmological information about meteors. In some instances, for example the delineation of meteor orbits, both the original observations and the computational mechanics are generally accepted. In others, such as the question of interstellar meteors, widely different interpretations can be placed on the findings depending on what data are selected and how they are analyzed.

6-1. Meteor showers. As was pointed out in the opening chapter, observations of meteor streams have formed the backbone of meteor science for the past hundred years. Olivier (1925) has enlivened his summary of the earlier visual work with much intimate detail about the individuals and places concerned. The story of the optical work has been brought more up to date by Porter (1952), who has related it closely with the history of cometary researches. Porter's book also includes practical discussions of the computational methods used in deriving orbital parameters. The two books by Hoffmeister (1937, 1948) should not be overlooked, particularly the more recent one on meteor streams. However, the reader may find that some potentially useful and fundamental information has been effectively concealed by the manner in which Hoffmeister treats the data while developing his major thesis on the distribution of meteor streams in space and time—a thesis which is open to criticism since he has relied on visual data almost exclusively. The best modern review of meteor showers is to be found in "Meteor Astronomy" by Lovell (1954). Here the reader will find critical and detailed discussions of all the prominent meteor streams. Lovell's interest in this particular area probably stems from the important contributions that he and his colleagues have made to the subject, because the Jodrell Bank pioneering work on the precise delineation of the daytime streams undoubtedly ranks as an outstanding postwar highlight in the study of meteor showers.

In this section we present in tabular form a condensed summary of the elements of the recognized meteor showers, together with some commentary where appropriate. The source material is to be found in the books mentioned above and in many contemporary papers, including ones by Millman (1954a, 1955), Ellyett and Roth (1955), Whipple (1954, 1955b), and Whipple and Hawkins (1959). Visual observations collected over many years by Olivier, Prentice, McIntosh, and Ceplecha have been valuable, particularly in assessing rates. For the other parameters the more accurate instrumental data have been utilized whenever they were available. Some degree of judgment has been exercised in selecting material and in weighting parameters wherever the published data diverged significantly.

Table 6-1 lists a number of the more prominent showers: the ones in boldface type are the stronger and more consistent. Bracketed figures indicate less reliable data. Most of these showers appear consistently each year, although the Leonid rates show strong enhancement every 33 years and the Phoenicids are as yet not well determined. A shower is usually named after the constellation in which the radiant appears. If more than one radiant happens to occur within a given constellation, the name is prefixed in each case by the Greek letter designation of the nearest prominent star. The Quadrantids were named after an obsolete constellation "Quadrans Muralis," which was located between Draco and Boötes just east of the handle of the Big Dipper. There are a few exceptions to this general rule, whereby the shower is named, not after the constellation, but after the discoverer of the associated comet, e.g., the Giacobinids (see Table 6-2) after the codiscoverer of the Giacobini-Zinner comet and the Bielids after Biela's famous dichotomous object. Some efforts are being made to restore the purity of the nomenclature by converting Bielids to Andromedids and Giacobinids to Draconids, with only partial success in the face of a popular adherence to the cometary terms. This resistance to conformity may have some minor merit in avoiding confusion since in addition to the Giacobinid-cum-Draconid shower there is another recognized Draconid stream in June (not listed in these tables because of its low activity).

The second column in Table 6-1 gives the date of peak activity. The right ascension and declination of the radiant at the time of maximum activity are given in column 3. The radiants move in an easterly direction across the sky, typically at the rate of about 1° per day in right ascension with smaller motions in declination. The extreme dates between which at least a few meteors of the shower should be seen are shown in column 4. The duration in days (column 5) is a measure of the

Table 6-1. The Major Meteor Showers

(1) Shower	(2) Date of peak activity	(3) Radiant coordinates R.A.	(3) Dec.	(4) Dates of detectable meteors	(5) Duration of peak, days	(6) Approx. local time of radiant transit	(7) Observed velocity V_0, km/sec	(8) Equivalent visual hourly rates
Quadrantids	Jan. 3	231°	+50°	1–4 Jan.	0.5	0835	41	50
Corona Australids	Mar. 16	245	−48	14–18 Mar.	(5)	0445	:	(5)
Virginids	Mar. 20	190	00	Mar. 5–Apr. 2	(20)	0050	30	(<5)
Lyrids	Apr. 21	272	+32	19–24 Apr.	2	0410	48	5
Eta Aquarids	May 4	336	00	Apr. 21–May 12	10	0735	64	20
Arietids (D)	June 7	45	+23	May 29–June 19	20	1000	39	60
Zeta Perseids (D)	June 9	62	+24	1–17 June	15	1100	29	40
Ophiuchids	June 20	260	−20	17–26 June	(10)	2325	:	(20)
Beta Taurids (D)	June 29	87	+20	June 24–July 5	10	1115	31	20
Capricornids	July 25	315	−15	July 10–Aug. 5	(20)	0050	:	(20)
Southern Delta Aquarids	July 29	339	−17	July 21–Aug. 15	15	0210	41	20
Northern Delta Aquarids	July 29	339	00	July 15–Aug. 18	20	0210	41	10
Pisces Australids	July 30	340	−30	July 15–Aug. 20	(20)	0210	:	(20)
Alpha Capricornids	Aug. 1	309	−10	July 15–Aug. 20	(25)	0000	23	5
Southern Iota Aquarids	Aug. 5	338	−15	July 15–Aug. 25	(25)	0410	35	(10)
Northern Iota Aquarids	Aug. 5	331	−6	July 15–Aug. 25	(25)	0110	30	(10)
Perseids	Aug. 12	46	+58	July 25–Aug. 17	5	0540	60	50
Kappa Cygnids	Aug. 20	290	+55	18–22 Aug.	(3)	2125	26	(5)
Orionids	Oct. 21	95	+15	18–26 Oct.	5	0420	66	20
Southern Taurids	Nov. 1	52	+14	Sept. 15–Dec. 15	(45)	0045	29	(5)
Northern Taurids	Nov. 1	54	+21	Oct. 15–Dec. 1	(30)	0055	30	(<5)
Leonids	Nov. 16	152	+22	14–20 Nov.	4	0026	72	(5)
Phoenicids	Dec. 5	15	−55	(Dec. 5)	(0.5)	2000	(13)	(50)
Geminids	Dec. 13	113	+32	7–15 Dec.	6	0205	35	50
Ursids	Dec. 22	217	+80	17–24 Dec.	2	0825	34	15

147

sharpness of the peak and is roughly the interval between the times when the shower activity is one-quarter of the maximum. It should be noted that this duration interval may be asymmetrically disposed within the longer period specified in the previous column, since the activity of many showers displays a slow rise and a rapid fall.

The approximate local time of transit of the radiant, given in column 6 of Table 6-1, may be of help in determining when to look for the shower. Other factors enter here, of course. The Corona Australids are not visible in Canada or Europe, and the reliable Perseids of the Northern Hemisphere make little impression in Australia or South Africa. Daylight, or rather the lack of it, is a vital consideration in optical work, and the daytime showers of Table 6-1, marked (D), can be detected only by radio methods. The Eta Aquarid stream shows just a hint of its potential brilliance to the visual observer, as dawn comes long before the radiant transits. The Quadrantid radiant is circumpolar at middle northern latitudes; hence the northern observer's horizon will not intrude to cut off the flow of meteors, but the short, sharp peak of the shower may favor North America one year and Asia the next, with or without accompanying darkness.

The observed velocity V_0 of the shower meteors has been listed in column 7 of Table 6-1 wherever a value has been available from photographic or radio observations. Accurate information is lacking for some of the Southern Hemisphere streams. The last column of the table shows the equivalent visual rates at maximum activity. In all cases, whether visual, photographic, or radio, the published rates have been amended to equate them to the hourly numbers that a single naked-eye observer would see, assuming a clear dark night and a radiant elevation of 45°. The rates given are for the shower meteors and are in addition to the normal background rates characteristic of the time of day and the date. The values are intended to indicate long-term averages only. Even the "Old Faithful" showers, such as the Perseids and Geminids, will deviate appreciably from these average rates from year to year, and there will be marked variations from hour to hour.

No prominent annual showers occur in February or September. Several very minor showers can be found in the records for these months, though some are of doubtful authenticity. The whole interval after the Quadrantids in early January to the Eta Aquarids in early May is rather devoid of noteworthy activity, as even the present-day Lyrid shower is but a ghost of its ancient splendor. On the other hand, both the day and the night streams of May to August are numerous and rich in both the Northern and Southern Hemispheres—even more so than the list in Table 6-1 would suggest. The Leonids were formerly a strongly periodic stream, but perturbations have so affected the orbit that the expected enhancements at 33-year intervals, while noticeable, have been scarcely remarkable since the last major spectacle of 1866. The few but consistent numbers that appear now each year may qualify the Leonids as an annual shower.

The Jodrell Bank publications have listed as many as eleven daytime meteor showers (Lovell, 1954). Table 6-1 includes only the three which have repeated most consistently over several years and which have relatively high hourly rates. Others, like the Omicron Cetids (Almond, 1951), may turn out to be periodic rather than annual showers, and still others may be differently delineated when further and more accurate observations have been made.

About half of the showers enumerated in Table 6-1 show some evidence of long-term periodicities. In the remainder the variations from year to year are not statistically significant. Among the latter are included the four Aquarid and the three Taurid showers. The radiant complex that is active in and near Aquarius during the latter part of July and early August is most remarkable. So far, only the photographic technique can separate the fine detail, and to date not enough measurements have been made to clarify the picture fully. The Taurid stream, through which the earth passes for at least two months each year, must be about twenty million miles in width. Many years ago Whipple (1940) suggested that after perihelion passage the Taurids should provide a daytime shower which would, however, be invisible except as a few fireballs in late June and early July. This prediction was brilliantly verified by radar observations seven years later at Jodrell Bank with the discovery of the Beta Taurid meteors coming from the direction of the sun (Clegg, Hughes, and Lovell, 1947).

Two of the showers listed in Table 6-1 are recently discovered nighttime streams, namely, the Ursids and the Phoenicids. The Ursids of late December were first announced in 1945 by Bečvář of the Skalnaté Pleso Observatory in Czechoslovakia. A strong connection between the Ursids and Comet Tuttle has been suggested (see Table 6-2). The hourly rates of the Ursids appear to vary widely from year to year, but not enough data have been collected yet to yield any reliable evidence of periodicity. The Phoenicids were observed in 1956 in Australia, both visually and by radar (Weiss, 1958). The shower has been tentatively associated with Comet 1819 IV Blanpain. Visual observations showed that bright, slow fireballs appeared to be characteristic of this stream, although the velocity has not yet been measured accurately by instrumental methods (the value listed in Table 6-1 is based on the probable orbit of the meteors). It is too early to say if the Phoenicid shower will continue to be a regular feature of the southern skies in early December. The stream may be periodic; Bowen (1957b) has predicted a period of

5.6 years from his rainfall–meteor-shower correlations (see Sec. 10-4). The very slow geocentric velocity and the comparatively high visual rates of the Phoenicid meteors add interest to the study of this shower.

In general, the diffuseness of a shower radiant appears to increase with the age of the stream as the individual meteor orbits diverge because of many complex effects, such as collisions between particles, sputtering by solar radiation, the Poynting-Robertson effect, and gravitational perturbations caused by the planets, chiefly by Jupiter. The individual meteor radiants of the Giacobinid shower are estimated to lie within $0°.1$, perhaps less, of the mean radiant point. Whipple has found that this cosmic spread of the radiant amounts to about $0°.2$ for the Leonids and Geminids. The Perseids and the Southern Delta Aquarids are each grouped within $0°.7$ to $0°.8$ and the Northern Taurids within about $1°$. If the radiant spread is plotted against the time in days that the earth takes to pass through the stream (approximately the interval shown in column 4 of Table 6-1), a straight line is obtained. Very diffuse radiants like the Northern Iota Aquarids $(1°.3)$ and the Southern Iota Aquarids $(1°.8)$ depart from this empirical line since their stream widths (roughly forty days) are little greater than that of the Northern Taurids. The Alpha Capricornids have the greatest radiant spread yet determined, more than $2°$, though the stream width is only about twenty days.

6-2. Meteor streams and cometary associations. In the century which has elapsed since Schiaparelli announced that the Perseids moved in the same orbit as Comet 1862 III, some fifteen or more examples of cometary associations have been put forward. A partial list is given in Table 6-2, where the elements of the meteor orbits may be compared with those of the comets. Not all of the postulated associations have the same degree of plausibility. The relation between either the Eta Aquarids or the Orionids and Halley's striking comet is tenuous and uncertain, though still an attractive possibility. On the other hand, the connection between the Giacobini-Zinner Comet 1946 V and the comparatively young Giacobinid shower is unquestionable. The elements for each agree so closely that, until dissipative effects disperse the meteors more widely, we shall adopt the well-determined cometary parameters for the meteors also (see Table 6-2 and Fig. 6-1). Note that in Figs. 6-1 to 6-3, the orbits of the meteors and comets have been projected on the plane of the ecliptic. The dotted portions of the orbits are below the plane, and the positions and dates of the ascending or descending nodes have been marked where they intersect or come close to the earth's orbit. The time of the node is not necessarily the time of closest approach of the two orbits, particularly for low-inclination orbits, but the difference is usually of no consequence.

Figure 6-1 shows both the orbit of Biela's comet and the path of the

Table 6-2. The Orbital Elements of Some Meteor Streams and of Their
Associated Comets

Meteor stream or *Comet*	P, years	q, au	e	ω, deg	Ω, deg	i, deg
Lyrids	161	0.92	0.97	214	32	80
1861 I	415	0.921	0.983	213.4	29.9	79.8
Eta Aquarids	8	0.70	0.83	109	44	158
Orionids	21	0.54	0.93	87	30	163
1910 II (Halley)	76.0	0.587	0.967	111.7	57.3	162.2
Beta Taurids (D)	3.3	0.34	0.85	246	276	6
Southern Taurids	3.5	0.37	0.84	112	45	5
Northern Taurids	3.1	0.32	0.85	298	222	3
1954 IX (Encke)	3.30	0.338	0.847	185.2	334.7	12.4
Alpha Capricornids	4.1	0.57	0.78	271	133	4
1954 III (Honda-Mrkos-Pajdušáková)	5.22	0.559	0.814	184.0	233.1	13.2
Perseids	95	0.94	0.96	151	138	114
1862 III (Swift-Tuttle)	119.6	0.963	0.960	152.8	137.5	113.6
Giacobinids (October Draconids)	6.59	0.996	0.717	171.8	196.2	30.7
1946 V (Giacobini-Zinner)	6.59	0.996	0.717	171.8	196.2	30.7
Bielids (Andromedids)	6.1	0.75	0.78	242	224	6
1852 III (Biela)	6.62	0.861	0.756	223.3	245.9	12.6
Leonids	45	0.97	0.92	174	235	163
1866 I (Tempel)	33.2	0.977	0.905	171.0	231.4	162.7
Ursids	14	0.92	0.85	212	265	53
1939 X (Tuttle)	13.6	1.022	0.821	207.0	269.8	54.7

rediscovered Bielid (or Andromedid) meteors. Hawkins, Southworth, and Stienon (1959) found 23 photographic meteors over the period 1952–1956 which appeared to follow closely the orbit of Biela's comet, and they state that these represent the remnants of the once magnificent Bielid shower. It is estimated that the present-day visual rates are perhaps one Bielid in five hours—a mere vestige of the thousands of shooting stars seen per hour during the peak periods in 1872 and 1885. Observations of the Bielids have dropped almost to the vanishing point during the past fifty years, and many persons considered that the shower was lost. True, the few now being detected will fail to excite the average observer, but the demonstration that some members of the stream are still striking the earth is important—then, too, the faint possibility remains that further perturbations by Jupiter may swing the main stream back to the earth in future years.   The June Draconids (radiant at right ascension 215°, declination +55°, on June 28) are associated with the Pons-Winncke Comet 1951 VI, which has a period of about six years (not listed in Table 6-2).   The June Draconid shower of 1916 was fairly strong, but succeeding appearances of the shower have been weak, and no Draconid meteors have been reported since 1927.   The perihelion distance of the comet's

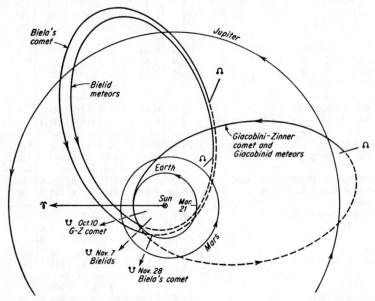

Fig. 6-1. Orbits of Biela's Comet and the Bielid meteor stream, and the orbit of the Giacobini-Zinner Comet and the Giacobinid meteors.

orbit is now well outside the earth's orbit; hence it is rather improbable that many Draconid meteors will be seen in the future.

The path of Encke's Comet 1954 IX* is shown in Fig. 6-2.   The orbit of the Southern Taurids is also plotted for comparison.   The ascending node of the Southern Taurids occurs near the earth's orbit on Nov. 8 while the descending node of the comet is well inside the earth's orbit.

* The nomenclature "1954 IX" means that this was the ninth comet observed to come to perihelion passage in 1954, not that 1954 was the first year the comet was seen.   Encke's comet also bears several other similar designations, e.g., 1948 III. If the comet is clearly periodic the name is sometimes prefixed by P/, as P/Encke.

There is little doubt, though, that the Southern Taurids are intimately associated with the comet.   On the scale of this projection it is difficult to separate the orbit of the daytime Beta Taurids from that of the comet. The ascending node of the Beta Taurids is marked at June 28 on the cometary orbit.   The origin of the Taurid complex has been traced back about five thousand years, during which time the inclinations of the various stream components have spread over fifteen degrees, extending both above and below the ecliptic.

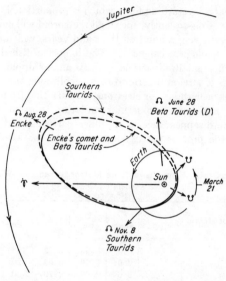

Fig. 6-2. Orbit of Encke's Comet compared with that of the Southern Taurid stream. The orbit of the daytime Beta Taurids corresponds closely with that of the comet; the ascending node for the Beta Taurids is indicated on the cometary orbit.

A meteor stream whose orbit has a high inclination to the ecliptic may be thought to have a greater chance of preserving its identity over the centuries, because it should stay well clear of Jupiter's perturbing influence.   This does tend to be true, but there are some exceptions.   We have already remarked on the survival of the Taurids after two thousand revolutions in planes close to those of the planets.   On the other hand, we might have expected the Leonid orbit to be quite stable, both because it is tilted at a greater angle to the plane of the ecliptic than are the Taurid orbits, and because the Leonid motion is retrograde, which means that the meteors will not linger as long within Jupiter's sphere of influence.   Despite these presumably more favorable circumstances the

Leonid stream suffered severe Jovian perturbations in the nineteenth century, from which it may never recover. The Lyrids ($i = 80°$) and the retrograde Perseids ($i = 163°$) do conform to our intuitive notion that high-inclination streams should be long-lived.

There are other influences, besides the gravitational one, which may alter both the course and the character of a meteor stream. One of the most important is the combination of radiation pressure and relativistic considerations known as the Poynting-Robertson effect. To put it very briefly, a small particle absorbs heat from the sun, and the reemission of this energy creates a retarding force which is proportional to the velocity of the particle. Consequently, the small meteoroid will eventually spiral into the sun, perhaps in a hundred thousand years, which is a very short time on the cosmological calendar. The long-established showers thus will have lost their smallest particles (Wyatt and Whipple, 1950). Other probable causes of stream deterioration are collisions among the meteoroids themselves or with ions or electrons. Sputtering from the surface of the meteoroid, owing to corpuscular radiation from the sun, can also account for the disappearance of the finer particles, and the estimated time scale of the process agrees very well with the available evidence (Kresák, 1960).

Table 6-3. The Orbital Elements of Some Meteor Streams for Which There Are No Associated Comets

Meteor stream	P, years	q, au	e	ω, deg	Ω, deg	i, deg
Quadrantids....................	6.3	0.97	0.72	168	283	74
Arietids (D).....................	2.0	0.09	0.94	29	77	21
Zeta Perseids (D)................	2.0	0.35	0.79	60	78	0
Southern Delta Aquarids..........	4.2	0.06	0.976	154	302	29
Northern Delta Aquarids..........	4.2	0.07	0.973	333	139	20
Southern Iota Aquarids...........	4.9	0.23	0.92	128	311	6
Northern Iota Aquarids...........	2.3	0.27	0.84	308	151	5
Kappa Cygnids..................	8.3	0.97	0.76	204	144	37
Geminids	1.64	0.140	0.900	324.3	261.2	23.9

Table 6-3 gives the elements of several meteor orbits with which no known comets can reasonably be associated. There is, however, an interesting and probable connection between the daytime Arietids and the Delta Aquarid complex. One of the latter streams, the Southern Delta Aquarids, has been plotted in Fig. 6-3, and the orbit of the daytime Arietids is shown for comparison. Despite the seemingly loose fit of the ellipses, which may be due to observational errors, the evidence is strong that we are encountering the same broad meteor stream twice, both in late July as the Delta Aquarids come toward the sun from below the ecliptic and in early June when the meteors strike the earth from above the ecliptic after swinging round the sun.   Mention has been made of a possible connection between the Delta Aquarids and either Comet 1954 III (this comet does fit rather well with the Alpha Capricornids—see Table 6-2) or the asteroid Icarus, but neither association seems plausible.

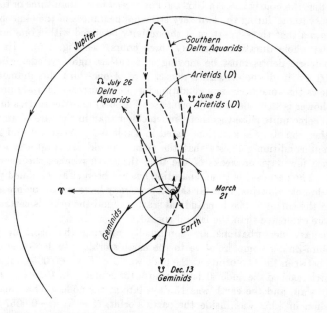

FIG. 6-3. Comparison of the orbit of the daytime Arietids with that of the Southern Delta Aquarid stream.   The Geminid orbit is also shown.   No known comets are associated with any of these meteor streams.

The orbit of the Geminid stream has been plotted in Fig. 6-3.   This orbit is smaller than those of any other recognized meteor streams or of any known comets.   Two or three asteroids have slightly smaller orbits, but no connection is suggested between them and the Geminid stream. The records of the Geminid shower do not go back more than about one hundred years, and the future life of this currently prolific shower has been estimated to be only of the order of another hundred years.

The history of the Giacobinid meteor stream has been discussed in considerable detail by Davies and Lovell (1955).   The first definite observation of the shower was in 1926, when the visual rate was about

15 hr^{-1}. In 1933 and 1946 phenomenally high rates of 4,000 to 6,000 hr^{-1} were recorded. No meteors were seen in 1939 or 1940, because the predicted time of maximum occurred in daylight: whether or not there were showers is unknown. The Jodrell Bank radio apparatus detected 180 Giacobinid meteors per hour during the 1952 daylight return. Since that time only a few isolated meteors have been seen. In particular, the expected 1959 return was extremely disappointing. Visual reports indicated that the hourly rates in 1959 did not exceed more than three or four.

Observations during the two very strong appearances of the Giacobinids showed that three-quarters of the activity occurred within one hour, and the whole duration was only three hours (see Fig. 1-5). Hence the meteoric debris must be moving as a rather tight cylinder about 300,000 km in diameter with a denser core of one-third this diameter. It follows that one necessary condition for the occurrence of an appreciable shower is that the comet's orbit (see Fig. 6-1) and the earth's orbit should come quite close together—much closer than in the case of any of the other cometary associations listed in Table 6-2. A second and less stringent condition suggests that the comet should arrive at the node within a few days or weeks of the time the earth reaches the nearest point. The permissible time separation has not been clearly defined yet, as we do not know just how far the meteors may have spread before and behind the comet. The longitudinal scatter round the orbit is certainly far more extensive than the lateral spread.

Planetary perturbations are continually altering the orbit of the Giacobini-Zinner comet relative to the earth's orbit. In 1933 the distance between the two orbits at the node was $C - E = +0.0054$ au, and the earth reached the node 80 days ahead of the comet. In 1946, $C - E = +0.0014$ au, and the earth was 15 days late at the node. The comet's perihelion in 1952 was inside the earth's orbit, $C - E = -0.0057$ au, and the earth was 172 days behind the comet. The 1959 observations of the comet showed that, although the earth was only 21.6 days ahead at the node, the comet's perihelion had moved in further toward the sun, to $q = 0.936$ (compared with the 1946 value $q = 0.996$, Table 6-2). The corresponding value of $C - E = -0.058$ au is ten times the greatest separation observed on the previous shower occasions. This could well account for the lack of meteors, despite the reasonably small time differential. (We are indebted to Dr. Elizabeth Roemer and Rev. Cameron Dinwoodie for the private communication of some of these unpublished data.)

If this trend continues, as it seems likely to do, the Giacobinids may, like the passenger pigeons, become a memory in the minds of men. This would be a great pity, not solely because the Giacobinid showers have been the most striking of the twentieth century, but because the meteors themselves, in their physical characteristics, are quite like no other meteors. The hypothesis of the fragmenting meteoroid originated in an endeavor to explain some peculiar photographic results obtained during the 1946 shower (Jacchia, Kopal, and Millman, 1950). We now believe that most meteoroids crumble readily on impact with the upper air, but attention was first drawn to this general possibility by the anomalous behavior of the Giacobinids, which seem to be extremely fragile dustballs. One can only speculate how long our understanding of this aspect of meteoric phenomena would have been retarded if Millman had failed to enlist the cooperation of the Royal Canadian Air Force in a dramatic emergency operation on the night of Oct. 9–10, 1946. An ominous cloud bank hung over the Ottawa area where cameras and observers were waiting for the onset of the shower, and only by making a frantic last-minute dash by a special RCAF plane to North Bay, Ontario, where clear skies prevailed, were they able to obtain the vital evidence. It now appears that the more than two hundred photographic specimens captured with the rotating-shutter camera by Millman on that eventful night may be both the first and last ever to be taken in any appreciable numbers from this unique stream.

6-3. The interstellar meteor question. Ever since Schiaparelli's original attack on the problem, nearly a century ago, scientists have sought definitive answers to the cosmic questions posed by the arrival of meteoric particles from outer space. Where do they come from? Are they all members of the solar system, miniature planets of our own sun? No one doubts the evidence of the recognized annual meteor streams, which demonstrates clearly that an appreciable fraction of the total numbers striking the earth must now be traveling in elliptical orbits, whatever the origin of the particles may have been. However, the non-shower meteors comprise an even larger proportion of the population, and prior to the era of precise instrumental observations there was ample scope for the thesis that most of these meteors came to us from interstellar space. Some mention has been made in Sec. 5-3 of the analytic techniques used to arrive at this conclusion from the visual data then available. Hoffmeister (1937, 1948) and Öpik (1941) at one time were of the opinion that 60 to 70 per cent of the sporadic meteors could have hyperbolic velocities, the range extending up to three times the parabolic velocity. More recent publications by these authors (Hoffmeister, 1955; Öpik, 1956a) have indicated that they now consider these estimates, both of numbers and velocities of hyperbolic meteors, should be reduced considerably.

Lovell (1954) has devoted five chapters of his book almost entirely to the interstellar meteor problem. In one chapter he has attempted to summarize Öpik's work as described in preliminary publications of the rocking-mirror visual observations made in Arizona and at Tartu in Esthonia, without being able to reconcile the results with those obtained by photographic and radio observations. Some later papers by Öpik have brought about a closer *rapprochement* between the instrumental and the visual conclusions. In making his final analysis of the rocking-mirror observations, Öpik (1956a, 1958b) was able to resolve some of the apparent anomalies satisfactorily. He nevertheless retained the viewpoint that a significant, though small, component (perhaps 3 per cent) of the sporadic meteor complex may be interstellar in origin.

The instrumental techniques have now demonstrated fairly conclusively that relatively few meteors in the visual range, that is, fifth mag-

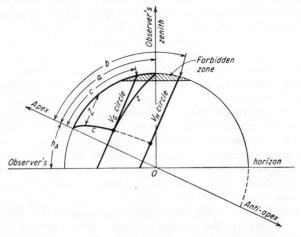

Fig. 6-4. Geometry for synthesizing theoretical radiant and velocity distributions.

nitude and brighter, can be following hyperbolic orbits. However, definite conclusions have not yet been reached for either very bright or very faint objects. Meteorite-dropping bolides occur so rarely that to date only one specimen (which had an elliptical orbit) appears to have been photographed (Ceplecha, Rajchl, and Schnal, 1959). The range of fainter meteors from fifth magnitude to the incandescent limit remains to be explored fully. We know very little indeed about the orbital characteristics of micrometeorites, which by their nature defy study by photographic or radio methods.

The Jodrell Bank and the Ottawa radio-velocity measurements will be described briefly, not because they presented the unassailable answer to the question—nothing short of precise orbital data for every observed meteor could do that, together with the assurance that the sampling is truly representative—but because the large number of reasonably accurate velocities obtained on these two programs appeared to justify a fresh approach to the problem. Because no radiant information was available in the Ottawa work (McKinley, 1951b), various assumed radiant distributions were tried out. A non-uniform distribution was adopted by postulating more radiants with $b > 90°$ than with $b < 90°$, which in effect implies that more of the orbits will be direct. Here, b is the angle on the celestial sphere between the apex of the earth's way and the true radiant position (see Fig. 6-4). Each radiant point on a given V_H circle of Fig. 6-4 transforms by means of Eqs. (5-12) and (5-13) to a point on the corresponding V_G circle, and the observed velocity V_0 is given by these same equations together with Eq. (2-6). The radiants were taken to be uniformly distributed around each V_H circle. It was further assumed that half of the meteors had $V_H = 36$ km/sec and half had $V_H = 42$ km/sec.

The probability function for the Ottawa radar (Fig. 5-6) was then used to convert the theoretical radiant distributions to predicted distributions of velocities as detected by the radar. To carry out the conversion three representative values were selected for the elevation of the apex above the horizon, $h_A = -45, 0, +45°$. The calculated curves are shown in Fig. 6-5 as dashed lines. Observed distributions for the times

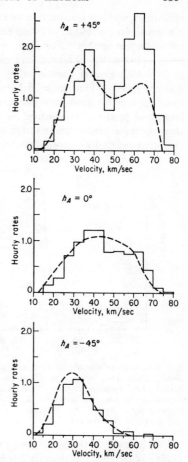

FIG. 6-5. Comparison of observed and predicted nonshower velocity distributions, Ottawa data. *Solid-line histograms*, observed distributions for three elevations of the apex, $h_A = +45°$, 0°, −45°; the numbers of meteors in each distribution were 1157, 975, and 250, respectively. *Dashed lines*, calculated distributions; all three are normalized to the observed distribution for $h_A = 0°$.

corresponding to these apex elevations were extracted from the basic data (which have been summarized by the over-all curve given in Fig. 5-16, *solid-line graph*), after deleting as far as possible the contributions from the recognized showers. These have been plotted in Fig. 6-5 as the solid-line histograms. For $h_A = -45$ and $0°$, particularly, the agreement between the observed and calculated distributions is good. For $h_A = +45°$ a greater number of high-velocity meteors was observed than was predicted. This may be because no allowance was made in the computations for a possible increase of ionization with velocity. If the ionization produced is assumed to vary as V^n, where n may be greater than unity, a better quantitative agreement may be obtained between the predicted and observed distributions for $h_A = +45°$.

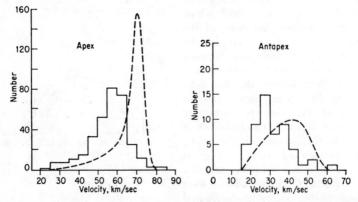

Fig. 6-6. Comparison of observed and predicted nonshower velocity distributions, Jodrell Bank data. *Solid-line histogram*, observed distributions for a selected *apex* period when the apex elevation was high, and for an *antapex* period when the apex elevation was low; the numbers of meteors in each distribution were 298 and 53, respectively. *Dashed lines*, calculated distributions; each is normalized to the corresponding observed distribution.

Concurrently with the Ottawa program, Almond, Davies, and Lovell (1951, 1952, 1953) at Jodrell Bank conducted a similar series of radio observations which were tailored rather more specifically to determine whether or not there were appreciable numbers of hyperbolic meteors. They used a directive antenna to narrow down the region of the sky from which detectable meteors could come, but the individual meteor radiants were not determined. Furthermore, they observed mainly during two selected times of the day, over periods of several months, one when the apex was highest in the sky—the "apex" experiments—and the other when the apex was lowest—the "antapex" experiments. Theoretical velocity distributions corresponding to these apex elevations were computed by Clegg (1952), assuming $V_H = 42$ km/sec. The histograms in Fig. 6-6 show one example of the apex observations and one from the antapex experiments, together with the predicted distributions (dashed lines). The observed distributions in both cases show trends to lower velocities than the theory predicts, which Lovell attributes in part to oversimplification of some of the theoretical premises, but the fact that the tendency is toward lower velocities suggests that the majority of the heliocentric velocities were less than 42 km/sec.

The purpose of these comparisons between observed and synthesized distributions is to try to utilize all the observed velocities in a selected period rather than to consider only the marginal geocentric velocities. Inspection of the over-all velocity distribution for any period will quickly show if any velocities exceed $V_0 = 72$ km/sec, but the more involved analyses given above help to demonstrate that the statistical distribution of velocities less than $V_0 = 72$ km/sec is compatible with the assumption of elliptical heliocentric velocities. Still other theoretical distributions can be fitted to the observations with fair success because of the number of adjustable parameters. There seems to be little point in trying to carry the analysis any further along these lines. The problem is very similar to the one discussed in Sec. 5-3, the only difference being that we have here substituted rates and velocities for rates and radiants as primary data.

The reality of the "fringe" of hyperbolic velocities in the radio data has been the subject of much discussion. Planetary perturbations, among other causes, can certainly divert elliptical meteors into hyperbolic orbits about the sun. It has been suggested that some meteors in the fringe area may indeed have had assistance from Jupiter but, as Öpik has pointed out, the numbers intersecting the earth would be very few, far too few to account for the fringe. Experimental error may be responsible for the majority, though perhaps not all, of the hyperbolic values—the average velocity error resulting with the rapid reduction methods employed at Ottawa was estimated to be about 5 per cent and the greatest error about 10 per cent. Thirty-two meteors out of nearly 11,000 had observed velocities in the range 75 to 79 km/sec; none were in excess of 80 km/sec. One cannot say with any degree of certainty, of course, just what fraction of the number of meteors with velocities less than 72 km/sec may have had heliocentric velocities in excess of 42 km/sec, but the distributions of Figs. 6-5 and 6-6 lend support to the conclusion that both the fraction and the excess of velocity must be relatively small.

The real question to be answered is whether or not the radio methods are detecting all the high-velocity meteors. In the light of remarks made in Sec. 8-6 it now seems likely that the older radio methods may have failed to provide a satisfactory sampling of the faint high-velocity meteors. At the time the original experiments were done, the effectiveness of the underdense-type echo ceiling was not fully realized. Because the average sensitivity of the Ottawa equipment was around eighth or ninth magnitude, the statement was made (McKinley, 1951b) that the results might be applied to meteors as faint as the eighth magnitude—which was undoubtedly correct for meteors with $V < 50$ km/sec, but it may not have been so for faint meteors with $V > 75$ km/sec (see Sec. 8-6). However, the underdense-echo ceiling does not apply to overdense-type echoes, i.e., to meteors with $M \leq 5$. We are reasonably safe, therefore, in saying that the conclusions are valid to at least the limit of visual magnitudes, where the trails begin to be underdense.

It is, of course, quite possible that the true velocity distributions in the faint magnitude ranges are lacking in high velocities, but the velocity-only type of experiment cannot confirm this. Davies's more recent work on orbits (Sec. 6-4) is not entirely free from criticism based on high-velocity ceiling considerations, but he is at least one step further ahead because he derives orbital distributions. Whipple (1955a) has indeed suggested that a real difference in the orbital distributions could occur between the photographic and the radio magnitude ranges. The most recent results of the Super-Schmidt program (Sec. 6-4) tend to favor this conclusion. Öpik (1958b) found $r = 2.80$ for retrograde meteors, compared to $r = 3.56$ to 3.66 for direct meteors, which also suggests that the numbers of meteors with high observed velocities, relative to the numbers with low observed velocities, should decrease with increasing magnitude.

As the antapex distributions show (Fig. 6-5, $h_A = -45°$, and Fig. 6-6, *antapex*), there were few if any radio meteors detected above 60 km/ sec. During the apex periods appreciable numbers were seen up to $V = 75$ km/sec. Therefore, the lack of high-velocity meteors during the antapex periods must be a true one—even the rather stringent and undoubtedly low theoretical ceiling which we have computed in Sec. 8-6 does not account for it. The conclusion that all, or nearly all, meteors are moving in elliptical orbits can be applied down to the limits of the visual range at least and possibly to somewhat fainter meteors. Improved radio techniques will have to be evolved before anything really definitive can be said about meteors much fainter than $M = 5$.

The sun's motion relative to the neighboring stars is about 20 km/sec in the general direction of the constellation Hercules. If particles of meteoric sizes exist in the vast reaches between the stars, their mean velocity relative to the sun could also be about 20 km/sec. When such particles reach the earth's distance from the sun, the resultant heliocentric velocity is found not by adding 20 and 42 km/sec vectorially, as might be thought at first glance, but by using the energy equation for velocities, $V_H^2 = 20^2 + 42^2$. Thus $V_H = 46.5$ km/sec, not 62 km/sec, and the maximum V_G that would result (now one does add vectorially) is 76.5 km/sec, not 92 km/sec. The concern over the relatively small numbers in the fringe area of velocities is therefore understandable.

Interstellar meteors, if proven to exist, would be of important cosmological significance because they would be our only tangible evidence of macroscopic material from beyond the solar system—very tangible indeed in the case of meteorites. Perhaps the famous Pultusk meteorite (Galle, 1868) had an interstellar origin—Öpik (1958a) states that it is the only case of a meteorite with well-observed hyperbolic velocity. In a speculative mood, we might assert that if the instrumental methods were to record even but a few meteors which were agreed by all concerned to be incontrovertibly hyperbolic (well beyond the current fringe area), it is probable that both schools of thought would feel well vindicated. The evidence to date does not deny the possibility, but it does underline the probable rarity of such events. The interstellar proponents would have their thesis proved, in principle at least, and the photographic and radio workers would have positive assurance that their instruments were fully capable of detecting hyperbolic meteors. Discoveries of this nature would confirm rather than negate the current conclusion that the great majority of meteors seen by instrumental methods up to the present do belong to the solar system.

6-4. Distribution of meteor orbits in space. A random selection of 360 meteors was taken by Hawkins and Southworth (1958) from the Harvard Super-Schmidt collection. Figure 6-7 shows the radiant points of these meteors plotted in celestial coordinates. In this particular projection the apex of the earth's way is at the center of the chart. This diagram (kindly furnished in advance of publication by Dr. Hawkins) shows one concentration of radiants near the longitude of the antihelion point, 180° away from the sun. Some shower meteors have been identified in the data; the major shower radiants are shown by the named squares, and minor showers, which have been segregated by a criterion proposed by Hawkins and Southworth (unpublished), are indicated by circles. Owing to the restriction imposed by daylight, the area near the solar point could not be explored, nor has the deep Southern Hemisphere been observed. Hawkins (1956a) used the early Jodrell Bank radar data to fill in the solar region on the chart. He found that the daylight meteor activity provided a third concentration of radiants near the sun's longitude. Öpik (1956a) has published a comparable chart of sporadic stream density, based on the visual observations made on the Arizona Meteor Expedition.

A similar general grouping of radiants for meteors down to seventh magnitude was observed by Davies (1957) in his work on the orbits of radio meteors. In Fig. 6-8 he has plotted the relative density of 2,400 radiants (corrected for observational selection) as a radius vector in the

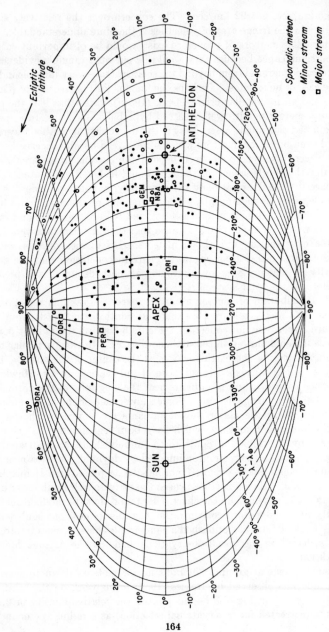

FIG. 6-7. Distribution of radiants of major streams, minor streams, and sporadic nonshower meteors, from randomly selected photographic data. (*Courtesy of G. S. Hawkins.*)

plane of the elliptic.   The apex concentration is due to the earth's motion and contains a large proportion of high-latitude radiants.   The other two groups, at longitudes roughly 60 and 295° respectively, include the majority of the meteors.   Low-inclination orbits are predominant in these latter groups.   Although day-light was no hindrance to the radio observations, the deep southern radiants were again beyond reach.

When one examines the variation of numbers with orbital size, it is convenient to plot the distributions against $1/a$, the reciprocal of the semimajor axis expressed in astronomical units.   Elliptical orbits will range from the smallest $(1/a = 2)$, which lie inside and just touch the earth's orbit, to the parabolic limit $(1/a = 0)$.   Negative values of $1/a$ represent hyperbolic orbits.   Figure 6-9 presents two sets of photographic data: the dots and solid-line graph refers to 144 small-camera meteors of magnitude zero and brighter (Whipple, 1954), and the stepped histogram shows the distribution of 2,529 Super-Schmidt meteors of third magnitude and brighter (McCrosky, unpublished).   In the bright-meteor distribution there are no meteors with $1/a > 1$; that is, there are none with orbits as small

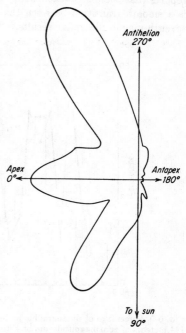

FIG. 6-8. Distribution of nonshower meteor radiants with ecliptic longitude, from the Jodrell Bank program of radio orbits. (*Davies*, 1957.)

as that of the earth.   The majority are grouped about $1/a = 0.3$, and there is a strong component near the parabolic value.   The Super-Schmidt distribution does extend beyond $1/a = 1$, showing that the percentage of short-period orbits increases with fainter magnitudes.   In a comprehensive paper Öpik (1958b) has discussed the distribution of meteor streams over the celestial sphere, as deduced from visual observations.   One point in this paper, of particular interest here, is that the increase of numbers per magnitude r is greater for meteors in direct short-period orbits than for those in retrograde orbits, which as a group have longer periods.

Davies's distribution of numbers versus $1/a$, for radio meteors down to the seventh magnitude, is given in Fig. 6-10.   The numbers have been weighted for observational selection.   An even higher proportion of short-period orbits is strikingly apparent in the radio distribution.   Davies has recently carried out a radio survey to a limit of fourth magnitude.   He reports that the distribution with $1/a$ of these orbits showed that there is a smooth transition between the photographic distributions and the seventh-magnitude radio results.   This survey has brought the total

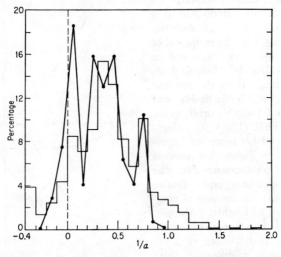

FIG. 6-9. Percentage of photographic meteors versus $1/a$.   *Dots and solid-line graph,* 144 meteors of zero magnitude and brighter (*Whipple, 1954*); *histogram,* 2,529 meteors of third magnitude and brighter (*courtesy of R. E. McCrosky*).

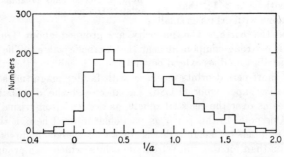

FIG. 6-10. Numbers of radio meteors versus $1/a$, for 2,400 meteors of seventh magnitude and brighter.   (*Davies, 1957.*)

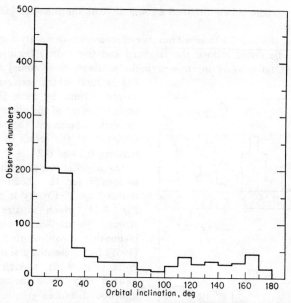

FIG. 6-11. Distribution of 2,529 photographic meteors with orbital inclination i. (*Courtesy of R. E. McCrosky.*)

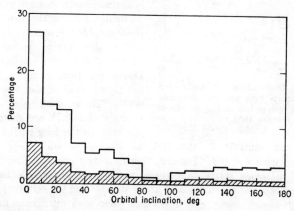

FIG. 6-12. Distribution of radio meteors with orbital inclination i. *Open histogram*, orbits with $q' > 3$ au; *shaded histogram*, orbits with $q' > 10$ au. (*Davies, 1957.*)

number of radio orbits obtained at Jodrell Bank up to about 4,000 as of early 1960.

In Figs. 6-9 and 6-10 a small number of meteors with negative values of $1/a$ may be noted. Both the Harvard and the Jodrell Bank workers state that no meteors in these hyperbolic fringes were found to have

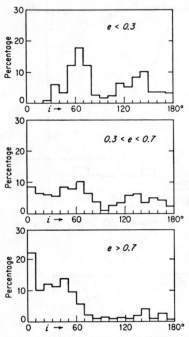

FIG. 6-13. Distribution with inclination of radio orbits with aphelion distances $q' < 3$ au, grouped according to eccentricities. (*Davies*, 1957.)

$1/a$ values which exceeded the parabolic limit by more than the probable error of the observations. In each experiment the standard deviation of the errors in $1/a$ lay between 0.1 and 0.2.

The distribution of orbital inclinations i for the 2,529 meteors reduced by McCrosky is given in Fig. 6-11, which illustrates the strong preponderance of low-inclination direct orbits. Davies (1957) has presented a similar diagram (Fig. 6-12), though he has plotted only those meteors with aphelion distances greater than 3 au (open histogram) and those greater than 10 au (shaded histogram). The ecliptic concentration is again evident, though it is not as pronounced as in the case of the photographic meteors.

The short-period radio orbits with $q' < 3$ au were subdivided by Davies into three groups according to their eccentricities (see Fig. 6-13). Those with high eccentricities ($e > 0.7$) are distributed similarly to the long-period orbits. In marked contrast is the lack of low-inclination orbits among the group with $e < 0.3$. Instead, there are two peaks at $i = 60°$ and $i = 140°$. Davies states that these meteors are observable the year round and represent a complex of orbits intersecting the ecliptic plane at very high angles, some with direct and some with retrograde motions. The proportion of meteors in these short-period, almost circular orbits appears to increase rapidly with magnitude. One should not overlook the possibility that the scarcity of this type of orbit at low inclinations might be due to a kind of observational selection. The geocentric velocities of these meteors are very low, and hence the fainter ones may escape detection because of their comparatively poor ionizing efficiency (this effect should not be confused with that caused by the high-velocity, underdense-type echo ceiling). However, the fainter Super-Schmidt meteors also show signs of the same trend toward relatively few orbits with both low inclinations and low eccentricities. Either a similar kind of luminous selection effect is beginning to operate, or the trend is real.

6-5. The origin of meteors. We have seen that several meteor streams can be clearly associated with comets through the close similarity of their orbital elements. Although we have no direct evidence that disintegration of the comet itself gives rise to these streams, it seems reasonable to assume that the meteoroids of these streams would be composed of cometary material. Whipple (1951) has evolved an "icy-conglomerate" model of a comet which has been widely accepted. In brief essence, the comet's nucleus is assumed to consist of small mineral particles, perhaps in loosely bound matrices (dustballs), immersed in an ice of frozen gases, such as H_2O, NH_3, CH_4, and CO_2. Spectroscopic observations of comets do show CN, C_2, CO^+, and other unstable molecules which could have been released from the stable compounds forming the ices. As the comet swings about the sun, the frozen gases melt and vaporize, and dustballs are set free—perhaps ejected forcibly by pressure created in gas pockets. The evidence from the photographic light curves of meteors suggests strongly, without proving conclusively, that the meteoroids which give rise to practically all visible meteors are porous and crumbly in nature with bulk densities less than that of water. The physical meteor data and the comet model are compatible, which lends additional support to the theory that meteors are likely to be made of cometary material.

Some minor anomalies arise in developing the comet-meteor hypothesis. For example, the Geminid orbit (Fig. 6-3) is smaller than that of any comet known to recorded history. Furthermore, the Geminid meteors appear to have a density from two to three times that of the average meteor, though this derived density is still too small for solid mineral bodies. The Geminids could be the residue from the central nucleus of a very large comet, though the original object must have been a giant of the comet family in order to survive such close passages to the sun ($q = 0.14$ au) in its contraction from Jupiter's orbit. The faint radio meteors with short-period orbits also appear at first glance to lack cometary progenitors. It may be shown, however, that if these particles were originally moving in long-period orbits, the combined effect of planetary perturbation and the Poynting-Robertson effect would cause the orbits to contract to their present dimensions within a few million years. Again, there are small but significant physical differences between the members of one major shower and another.   These variations imply that the parent comets themselves have or had their individual characteristics, but in no cases are the deviations from the mean great enough to cast serious doubts on the probable cometary origin of the showers.

Only a very few of the brightest fireballs are now considered to be solid bodies with the density of stone or iron.   This type of meteoroid, which may be both large enough and strong enough to survive as a meteorite, is thought to be asteroidal material.   The origin of the asteroids themselves is highly conjectural.   One hypothesis is that they were formed by a "rear-end" collision between two small planets, moving at nearly the same orbital velocity, and that additional collisions and grindings of the larger fragments have produced the spectrum of rock and iron fragments which bombard the earth at an average rate of perhaps 1 hr^{-1}.   This asteroidal theory is incomplete, and there are many unanswered questions, but no attractive alternative is available at the moment.   Some selection mechanism may be operating to remove asteroidal debris smaller than the meteorites, since there is little or no positive proof of its existence in the photographic range.

Micrometeorites, at the other extreme of size, are probably single solid particles, and the suggestion has been made that they may be asteroidal dust.   This thesis seems unacceptable, first because of the peculiar lack of evidence of asteroidal particles in the intermediate range of meteor sizes, and second because quantitative problems arise in accounting both for the large (estimated) total mass of the micrometeorites and for their continued existence so long after the original catastrophic event, in view of the influences which should act to sweep fine material into the sun relatively quickly.   Fewer difficulties are apparent if we consider micrometeorites to be made of cometary material.   They may also be the basic particle constituents of the meteor dustballs.   A reasonable rate of capture of comets from Oort's almost inexhaustible cloud (see later in this Section) is quite adequate to account both for the micrometeorites and for the fine dust particles which cause the zodiacal light.

We might assemble three tables of orbital elements, one of the asteroids, one of the comets, and one of the meteors, and then endeavor to determine whether meteor orbits as a class are more closely associated with comet orbits or with asteroidal orbits.   We soon would find that simple intercomparisons led to no conclusions, owing to the difficulty of identifying consistent patterns among the five different parameters involved.   Whipple (1954) devised an ingenious formula to aid in separating the various types of orbits.   His empirical "K criterion" is

$$K = \log_{10}\left[\frac{a(1 + e)}{1 - e}\right] - 1$$

The quantity in the square bracket is the inverse square of the orbital velocity at the aphelion point. Only three of the 1,600 known asteroids yield positive values of the K criterion. On the other hand, all of the ten cometary orbits with perihelion points inside the earth's orbit have positive Ks, as do 75 per cent of those with periods less than 25 years. Hence the K criterion is a fairly effective device for discriminating between cometary and asteroidal orbits. When Whipple's 144 orbits of bright photographic meteors are inserted in the formula it is found that 90 per cent have positive K values. This may be regarded as confirmatory evidence of the cometary character of these particular meteor orbits.

The K criterion has no fundamental physical significance, of course. Inconclusive results are obtained when it is applied to the group of meteors moving in short-period orbits of low eccentricity. For these we have to fall back on the observations of the photographic light curves and measured decelerations. These data reveal no significant differences between the physical properties of known cometary meteors and of meteors with asteroidal-type orbits. We are just beginning to accumulate the equivalent information for the faint radio meteors. Recent experiments lend tentative weight to the conclusion that they too are dustballs, down to the present limits of radio detection, and therefore they are also likely to be cometary stuff.

In thus identifying ordinary meteors with comets, we have only succeeded in shifting the burden of explanation to the problem of the genesis of comets—a puzzle which has perplexed scientists for centuries. The distribution of cometary velocities shows a kind of hyperbolic fringe area which is similar to that appearing in the distributions of meteor velocities. Most of the orbits are elliptical, though many are large, and the weight of current opinion favors the notion that comets have always been members of the solar system (Porter, 1952). The theory put forward by Oort (1951) envisages a vast cloud of comets, perhaps 10^{11} in number, moving around the sun in tremendous orbits at distances ranging up to 150,000 au. These distances are comparable with those of the nearest stars; hence, from time to time, stellar perturbations may throw a comet into an orbit which will bring it within our earthly ken. Capture of these comets by Jupiter would then account for the short-period orbits. How the comet cloud was created is a part of the enigma of the solar system. Future research in meteoric phenomena will undoubtedly forge some new and important links in the long chain of evidence binding together our understanding of the solar system.

CHAPTER 7

Physical Theory of Meteors

7-1. The classical physical theory of meteors. The physical phenomena of meteors are closely interwoven with the properties of the upper atmosphere. Prior to the era of rocket flights, Whipple (1938, 1943) was able to derive amazingly accurate estimates of air densities and temperatures at meteoric heights from his photographic observations of meteor luminosities and decelerations. His calculations were based on what we shall term the classical theory of meteors, which combines conventional aerodynamic ballistics with plausible assumptions about atomic collisions and light-emission processes.

We are now passing through a transitional period and approaching the time when the rocket data (see Appendix) should become sufficiently well established to enable the problem to be worked in reverse. This is particularly important because in recent years we have been forced to the conclusion that most meteoroids in the visible range are porous or crumbly objects, which do not follow the rules for solid mineral bodies. The success of the classical theory appears to have been due in part to the fortuitous selection of very bright meteors in the early camera programs, meteors which were large objects, though not necessarily solid ones, penetrating deeply into the atmosphere. When the same treatment is applied to the majority of visual meteors, a significant lack of agreement may be remarked between predictions and observations.

The discussion in this chapter will be based mainly on the luminous aspects of meteors. One important manifestation of the meteor's passage, the ionization, will receive more detailed attention in Chap. 8. For three reasons we shall devote some time to an outline of the classical theory, despite its limitations. First, it serves quite satisfactorily for some of the brighter meteors at least. Second, the developments in meteor ionization theory (Chap. 8) have stemmed directly from the classical optical theory. The ionization theory seems to have worked quite well in many applications, whether or not it ought to have in the light of current views on the nature of meteoroids. Third, although the "neoclassical" theory of the crumbling meteoroid is being built around

172

the older hypotheses, it is not yet susceptible of complete delineation in the form of convenient equations—it is in a state of continuous flux, of cut-and-try, and its tenets take the form of empirical tables subject to change.

The classical theory is largely the work of several eminent scientists during the period 1920–1940, including Lindeman and Dobson (1923), C. M. Sparrow, H. B. Maris, and J. Hoppe. Perhaps the greater share of the credit should go to two men: E. J. Öpik, who, in addition to being an indefatigable observer, has displayed a keen insight into the details of the physical processes, and F. L. Whipple, who has supplied accurate observational material and further streamlined the theory. The interested reader may find the historical highlights well covered in several summary papers, notably by Öpik (1937, 1955c, 1955d), Whipple (1938, 1943), Levin (1956), and Herlofson (1948a). Much of the following development of the classical theory is derived from these same papers, though with a distinct leaning toward Whipple's form of presentation, which in turn is based on pioneer work by Hoppe and Öpik.

7-2. The drag and differential mass equations. To begin with, the shape, mass, and density of the meteoroid are all unknown. We may define a dimensionless *shape factor* A such that $A(m/\rho_m)^{2/3}$ is the effective cross-sectional area of the object, where m is the mass and ρ_m the effective density of the body. A simple calculation will show that $A = (9\pi/16)^{1/3} = 1.2$ for a sphere. For a cube $A = 1.0$ to 1.7, depending on its orientation. Long narrow bodies may have $A < 1$ for the streamlined aspect and $A > 1$ for the broadside-on aspect. In general, irregularly shaped bodies may have a mean A of the same order as that for the sphere, owing to rotation. We shall assume A to be close to unity.

Air particles colliding with the meteoroid will decrease its forward momentum. In time dt the mass of air intercepted by the body will be $dm_a = A(m/\rho_m)^{2/3}\rho_a V dt$, where ρ_a is the air density. The air particles in this volume will gain $\Gamma V dm_a/dt = \Gamma A(m/\rho_m)^{2/3}\rho_a V^2$ units of momentum per second. Here Γ is a dimensionless quantity, known as the *drag coefficient*, which depends chiefly on the shape of the meteoroid, though it may be affected to some extent by other factors such as V and H and whether or not the particle is rotating. Values for Γ vary from 0.5 to 1.0. The meteoroid will lose $m dV/dt$ units of momentum per second, which may be equated to the momentum gained by the air particles, to yield the *resistance* or *drag equation*

$$\frac{dV}{dt} = -\frac{\Gamma A}{m^{1/3}\rho_m^{2/3}}\rho_a V^2 \tag{7-1}$$

The kinetic energy of the meteoroid is converted to heat, light, and ionization by the collisions with air particles, though the fraction which appears as heat greatly exceeds the other two. Atoms of the meteoroid are vaporized from the surface of the parent body. Various processes for the ablation of atoms may be visualized, which are conditioned by the composition and size of the meteoroid and the height at which the action is taking place. When the mean free path of the air particles is greater than the radius of the meteoroid, the atoms leave the body without serious mutual interference. Lower down in the atmosphere a shielding effect may arise, owing to a layer of vaporized atoms about the meteoroid. Lower still in the atmosphere, and particularly for larger bodies, an air cap may develop ahead of the meteoroid. These considerations are fully developed by Öpik (1958a). Whatever the mechanism may be, we shall assume that the rate of loss of mass is proportional to the kinetic energy transferred to the intercepted air mass. Thus we may write down the *differential mass equation*

$$\frac{dm}{dt} = - \frac{\Lambda A}{2\zeta} \left(\frac{m}{\rho_m}\right)^{2/3} \rho_a V^3 \tag{7-2}$$

where ζ (dimensions L^2, T^{-2}) is the heat of ablation of the meteoroid material (usually taken to lie in the range 0.2 to 1.0×10^{10} ergs/g), and Λ is the dimensionless *heat-transfer coefficient*. The heat-transfer coefficient is a measure of the efficiency of the collision process in converting kinetic energy to heat: values of Λ in the range 0.6 down to 0.1 or less have been proposed.

7-3. The luminosity and ionization equations. The ablated atoms are moving with the velocity of the meteoroid, and hence their kinetic energies will range from a few tens to some hundreds of electron volts. For example, if we adopt an atomic weight of 30 as a mean value for atoms of stony meteoroids, such an atom moving at 60 km/sec will possess a kinetic energy of $\frac{1}{2} \times 30 \times 1.67 \times 10^{-24} \times (60 \times 10^5)^2 = 9 \times 10^{-10}$ erg, which is equivalent to $(9 \times 10^{-10})/(1.6 \times 10^{-12}) = 560$ ev. This kinetic energy is more than adequate to excite and also to ionize the atoms of the meteor, for which typical excitation or ionization potentials range from about 2 to 15 ev. The excited atoms emit radiation. If we consider the visible light radiated in the range 4,000 to 7,000 A (see Sec. 2-2), we may define a dimensionless *luminous-efficiency factor* τ_I by assuming that the luminous power I radiated in this wavelength band is proportional to the rate of loss of the kinetic energy of the ablated atoms:

$$I = - \frac{1}{2} \tau_I \frac{dm}{dt} V^2 \tag{7-3}$$

Substituting for dm/dt from Eq. (7-2), we have the *luminosity equation*

$$I = \tau_I \frac{\Lambda A}{4\zeta} \left(\frac{m}{\rho_m}\right)^{2/3} \rho_a V^5 \tag{7-4}$$

The factor τ_I is not easy to evaluate. Various investigators have used estimates which have varied by two orders of magnitude from $\tau_I = 2 \times 10^{-2}$ to 2×10^{-4}. Öpik believes τ_I to be the sum of three factors, the first representing the impact efficiency, the second the temperature-radiation efficiency, and the third the black-body radiation efficiency; of these, the first is the only important component for the average visual meteor. Many years ago Öpik evaluated τ_I from laboratory evidence and theoretical considerations based on the laws of atomic interactions. His conclusions can best be expressed in sets of empirical tables, since the calculated τ_I values depend on the meteor velocity, on the substance of the particle, e.g., whether it is iron or stone, and on whether the meteoroid is a solid body or a dustball. In this brief account we cannot attempt to reproduce all the tables and the reasoning behind them: the reader may be referred to the book by Öpik (1958) for full details. A convenient, though rather sweeping, simplification of these data was produced by Whipple, in the form

$$\tau_I = k_0 V \tag{7-5}$$

where $k_0 = 8.5 \times 10^{-5}$ sec/km. This relation is applicable to the brighter photographic meteors only, and even in these cases its validity is now regarded skeptically. For fainter meteors as seen by the eye, τ_I appears to vary more slowly than the first power of V—perhaps even as a negative power of V for faint dustballs.

The power going into the production of ionization, like the luminous power, is also assumed to be proportional to the kinetic power loss of the ablated atoms. If q is the number of electrons (or ions) produced per unit path length and η (dimensions M, L^2, T^{-2}) is the mean ionization potential per atom involved, then the energy of the ionization created per second is

$$qV\eta = -\frac{1}{2}\tau_q \frac{dm}{dt} V^2 \tag{7-6}$$

where τ_q is the dimensionless *ionization-efficiency factor*. Again substituting for dm/dt from Eq. (7-2), we obtain the *ionization equation* for the number of electrons created per unit path length,

$$q = \tau_q \frac{\Lambda A}{4\zeta\eta}\left(\frac{m}{\rho_m}\right)^{\frac{2}{3}}\rho_a V^4 \tag{7-7}$$

From the combined radio and visual data on Geminid and Perseid meteors, Millman and McKinley (1956) found that the ratio τ_q/τ_I (which is the same as the ratio $qV\eta/I$) varies from about unity for $V = 35$ km/sec to nearly three for $V = 60$ km/sec; hence τ_q/τ_I varies approximately as V^2 (see Sec. 8-13). Whipple (1955a) reached the same conclusion from an independent study of radio and photographic rates.

An alternative path to the ionization equation was followed by the Jodrell Bank workers, who defined the dimensionless *probability factor* β as the probability that a single ablated atom, with a mass μ, would produce a free electron on collision with an air particle. A given meteor atom can, of course, produce more than one electron before it is slowed down to thermal velocities through multiple collisions. The mass of the *ions* produced per second will be proportional to the mass lost by the meteor per second; that is,

$$qV\mu = -\beta \frac{dm}{dt} \qquad (7\text{-}8)$$

It follows immediately from Eqs. (7-6) and (7-8) that the link between τ_q and β is given by

$$\tau_q = \frac{2\eta}{\mu V^2} \beta \qquad (7\text{-}9)$$

Hence, from the above observational evidence that $\tau_q/\tau_I \sim V^2$, one may conclude that $\beta/\tau_I \sim V^4$. If τ_I varies as V^n, as was suggested earlier, then β will vary as V^{4+n}. The Ottawa data (Millman and McKinley, 1956) yielded values that ranged from $V^{3.5}$ for fifth-magnitude meteors to $V^{4.5}$ for zero-magnitude meteors. Hawkins (1956c), using similar observational information, found that on the average $\beta/\tau_I \sim V^{4.56}$. On the other hand, Kaiser (1953) and Evans and Hall (1955) have concluded that β is of the order of 0.1 and is practically independent of the velocity. Further investigations will be needed to resolve these apparent anomalies. In the meantime, the bulk of the evidence appears to support the relations $\beta \sim \tau_q V^2 \sim \tau_I V^4$.

An alternative ionization equation defining q in terms of β and other parameters of the meteor may be derived by substituting for dm/dt in Eq. (7-8) from Eq. (7-2) as follows:

$$q = \beta \frac{\Lambda A}{2\zeta\mu} \left(\frac{m}{\rho_m}\right)^{2/3} \rho_a V^2 \qquad (7\text{-}10)$$

Note that Eq. (7-4) is a power equation, whereas Eqs. (7-7) and (7-10) have the dimensions of inverse length despite their superficial similarity to Eq. (7-4).

7-4. The integrated mass equation. The four basic equations developed in the previous two sections, together with their ancillary equations, may be manipulated to yield a number of interesting and useful results. The deceptively simple elegance of some of these derivations should not cause the reader to forget the tenuous nature of the underlying hypotheses.

The directly observable variables in these equations are V, t, dV/dt, and I. The electron line density q may be included in this list, though it might better be regarded as an indirectly observed variable deducible from directly observed quantities through the application of a theory which is in process of being established (see Chap. 8). The mass of the meteoroid at any instant is an unknown variable, and its density is a parameter which is also unknown. Several of the remaining parameters, e.g., A, Γ, ζ, may be tentatively assumed to be known to better than an order of magnitude for the average meteor if not for a specific individual, and furthermore they may be considered constant to a first approximation over most of the meteor's flight. Other parameters, such as τ_I, τ_q, and β, have not been well determined, and they may be far from constant. Rather than attempt to measure each unknown separately—there are simply not enough independent equations to do this—we shall group them into certain combinations or ratios which can be evaluated from the observational data. One example of this technique has been mentioned in the previous section, where it was pointed out that the ratios τ_q/τ_I or β/τ_I can be found, though the absolute values remain indefinite.

We may integrate Eq. (7-3) from a given instant t on the light path to the time t_e when the meteor disappears at the end of its flight, to obtain the mass m_t at time t:

$$m_t = \frac{2}{\tau_I V^2} \int_t^{t_e} I \, dt \tag{7-11}$$

For this purpose the change in velocity right up to the end of the meteor may be neglected, and V^2 may be brought out from under the integral sign. Note here that the product $m_t \tau_I$ can be measured in terms of observable quantities but that neither one alone is determinable. Equation (7-1) is now cubed and the mass therein replaced by the value given in Eq. (7-11) to yield

$$(\Gamma A)^3 \frac{\tau_I}{\rho_m^2} = -\frac{2}{\rho_a^3 V^8} \left(\frac{dV}{dt}\right)^3 \int_t^{t_e} I \, dt \tag{7-12}$$

The parameters on the left may thus be evaluated as an ensemble in terms of known and observable quantities on the right.

Another observable combination of parameters may be found by dividing Eq. (7-2) by Eq. (7-1) and then substituting for m from Eq. (7-11) and for dm/dt from Eq. (7-3). This gives

$$\frac{2\Gamma\zeta}{\Lambda} = -\frac{V}{I} \frac{dV}{dt} \int_t^{t_e} I \, dt \tag{7-13}$$

We have taken it for granted that the properties of the upper atmosphere are known, e.g., ρ_a in Eq. (7-12), even though a perusal of the tables in the Appendix will show that the values may be uncertain by a factor of two in some cases. We shall now take a further step here and assume that the atmosphere at meteoric heights may be described as isothermal and homogeneous. This is not true over a great range of height, but it may be taken as approximately correct for small height differences. The air density in an isothermal atmosphere is given by $\rho_a = \rho_0 \exp(-H/\mathbf{H})$, where ρ_0 is sea-level density and $\mathbf{H}$ is the scale height at the true height H (see discussion in the Appendix). For a meteor coming from a radiant at a zenith distance Z, the incremental path length is $ds = dH/\cos Z$. Also, we have $V\,dt = ds$. Equation (7-2), when integrated from $s = -\infty$ on the path, where the mass has the no-atmosphere value m_∞, to the point s, becomes

$$m^{\frac{1}{3}} = m_\infty{}^{\frac{1}{3}} - \frac{\Lambda A}{6\zeta \rho_m{}^{\frac{2}{3}}} \int_{-\infty}^{s} V^2 \rho_a \, ds \qquad (7\text{-}14)$$

Carrying out the integration on the assumption of constant velocity we have

$$m^{\frac{1}{3}} = m_\infty{}^{\frac{1}{3}} - \frac{\Lambda A V^2 \mathbf{H}}{6\zeta \rho_m{}^{\frac{2}{3}} \cos Z} \rho_a \qquad (7\text{-}15)$$

as one form of the *integrated mass equation*. Another formulation, from which the atmospheric density and the meteoroid density have both been eliminated, may be derived by again dividing Eq. (7-2) by Eq. (7-1) and integrating directly.

$$\log_\epsilon \frac{m_\infty}{m} = \frac{\Lambda}{4\Gamma\zeta} (V_\infty{}^2 - V^2) \qquad (7\text{-}16)$$

It will be noted that the same combination of parameters appears in both Eqs. (7-16) and 7-13).

7-5. Maximum luminosity and ionization. As the meteoroid descends into denser air, the production of both luminosity and ionization increases to a maximum and then falls off as the size of the meteoroid dwindles. The condition for maximum light may be found by differentiating Eq. (7-4) logarithmically and equating to zero. We may operate similarly on Eq. (7-7) to determine the condition for maximum ionization. In the latter case, for example, the steps go as follows:

$$\frac{1}{q}\frac{dq}{dt} = \frac{1}{\tau_q}\frac{d\tau_q}{dt} + \frac{2}{3m}\frac{dm}{dt} + \frac{1}{\rho_a}\frac{d\rho_a}{dt} + \frac{4}{V}\frac{dV}{dt} = 0$$

The mass term in this expression becomes $(-\Lambda A \rho_a V^2)/(3\zeta m^{\frac{1}{3}}\rho_m{}^{\frac{2}{3}})$ on substituting for dm/dt from Eq. (7-2). The air-density term becomes $V \cos Z/\mathbf{H}$ with the adoption of a homogeneous isothermal atmosphere. By assuming $\tau_q \sim V^n$, the remaining two terms may be combined into $(4 + n)(dV/dt)/V$, which, except for very slow meteors, may be neglected in comparison with either the meteor-mass term or the air-density term.

These latter terms may now be equated to yield

$$\rho_{a(\max)} = \frac{3\zeta \cos Z}{\Lambda H A V^2} m_{(\max)}^{1/3} \rho_m^{2/3} \qquad (7\text{-}17)$$

where the subscript (max) refers to the values at the point of maximum line density, $q_{\max}$. The identical relation will be obtained for the air density at the point of maximum luminosity, starting with Eq. (7-4). A similar equation is derivable immediately for $p_{a(\max)}$, the atmospheric pressure at maximum light or ionization, since in our assumed isothermal homogeneous atmosphere we have $p_a = gH\rho_a$ (see Appendix), where g is the acceleration due to gravity:

$$p_{a(\max)} = \frac{3g\zeta \cos Z}{\Lambda A V^2} m_{(\max)}^{1/3} \rho_m^{2/3} \qquad (7\text{-}18)$$

Substitution of the expression for $\rho_{a(\max)}$ from Eq. (7-17) in Eq. (7-15) gives

$$m_{(\max)} = \frac{8}{27} m_\infty \qquad (7\text{-}19)$$

that is, at the point of maximum light or ionization, the idealized meteoroid has shrunk to $\frac{8}{27}$ of its original mass, or its radius has become $\frac{2}{3}$ of the initial radius.

If we put the value of $\rho_{a(\max)}$ given by Eq. (7-17) into Eq. (7-1) we obtain for the deceleration at maximum light or ionization

$$\left(\frac{dV}{dt}\right)_{(\max)} = - \frac{3\Gamma\zeta \cos Z}{\Lambda H} \qquad (7\text{-}20)$$

Note that this is independent of meteor size or velocity. The deceleration at maximum light should not be confused with the maximum deceleration, of course, which occurs near the terminal point.

We shall now deduce the connection between the meteor velocity and the height of maximum light or ionization. For meteors of a given density class and an average path inclination to the vertical, we may write the proportionality $\rho_{a(\max)} \sim m_{(\max)}^{1/3}/V^2$, from Eq. (7-17). From Eq. (7-4) we have $I_{\max} \sim \tau_I m_{(\max)}^{2/3} \rho_{a(\max)} V^5$. Eliminating $m_{(\max)}$ gives

$$\rho_{a(\max)} \sim \frac{I_{\max}^{1/5}}{\tau_I^{1/5} V^3} \qquad (7\text{-}21)$$

Similarly, from Eq. (7-7),

$$\rho_{a(\max)} \sim \frac{q_{\max}^{1/5}}{\tau_q^{1/5} V^{9/5}} \qquad (7\text{-}22)$$

If we adopt $\tau_q \sim \tau_I V^2 \sim k_0 V^3$, these equations become

$$\rho_{a(\text{max})} \sim \frac{I_{\text{max}}^{\frac{1}{3}}}{V^{19\frac{1}{3}}} \qquad (7\text{-}23)$$

and

$$\rho_{a(\text{max})} \sim \frac{q_{\text{max}}^{\frac{1}{3}}}{V^{11\frac{1}{3}}} \qquad (7\text{-}24)$$

If desired, $p_{a(\text{max})}$ may be written for $\rho_{a(\text{max})}$ in the above equations.

Let us now make use of the relation $\log_{10} \rho_a = 1.3 - (\frac{3}{40})H$ [Eq. (A-5)], where H is in kilometers and ρ_a in kilograms per cubic meter. On taking logs and substituting for $\log_{10} \rho_a$, we have

$$H_{(\text{max})} = \text{constant} + 44 \log_{10} V + 1.8 M_{\text{max}} \qquad (7\text{-}25)$$

where we have inserted $\log_{10} I_{\text{max}} \sim 0.4 M_{\text{max}}$ from Eq. (2-2). Two-figure accuracy seems adequate for the coefficients in view of the various uncertainties. Similarly, Eq. (7-24) leads to

$$H_{(\text{max})} = \text{constant} + 49 \log_{10} V - 4.4 \log_{10} q_{\text{max}} \qquad (7\text{-}26)$$

The differential variation of height with V alone has been calculated from Eq. (7-25) for a datum level at $V = 40$ km/sec. This is plotted on Fig. 5-9d as the dashed curve. The agreement is reasonably good between the theoretical curve and the empirical curve based on the observations. A loss of brilliance of 5 magnitudes results in a theoretical height increase of slightly less than 9 km, from Eq. (7-25). This is of the same order as that observed photographically (see Fig. 5-11). The same height increase should theoretically be obtained for a decrease in q by a factor 10^{-2}, though the observations do not appear to bear this out. The radio data in Fig. 5-11 show little height variation with magnitude because these data are based on the heights of the enduring echoes, not on the true heights of maximum ionization. The observed height of the enduring echo will tend to lie between 93 km and the height of maximum ionization.

If we had kept track of all the parameters involved in the above discussion, we should have arrived at numerical values for the constants in Eqs. (7-25) and (7-26). There would have been many uncertain quantities to be evaluated in the process, and it might be better to determine empirical values for these constants directly from the observational data. For example, from Fig. 5-11 (which has already been adjusted to $V = 40$ km/sec) we note that the maximum light curve goes through $H = 93$ km, $M_{pm} = 0$. Since $44 \log_{10} 40 = 70$, it follows that constant = 23 is a reasonable value for Eq. (7-25). Obviously the theoretical straight line between H and M can only approximate to the observed relation.

Similarly, we may use the same fiducial point for the radio echoes, since at $H = 93$ km, where $M_{pm} = 0$, the point of maximum ionization coincides with the height of maximum echo endurance.   Because of the color-index shift in Fig. 5-11, we have $M_v = 1.8 \simeq M_r$ when $M_{pm} = 0$.   From Eq. (2-3), $q = 2 \times 10^{15}$ when $M_r = 1.8$.   Equation (7-26) then becomes

$$H_{(max)} = 82 + 49 \log_{10} V - 4.4 \log_{10} q_{max} \qquad (7\text{-}27)$$

The variation of $H_{(max)}$ with velocity alone has been superimposed on Fig. 5-10 as the dashed curve for comparison with the radio observations.

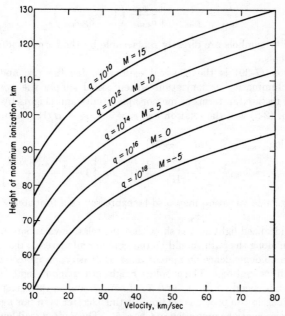

FIG. 7-1. Height of point of maximum ionization as a function of velocity, plotted for selected values of q in electrons per meter, or for the equivalent radio magnitudes.

The theoretical dependence of $H_{(max)}$ on V has been plotted in Fig. 7-1 for several values of q (or M).   These curves will be of interest in assessing the height limitation on the detectability of underdense echoes (Sec. 8-6).

7-6. Variation of mass, light, and ionization.   In Eq. (7-15) it will be noted that the coefficient of ρ_a is equal to $m_\infty^{1/3}/[3\rho_{a(max)}]$, from Eqs. (7-17) and (7-19).   Hence, the mass at any point is given by

$$m = m_\infty \left(1 - \frac{\rho_a}{3\rho_{a(max)}}\right)^3 \qquad (7\text{-}28)$$

in terms of the air density at that point, the air density at maximum light or ionization, and the original mass.

We may write down from Eq. (7-4), together with either Eq. (7-7) or (7-10), the following relative relations, making use also of Eq. (7-19):

$$\frac{I}{I_{max}} = \frac{q}{q_{max}} = \frac{\rho_a m^{\frac{2}{3}}}{\rho_{a(max)} m_{(max)}^{\frac{2}{3}}} = \frac{9}{4} \frac{\rho_a}{\rho_{a(max)}} \frac{m^{\frac{2}{3}}}{m_\infty^{\frac{2}{3}}}$$

It then follows immediately from Eq. (7-28) that

$$\frac{I}{I_{max}} = \frac{q}{q_{max}} = \frac{9}{4} \frac{\rho_a}{\rho_{a(max)}} \left(1 - \frac{\rho_a}{3\rho_{a(max)}}\right)^2 \qquad (7\text{-}29)$$

The density symbols are directly replaceable by the corresponding pressure symbols.

Equation (7-29) is the classical expression for the rise and fall of meteoric luminosity or ionization—often called simply the *light curve*. It can be restated in terms of meteor magnitudes and heights by making use of Eq. (2-2) and the relation $\log_\epsilon \rho_a = \log_\epsilon \rho_0 - H/\mathbf{H}$. Thus,

$$\log_\epsilon I - \log_\epsilon I_{max} = \frac{2.3}{2.5} [M_{max} - M]$$
$$= \log_\epsilon \frac{9}{4} + \frac{H_{(max)} - H}{\mathbf{H}} + 2 \log_\epsilon \left[1 - \frac{\epsilon^{(H_{(max)}-H)/\mathbf{H}}}{3}\right] \qquad (7\text{-}30)$$

The magnitude variation may also be expressed as a function of time, if desired.

These idealized light curves show that the relative variation in light or ionization along the path should be the same for all meteors; that is, there should be no dependence on meteor mass or density, on meteor velocity, or on path inclination. The absolute height of maximum light of a given meteor will depend on M, V, and Z, of course, and in these respects the theory given in the previous sections of this chapter is in fair agreement with the observations presented in Chap. 5. The ionized trail length (the length of path over which the ionization exceeds an arbitrary threshold level) is also dependent on M, V, and Z. The brighter and faster meteors create longer trails, as do meteors arriving from radiants near the horizon. The Stanford group have concluded that, on the average, an ionized trail length of 25 km is typical of a sixth-magnitude meteor (Manning, Villard, and Peterson, 1953; Eshleman, 1957).

Figure 7-2 shows three typical examples of observed light curves (solid lines) upon each of which theoretical light curves (dashed lines) have been superimposed. The agreement is good in Fig. 7-2a and quite reasonable in Fig. 7-2b despite the multitude of small-intensity outbursts or flares. In Fig. 7-2c the coincidence has been remarkable up to the moment when a large flare prematurely ended the meteor's career.   Very bright meteors such as these usually adhere fairly closely to the simple theoretical curve except for anomalous flare behavior.   However, when the observations of fainter meteors are checked against theory, a significantly different pattern develops.

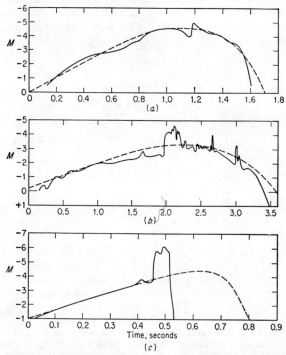

FIG. 7-2. *Solid lines*, observed light curves of three bright meteors; *dashed lines*, theoretical light curves.   Velocities: (a) 36 km/sec; (b) 25 km/sec; (c) 69 km/sec. (*Courtesy of L. G. Jacchia.*)

7-7. The fragmentation hypothesis.   Hawkins and Southworth (1958) made a random selection of some 360 meteors from the Harvard collection of Super-Schmidt photographs.   Many of these were second- and third-magnitude meteors.   The magnitude of each was measured at three points on the trail: at the beginning and end where the trail was just detectable, and at the point of maximum light.   The data are plotted in Fig. 7-3.   For each meteor two points are shown, which represent the differences between peak and beginning magnitudes and between peak and terminal magnitudes; each is plotted against the corresponding true height differential referred to height at maximum light. The theoretical light curve (Eq. 7-30) is also shown. Practically all of the observations lie inside the theoretical curve. This is strong evidence that the lengths of the fainter photographic meteor trails are considerably shorter than the classical theory predicts.

Jacchia (1955), after examining the light curves of faint photographic meteors, commented that the early part of the light curve frequently displays appreciable irregularities. This is in contrast to the relative smoothness of the initial rise for a very bright meteor. Many faint

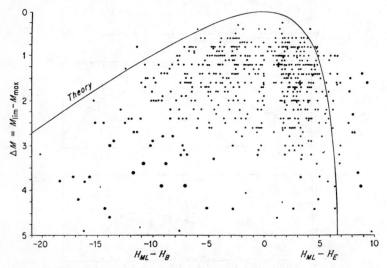

FIG. 7-3. Theoretical light curve compared with the beginning and end points of a random selection of Super-Schmidt meteors. H_{ML} = height at maximum light; H_B = height at beginning of trail; H_E = height at end of trail. (*Hawkins and Southworth*, 1958.)

meteors show a rapid rise of light followed by a steady decline—a reversal of the classical trend. The shutter breaks in the photographed trail of a faint meteor are not clear-cut. Sometimes the exposed segments become increasingly elongated and fuzzy until, near the end of the trail, they tend to fuse together (McCrosky, 1958). Furthermore, the observed deceleration of a faint meteor often increases much too fast to be explicable by the classical equations of motion for a solid meteoroid.

These observations can be explained if we assume that the average meteoroid has a fragile structure which breaks up easily into a cluster of small fragments on impact with the upper atmosphere. The small component particles will spread over an appreciable cross-sectional area larger than that of the parent body.   There will be a longitudinal spread as well, particularly near the end of the trail, which would account for the shutter-break blurring.   If the ultimate particles are true solid bodies, then presumably the classical equations could be applied to each one, but two difficulties arise.   First, neither the numbers nor the range of sizes of the component particles are known.   Öpik has estimated that the radius of an individual grain may lie in the range 0.001 to 0.05 cm.   The number originally packed together in the parent meteoroid may run from 10 to 1,000 for ordinary dustballs and to over a million for the Giacobinid meteors.   The second difficulty is that the particles are released in an abnormal environment, at lower heights and in denser air than they would have reached as independent bodies; hence their individual light curves will be appreciably shortened.   The presence of many other particles in close proximity also affects the analysis.   Practically all dustballs—which is to say almost all meteors—are now thought to break up into grains when the aerodynamic drag $\rho_a V^2$ reaches a value of about 2×10^4 dynes/cm$^2 \simeq 0.02$ atmosphere.   The effective density ρ_m of the parent meteoroid may be of the order of 0.05 to 0.5 g/cm^3, which would lead to an increase of nearly two orders of magnitude in the estimated masses of the meteors.

Enough has been said here to underline the new uncertainty that has crept into the physical theory of meteors.   At one time, the neat and tidy classical theory was made to serve for all meteors, to a first order of approximation.   The advent of more precise optical measurements has shown up its shortcomings, though the iconoclastic process has in many instances merely replaced old anomalies with fresh ones.   The effect of the fragmentation hypothesis may be felt even more strongly in the theory of radio echoes from meteors, which has been tied very closely to the classical concept of a single solid body.

The treatment in this chapter has been mainly phenomenological in nature.   We have not delved deeply into the basic physics and chemistry of the problem.   It would be unwise to attempt to deal superficially with the intricate details of the collision and ablation processes, sputtering, the "jet" effect, shock-wave phenomena, and the various theories of energy transfer.   The interested reader may be directed to the books by Öpik (1958a) or Levin (1956), or to the series of papers on these subjects from Harvard (e.g., Cook, 1954; Jacchia, 1955; Whipple, 1955a), but he should be cautioned that an adequate grounding in fundamental physics would be most helpful, if not indeed essential, to a critical comprehension of those treatises.

CHAPTER 8

Radio Echo Theory

The theory of radio echoes from meteor trails is ancillary to the basic physical theory of meteors and arises from the need to interpret the special properties of radio observing methods. We shall use the same elementary model that was introduced in Chap. 7 with the same fundamental physical assumptions about the meteor trail and its environment. It follows that the present extension of the discussion might appropriately be called the classical radio echo theory. This chapter deals mainly with backscatter-echo phenomena; Chap. 9 will consider the extension to the forward-scatter case.

Electromagnetic radiation is involved in both the optical and the radio methods. The difference is that in the optical case the radiation is incoherent since it comes from a myriad of independent oscillators, namely, the excited and ionized atoms of the trail. The received wave is the scalar or power sum of the outputs from the individual oscillators, which have not only random phases but also different frequencies. In the radio method, one coherent wavefront from a distant oscillator illuminates all parts of the trail in turn. The wavelet scattered from any given electron is in phase with the incident wave passing that particular point of the trail. The total reflected wave is the vector or field-strength sum of many such coherent and monochromatic wavelets. The resultant aspect sensitivity of the trail, which can be both an asset and a limitation, is but one of several new facets of meteor research which have been introduced by the radio techniques. This particular property happens to be quite useful in determining the geometrical path of the meteor, but it makes it harder to trace out the complete ionization curve in the way the light curve can be recorded by the camera.

Our discussion here of the classical radio echo theory will be couched in fairly elementary terms. In a general text it is inadvisable to reproduce in any detail the rather difficult mathematical arguments dealing with certain aspects of the subject, particularly when a redrafting of the theory may be required in the light of some recent observational evidence. Several competent applied mathematicians have taken an active interest

186

in these analytical developments, and on occasion the aid of powerful electronic computers has been invoked to solve complicated or intractable equations. Perhaps it would be both premature and unjust to suggest that some of this advanced work may have to be discarded—premature because we are not yet sure what impact the concept of the fragmenting meteoroid may have on the classical radio theory (for that matter we are not yet positive that the faint radio meteors actually are dustballs) and unjust because no first-class creative efforts are ever really wasted and only by examining the properties of the model in detail, painstaking and laborious as the process may be, can we discover its shortcomings and devise a better approximation. In recapitulating the findings of those who have mined this field before, we shall therefore restrain the temptation to stray down some of the more rugged mathematical passages in search of higher-grade ore, not so much because of the thought that these shafts would be the first to be sealed off if the direction of the main vein were to change, but because an adequate exploration would demand more space than we can afford in this book. It must suffice to examine the nuggets uncovered in these less accessible tunnels without partaking in the arduous operations which led to their discovery.

8-1. The basic model of the underdense trail. The first step in developing the simple model is to assume that in the wake of the meteor a stationary column of free electrons is created, with a diameter that is small in comparison with the wavelength. The column does not expand radially, nor do the electrons recombine, attach, or diffuse. The trail, once created, extends from $s = -\infty$ to $s = +\infty$, where s is distance measured along the meteor path relative to an origin at the minimum range point (R_0, t_0) [see Fig. 8-1; we have $R^2 = R_0^2 + s^2 = R_0^2 + V^2(t - t_0)^2$]. The incident radio wave penetrates the column and is scattered by the individual free electrons, which oscillate freely in the applied field without colliding with other particles to any great extent. Each electron behaves as if no other were present—secondary radiative and absorptive effects may be neglected. This condition defines the *underdense* trail. The equivalent echoing area, or scattering cross section of a free electron is $\sigma_e = 4\pi e^4/m^2 c^4 \sin^2 \gamma = 4\pi r_e^2 \sin^2 \gamma$, where e, m, and r_e are the charge, mass, and classical radius of the electron, c is the velocity of light, and γ is the angle between the electric vector of the incident wave and the line of sight to the receiver. For backscatter, $\gamma = 90°$ and $\sigma_e \simeq 1 \times 10^{-28}$ m². [The constant in the older classical textbook expression for the electron cross section is $8\pi/3$, but this should be multiplied by 1.5 because the electron backscatters like a Hertzian dipole (see Sec. 2-9).]

At a point on the trail a distance R from the radio transmitter, the power flux of the incident wave is $P_T G/4\pi R^2$ watts/m², where P_T is the transmitted power and G is the antenna gain in that direction, relative to an isotropic radiator.   Assuming that the same or an identical antenna is used for reception, the effective absorbing area of the antenna is $G\lambda^2/4\pi$ when the antenna impedance is matched to the receiver.   Thus the power delivered to the receiver by the wavelets scattered from a single trail electron is

$$\Delta P_R = \frac{P_T G}{4\pi R^2} \frac{\sigma_e}{4\pi R^2} \frac{G\lambda^2}{4\pi} = \frac{P_T G^2 \lambda^2 \sigma_e}{64\pi^3 R^4} \qquad (8\text{-}1)$$

Since all the electrons in a line element ds of the trail will scatter in phase, we must add their field vectors rather than their power fluxes.   At the receiver input the *peak* amplitude of the field vector due to a single

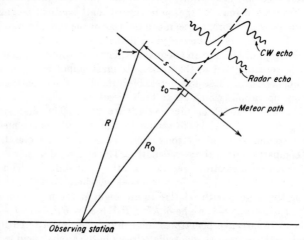

FIG. 8-1. The geometry of the meteor path relative to the observing station.

scattering electron in the trail is $(2\mathbf{r}\,\Delta P_R)^{1/2}$, where $\mathbf{r}$ is the receiver input impedance.   The absolute phase of the received wave, which has travelled a distance $2R$, is included in the time-varying expression $\sin(2\pi ft - 4\pi R/\lambda)$.   As R changes with time, a phase modulation of the wave is produced (Sec. 2-7).   Hence we may write

$$dA_R = (2\mathbf{r}\,\Delta P_R)^{1/2} q \sin\left(2\pi ft - \frac{4\pi R}{\lambda}\right) ds \qquad (8\text{-}2)$$

as the instantaneous amplitude of the echo signal received from all the electrons in the element ds, where q is the number per meter of path. The total field due to all the electrons in the trail between s_1 and s is then

$$A_R = (2\mathbf{r}\,\Delta P_R)^{1/2} q \int_{s_1}^{s} \sin\left(2\pi ft - \frac{4\pi R}{\lambda}\right) ds \qquad (8\text{-}3)$$

The parameter q may be taken out from the integral sign only if we assume it to be constant along the trail.

This integral is difficult to evaluate in general. The range changes very slowly with time near the t_0 point, though; so we can make the integral more tractable in this region by using the approximation $R \simeq R_0 + s^2/2R_0$. For convenience, we employ the transformations $\chi = 2\pi ft - 4\pi R_0/\lambda$ and $2s = x(R_0\lambda)^{\frac{1}{2}}$ to obtain

$$A_R = \frac{(2\mathbf{r}\,\Delta P_R R_0\lambda)^{\frac{1}{2}}}{2} q \int_{x_1}^{x} \sin\left(\chi - \frac{\pi x^2}{2}\right) dx \qquad (8\text{-}4)$$

or

$$A_R = \frac{(2\mathbf{r}\,\Delta P_R R_0\lambda)^{\frac{1}{2}}}{2} q(\mathbf{C} \sin \chi - \mathbf{S} \cos \chi) \qquad (8\text{-}5)$$

where $\mathbf{C} = \int_{x_1}^{x} \cos \frac{\pi x^2}{2} dx$ and $\mathbf{S} = \int_{x_1}^{x} \sin \frac{\pi x^2}{2} dx$

are the conventional Fresnel integrals of optical diffraction theory.

The maximum frequency with which the functions $\mathbf{C}$ and $\mathbf{S}$ vary with time is much less than the radio frequency f. We may therefore take a time average over an interval that is short compared with the smallest fluctuation period of $\mathbf{C}$ or $\mathbf{S}$ to obtain an expression for the quasi-instantaneous power P_R received from all the trail electrons between s_1 and s:

$$P_R = \frac{A_R^2}{2\mathbf{r}} = \frac{\Delta P_R R_0\lambda}{2}\left[\frac{\mathbf{C}^2 + \mathbf{S}^2}{2}\right] q^2 \qquad (8\text{-}6)$$

or, on substituting for ΔP_R from Eq. (8-1),

$$P_R = \frac{P_T G^2 \lambda^3 \sigma_e}{128\pi^3 R_0{}^3}\left[\frac{\mathbf{C}^2 + \mathbf{S}^2}{2}\right] q^2$$

$$= 2.5 \times 10^{-32} P_T G^2 \left(\frac{\lambda}{R_0}\right)^3 \left[\frac{\mathbf{C}^2 + \mathbf{S}^2}{2}\right] q^2 \qquad \text{watts} \qquad (8\text{-}7)$$

This is the basic expression for the echo power received from the model underdense trail during the formative stage.

The bracket in Eq. (8-6) has the value unity when evaluated from $s = -\infty$ to $+\infty$. The approximation that we used for R does not permit us to go very far in either direction from the t_0 point, of course, but it may be shown from tables of $\mathbf{C}$ and $\mathbf{S}$ (Jahnke and Emde, 1938) that the contributions from the remoter parts of the trail are negligible and that the value of the bracket is close to unity when taken over a few Fresnel zones on both sides of t_0.

The form of Eq. (8-6), with the bracket equal to unity, was first derived by Blackett and Lovell (1941) for the power scattered by a line of electrons, although at the time they were anticipating the possibility that the ionized line might be created by a cosmic-ray particle. Later work by

Lovell (1947, 1950) and by Lovell and Clegg (1948) extended the theory to the meteor case.

8-2. The diffraction echo. If we assume all the parameters in Eq. (8-7) to be constant for a given meteor we may write a simplified form of the equation as

$$P_r = F_r{}^2(C^2 + S^2) \qquad (8-8)$$

where $2F_r{}^2$ is the final echo-power level. The subscript r now refers to the power received from the meteor-reflected wave. This expression is identical with that which describes the optical pattern of diffraction fringes produced at a straight edge.

The detector may also receive a small fraction of the transmitted power directly. Mr. E. L. R. Webb of the NRC developed the analysis of this case, which applies to the simple cw system wherein transmitter and receiver are spaced a short distance D, just great enough to keep the receiver from being overloaded with the direct ground wave. We then have an additional field vector present at the receiver, defined by $B_R \sin [2\pi ft - (2\pi D/\lambda)]$, which must be added to the vector A_R in Eq. (8-5) before taking the short-term time average. When this is done, the total power at any moment is given by

$$P_{r+d} = F_r{}^2(C^2 + S^2) + F_d{}^2 + 2F_rF_d(C \cos \psi - S \sin \psi) \qquad (8-9)$$

or
$$P_{r+d} = (F_rC + F_d \cos \psi)^2 + (F_rS - F_d \sin \psi)^2 \qquad (8-10)$$

where $F_d{}^2$ is the power level of the direct wave and $\psi = 2\pi(2R_0 - D)/\lambda$ is the phase difference between the direct and reflected paths at time t_0.

The expression for P_r given by Eq. (8-8) increases slowly as t_0 is approached. As the meteor crosses t_0 the power rises quickly to a maximum; after this, oscillations of decreasing amplitude and increasing frequency occur about the final steady-state level. This is the ordinary noncoherent radar case. It appears in Fig. 8-2a as the dashed curve (see also Fig. 8-9, curve A). The square root of the power, i.e., the echo amplitude, has been plotted here because the ordinary radar receiver output is usually linear with voltage rather than with power. This theoretical curve may be compared with the observed radar records (Fig. 4-19).

For the cw case, Eq. (8-9) or (8-10), oscillations of increasing amplitude and decreasing frequency appear before t_0, as is shown by the solid curves, Fig. 8-2a to h, which have been plotted for selected values of the parameter ψ. The post-t_0 oscillations are also present. The value of ψ will determine whether the post-t_0 receiver output level is above or below that of the direct wave alone. These theoretical amplitude-time curves may be compared with the observed cw records (Figs. 4-9b, 4-10b, and 4-11).

A coherent detector, employing two outputs with quadrature injection of the reference wave, would eliminate the first two terms of Eq. (8-9) and yield only the third, which would simplify some of the analysis.

It should be emphasized that high-speed recording methods are needed, with time resolutions of the order of milliseconds, to bring out the fine structure of the oscillations. The ordinary radar range-time display, or a slow paper tape recorder, shows only the sudden rise in echo strength to the final mean level, and the fine detail of the oscillations is usually compressed and indiscernible.

We have avoided the use of the notation of the complex variable, although it would have enabled us to express the analysis in this and the preceding section in more compact form, because we have endeavored to keep the physical picture as clear as possible. In fact, it may be still easier to visualize the results if Eqs. (8-8) and (8-9) are expressed in terms of more familiar functions, by means of Cauchy's approximations for the Fresnel integrals. If we exclude the small region near t_0 where $-1 < x < 1$, and also assume x_1 to be effectively at minus infinity, then the Cauchy approximations become

$$\mathbf{C} = \frac{1}{\pi x} \sin \frac{\pi x^2}{2} \qquad \mathbf{S} = -\frac{1}{\pi x} \cos \frac{\pi x^2}{2}$$

for negative values of s, prior to t_0, and

$$\mathbf{C} = 1 + \frac{1}{\pi x} \sin \frac{\pi x^2}{2} \qquad \mathbf{S} = 1 - \frac{1}{\pi x} \cos \frac{\pi x^2}{2}$$

for positive values of s, after t_0. Hence, for the ordinary radar case,

$$P_r(-s) = \frac{F_r^2}{\pi^2 x^2} \tag{8-11}$$

and

$$P_r(+s) = 2F_r^2 + \frac{F_r^2}{\pi^2 x^2} + \frac{2\sqrt{2}}{\pi x} F_r^2 \sin \left(\frac{\pi x^2}{2} - \frac{\pi}{4} \right) \tag{8-12}$$

which are together equivalent to Eq. (8-8). Note the slow, nonoscillatory increase prior to t_0, followed by the rise to a maximum after t_0, with superposed oscillations about the final level $2F_r^2$.

For the cw or coherent-pulse radar case, before t_0,

$$P_{r+d}(-s) = \frac{F_r^2}{\pi^2 x^2} + F_d^2 + \frac{2F_r F_d}{\pi x} \sin \left(\frac{\pi x^2}{2} + \psi \right) \tag{8-13}$$

which shows that the slow rise in power begins at the level of the direct wave F_d^2 and the diffraction oscillations appear before t_0. After t_0, we have

$$P_{r+d}(+s) = \frac{F_r^2}{\pi^2 x^2} + E^2 + \frac{2F_r}{\pi x} E \sin \left[\frac{\pi x^2}{2} - \tan^{-1} \left(\frac{F_r - F_d \sin \psi}{F_r + F_d \cos \psi} \right) \right] \tag{8-14}$$

where $E^2 = F_d{}^2 - 2\sqrt{2}\,F_dF_r\sin\left(\psi - \dfrac{\pi}{4}\right) + 2F_r{}^2$.   Here the final power level is determined both by the relative values of F_d and F_r and by the phase angle ψ.   Note that post-t_0 oscillations should always be present, unless $E = 0$.   Since $E = 0$ only when $\sqrt{2}\,F_r = F_d$ and $\psi = 3\pi/4$ (see Fig. 8-2d) there should be very few cases of this nature.   In practice, though, an appreciable number of records show little or no sign of post-t_0 oscillations—an observation that has not yet been explained satisfactorily.

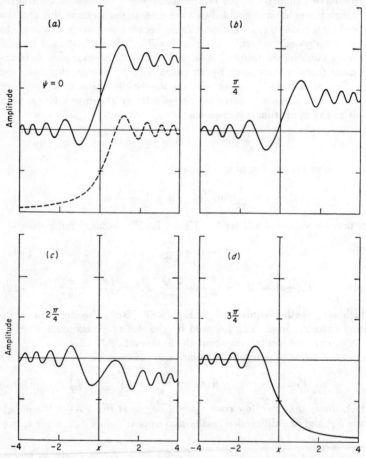

FIG. 8-2. Theoretical amplitude-time curves of meteor echoes based on the diffraction theory.   Receiver output voltage is plotted against the argument x of the Fresnel integrals, which is directly proportional to time.   The dashed curve in graph (a) is

A graphical representation of the diffraction echo may be obtained by plotting the C and S integrals orthogonally to produce the Cornu spiral shown in Fig. 8-3. For clarity, the variable x in the Fresnel integrals has been marked out along the curve only as far as $x = \pm 3.5$, though each spiral continues in to its center as $x \to \pm \infty$. To use the diagram, you mark the beginning and end points of the meteor trail on the curve. The line joining these points represents the total echo amplitude of that

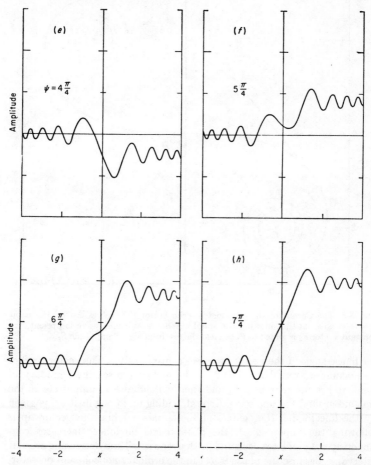

for the noncoherent radar case. The solid curves are computed for the cw or coherent-pulse radar case, for selected values of ψ, and for equal strengths of the reference voltage and the final meteor-echo voltage.

segment of trail, and its angular orientation with respect to an arbitrary fixed direction is the echo phase. You square the length of the line to obtain the echo power.

For the ordinary noncoherent radar case the origin of the meteor echo vector is held anchored at $x_1 = -\infty$. The F_r vector grows in amplitude as its tip follows around the lower left spiral and crosses the t_0 point, while

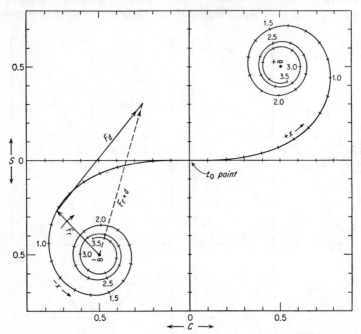

FIG. 8-3. The Cornu spiral. The meteor-echo vector F_r revolves around the point $x = -\infty$ with its tip following the spiral. When a reference wave is present, the constant vector F_d is added to F_r to yield the resultant signal amplitude F_{r+d}.

the phase angle of the vector increases continuously. The vector reaches its maximum around $x = +1.2$ as the meteor crosses the boundary of the first Fresnel zone past t_0, and then it fluctuates in amplitude as the tip goes around the upper-right spiral, ending up at the final value given by the line joining the centers of the spirals. While the vector tip is following the upper spiral, the phase angle no longer increases continuously but oscillates back and forth over a small and decreasing angular interval. Because the phase is lost in the ordinary noncoherent detector, only the amplitude variation will be recorded. This will be identical to the dashed curve in Fig. 8-2a.

In the case of a cw or coherent-pulse radar, a constant vector F_d due to the direct wave must be added to F_r (see Fig. 8-3). The resultant F_{r+d} vector will, in general, show both amplitude and phase fluctuations prior to t_0 as well as after t_0. An ordinary detector will reveal only the amplitude variations. The phase can be recovered if a quadrature detector is used which has two outputs, one combining F_r and F_d and the other combining F_r with F_d rotated by 90°. When the two outputs are displayed orthogonally on a cathode-ray tube, the Cornu spiral is created.

8-3. Velocity measurements. The oscillatory terms of Eqs. (8-12), (8-13), and (8-14) are the ones of chief interest in velocity measurements. In any of these terms we may replace $\pi x^2/2$ by $2\pi V^2\tau^2/R_0\lambda$, where $\tau = t - t_0$. Let the instantaneous frequency f_i be defined by $\sin(2\pi f_i\tau) = \sin(2\pi V^2\tau^2/R_0\lambda)$. Differentiating both sides with respect to τ we have

$$f_i = \frac{2V^2}{R_0\lambda}\tau \tag{8-15}$$

Thus the slope of a graph of f_i against τ is proportional to the square of the meteor velocity. Manning (1948) deduced the same expression for a "moving-ball" type of target. Actually, for the purpose of measuring velocities, there is little practical difference between the moving-ball interference theory and the cw line-diffraction theory, except near t_0. The moving-ball curves are symmetrical with respect to t_0 and show no post-t_0 shift (see Fig. 8-9, curve D), whereas the diffraction curves are in effect antisymmetrical with respect to t_0 (see Fig. 8-2) and are usually translated up or down after t_0.

If one excludes a few cycles near t_0, the observed relationship between f_i and τ is linear to less than one per cent for the better diffraction-echo records, some of which may show several hundred cycles prior to t_0. However, most small meteors produce only a few oscillations near t_0, where use of this technique can lead to rather large errors. Fortunately, the approximate position of the t_0 point can usually be located on the record, particularly in the cw method where the oscillations often appear on both sides of t_0. The radial component of wind velocity can cause some distortion of the diffraction waveform in the vicinity of t_0, but this effect is serious only for slow meteors and strong radial winds. The time taken by the average meteor to cross the first Fresnel zone is usually much less than the period of the body-Doppler fluctuations caused by wind drift. In most cases the phase angle ψ at t_0 can be determined to within ±45° from the record (rarely should the error be as great as ±90°) by comparison of the observed waveform with a catalog of calculated waveforms covering suitable ranges of ψ and of the ratio F_r/F_d. Starting from t_0, one can then count cycles backward in time. Let $\Delta\tau$ be the time interval between the mth and nth cycles (measured when feasible at the zero-crossing points where the slope is steepest—otherwise at the maxima). We have $\Delta\tau = t_n - t_m = (\sqrt{nR_0\lambda} - \sqrt{mR_0\lambda})/V$, or

$$V = \sqrt{R_0\lambda}\,\frac{\sqrt{n} - \sqrt{m}}{\Delta\tau} \qquad (8\text{-}16)$$

For convenience in reduction one may use perfect squares for m and n, e.g., the 4th and 9th cycles or the 9th and 16th cycles. The velocity error due to the uncertainty in ψ can easily be computed. The mth and nth zero crossings occur when $\pi x^2/2 \pm \psi$ equals $2\pi m$ and $2\pi n$, respectively. Let us take the particular case $m = 4$, $n = 9$ which was used to a great extent in reducing the Ottawa records. When $\psi = 0$ or $\pm 2\pi$, the expression $V\,\Delta\tau/\sqrt{R_0\lambda}$ equals unity and yields the correct value of V from the measured $\Delta\tau$. When ψ is near $\pm 90°$, the values of $V\,\Delta\tau/\sqrt{R_0\lambda}$, measured at the zero-crossing points, can range from 0.98 to 1.02, corresponding to an error in V of ± 2 per cent. The correct value for V at $\psi = \pm 180°$ can be found by turning the record over (thereby effectively shifting the phase 180°) and reading it as before. In between the points $\psi = 0$, π, and 2π, small errors in V will result from the use of the simple two-point formula, the errors decreasing for larger m and n. When $m = 4$, $n = 9$, the mean error over the whole range of ψ is $+1$ per cent if $\Delta\tau$ is measured at zero crossings, and -1 per cent if the maxima are used. A suggestion put forward by Mainstone (1960), that meteor velocities measured by an application of Eq. (8-16) will have a large systematic error on the low side, can be valid only if the analyst pays no attention at all to the waveform at t_0 and the information it contains regarding ψ.

The Jodrell Bank workers have developed similar formulas for use in measuring their radar amplitude-time records (Davies and Ellyett, 1949). In their experiments the diffraction-echo fluctuations were obtained only after t_0 and were independent of ψ.

The reduction of the diffraction-echo curves may be done automatically if the output of the receiver is fed directly into a recording frequency analyser of the type employed to register whistler phenomena on very low radio frequencies. Dr. L. A. Manning has kindly furnished some unpublished *frequency-time* records of meteor echoes obtained in this manner (see Fig. 8-4). The slopes of the echo curves near the t_0 points are proportional to the meteor velocities. In this particular experiment the transmitter and receiver were widely separated; hence the constant of proportionality depended both on the spacing of the stations and on the position and orientation of the trail (see Sec. 9-1). The geometry would be simplified and the ambiguities would be removed if the transmitter and receiver were placed close together, though fewer echoes would be seen. Note in Fig. 8-4 that some of the meteor echoes approach asymp-

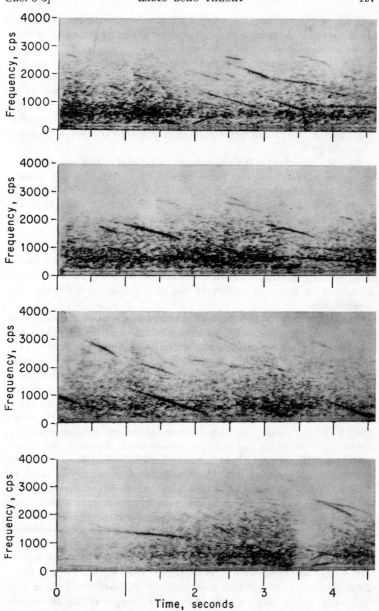

FIG. 8-4. Frequency-time records of meteor echoes obtained over a forward-scatter path. (*Courtesy of L. A. Manning.*)

totically to the limiting frequency corresponding to the head-on aspect of the meteor. Abnormal changes in slope of the frequency-time curve would indicate deceleration of the meteor.

This frequency-analyzing technique could be a great help in speeding up the velocity reductions, if high precision is not essential. As in the conventional records, the envelope of the amplitude-time variations can also be determined, though the frequency-time method yields this more directly. Any departure of this envelope from the theoretical envelope given by Eq. (8-8) could be interpreted in terms of variation of ionization along the path.

8-4. Modifications to the underdense trail model. The bare simplicity of our basic model requires many qualifications before it can hope to represent the complex conditions of the average meteor. We know that ionization is not distributed uniformly along the trail. The trail does expand radially, and it may have an effective initial diameter r_0 which is far from small in comparison with the radio wavelength. The effects of diffusion, recombination, attachment, turbulence, and wind shears must be considered; some of these will certainly be involved in the eventual dissipation of the trail. Let us first examine the influence these factors may have on the early history of the trail during the diffraction-echo observations.

The ions and electrons move out in an electrically neutral cloud (ambipolar diffusion). The radial expansion of the trail will proceed at a velocity of the order of the thermal velocities of the environment. This may be of the order of 0.5 km/sec, say. The meteor velocities range from 12 to 72 km/sec, and hence the trail is a narrow cone rather than a uniform cylinder, with a half-angle ranging from perhaps 2.5 to 0.5°. More accurately, the cone will not be right cylindrical but will have an exponential taper owing to the decrease in both r_0 and D with height (Sec. 8-6). This slight virtual realignment of the trail axis has a negligible second-order effect on the velocity measurement, though it would need to be taken into account in accurate radiant determinations.

Öpik (1955d) pointed out that the great penetrating power of the ablated meteor atoms, which have initial velocities comparable to that of the meteor, will very quickly create an ionized column which has an appreciable initial radius r_0. Many collisions are required to slow the atoms down to thermal velocities, though less than a millisecond is needed to complete the process. Replacing the line of electrons by an initial column of finite width created in less than a millisecond will not affect the velocity measurement, though it does have a bearing on the echo signal strength, as we shall see later. Öpik gives a table from which the initial radius may be computed for any height in the atmosphere.

As might be expected there is a slight velocity dependence, but Öpik's mean value for stony meteors moving at 40 km/sec may be taken as $r_0 = 1.1 \times 10^{-6} \rho_0/\rho_a$ meters, where ρ_0 is the atmosphere density at sea level. The ionized oxygen trail has been assumed here. By taking an average between the 1956 and 1959 ARDC density data in the Appendix tables we find that $\log_{10} \rho_a = 1.3 - 0.075H$ will represent the density fairly well for $75 < H < 120$ km. Hence

$$\log_{10} r_0 = 0.075H - 7.2 \qquad (8\text{-}17)$$

for the initial radius of the path, in meters. At 96 km, $r_0 = 1.0$ m.

Manning (1958) is of the opinion that the initial radius of the trail may be of the order of 14 ionic MFPs (mean free paths), again with only a slight dependence on velocity. The ionic MFP is about one-fifth of the neutral particle MFP, as listed in the Appendix tables. Since $\log_{10} \text{MFP}_{(neutral)} + \log_{10} \rho_a = -7.10$ from the Appendix tables, the following relation is obtained: $\log_{10} \text{MFP}_{(neutral)} = 0.075H - 8.4$. This is reasonably satisfactory for $75 < H < 120$ km. If we adopt Manning's conclusions, namely $r_0 \simeq 14 \text{ MFP}_{(ionic)} \simeq 3 \text{ MFP}_{(neutral)}$, we get

$$\log_{10} r_0 = 0.075H - 7.9 \qquad (8\text{-}18)$$

If the atom trail is adopted, on the thesis that ionization can occur while the atom trail is expanding, the constant in Eq. (8-18) would be -7.2, which agrees with that in Eq. (8-17). Experimentally, though, Eq. (8-18) as it stands seems to fit better with the evidence on ceiling heights (see Sec. 8-6).

To return to the velocity discussion let us insert some typical figures from the Ottawa experiments in Eq. (8-16). Here the mean $R_0 = 150$ km, $\lambda = 10$ m, $n = 9$, and $m = 4$. Thus, for the average meteor, $V \Delta\tau = 1.2$ km, and the $\Delta\tau$'s range from 0.017 to 0.1 sec. In this short path length, any likely variation in q could affect the echo amplitude somewhat, but it would create second-order phase errors only. Amplitude variations were indeed apparent in many of the records, particularly of the brighter meteors, though the f_i/τ curves were smooth and linear.

Wind drifts and shears can be more troublesome than any of the effects mentioned so far. Assume that a shear occurs between the path segment under observation and the t_0 point, with a radial velocity component of 10 m/sec, say. For a 72-km/sec meteor the translational shift between the $\Delta\tau$ segment and the t_0 point is $2 \times 10 \times 0.05 = 1$ m. The resultant phase shift of about $36°$ will add rather less than 1 per cent to the over-all velocity error. The same argument applies to the effects of a steady radial wind drift of the trail as a whole, which will create a similar phase shift between the $\Delta\tau$ segment and the t_0 point.* A very slow meteor, though, with five times this phase error, will lose or gain a half-cycle in the diffraction pattern between $\Delta\tau$ and t_0, and the velocity error may be several per cent. Kaiser (1955a) has examined the effects of wind shears in detail. In the light of our present knowledge of wind shears he concluded that the mean effect of shears on the velocity measurement of the average meteor would be about 1 per cent. Kaiser extended his analysis to show that the radiant determination errors were more seriously affected by wind shears. Average positional errors up to 3° may be ascribed to this cause.

If the contribution of the lower limit x_1 of the Fresnel integrals is not negligible, one may develop sets of predicted diffraction curves which are analogous to the optical diffraction fringes due to a rectangular slit, the slit width varying with time. Some of the observed records are clearly due to trails which have begun or ended fairly abruptly near t_0 or which have not come near t_0. It was pointed out some time ago (McKinley, 1951b) that in a few cases rapid diffusion might cause the lower limit x_1 to move in the direction of the meteor while it is still traveling down its path. Furthermore, if x_1 were to move with about the same velocity as the meteor, the target would be effectively a short-line segment traveling across the line of sight. The effect is complicated because the exponential decrease of D with H means that an initially short segment will not remain fixed in length as the meteor descends. This gives rise to a combination of diffraction and moving-ball effects.

Considerable study has since been devoted to this problem, which becomes increasingly important as the radio wavelength is decreased. Eshleman (1953) has discussed the influence which rapid diffusion has on echo rates observed on the higher radio frequencies, and in a later, unpublished report he derived quantitative expressions for the effective echoing area of a short-segment trail. The remarks of Hawkins (1956b) on the diffusion ceiling have already been noted. Flood (1957) developed the case where the segment is much shorter than the first Fresnel zone. In this situation the Fraunhofer diffraction theory of physical optics is more appropriate than the Fresnel theory. Qualitatively, the results mean that the echo from a faint underdense meteor trail, as observed on frequencies well above 100 Mc/sec, will be considerably weaker than if the trail were assumed to be several Fresnel zones in length around t_0. In addition, if the initial trail width is large in terms of wavelength, the

---

* To Mainstone (1960) goes the credit for demonstrating that the sign and magnitude of this progressive phase shift can be accurately determined by using one of the wind-drift methods described in Sec. 4-11. Furthermore, the technique allows one to remove any residual error in the determination of ψ at t_0, due to wind drift, which can be important for slow meteors (see Sec. 8-3).

signal will be further attenuated. On the other hand, the aspect sensitivity of the trail becomes less pronounced in comparison with the long-trail case, the echo strength does not fall off as rapidly on either side of t_0, and the echo curves become evenly symmetrical about t_0. The next two sections will cover some of these points in more detail.

8-5. The decay of the underdense trail echo. After the meteor has finished its course and has produced a trail of effective radius r_0, the most important factor in reducing the echo strength is ambipolar diffusion, which reduces the volume density without affecting the line density. Herlofson (1951), Huxley (1952), Kaiser (1953), and others have analyzed the problem by setting up and solving the differential equations for radial diffusion of a cylindrical distribution of electrons and positive ions, in the absence of a magnetic field.

A Gaussian distribution for the radial density of electrons will be adopted throughout this book as the most reasonable model, though other models have been treated (Herlofson, 1951; Kaiser and Closs, 1952; Eshleman, 1955). The standard form of the radial diffusion equation is

$$\frac{\partial N}{\partial t} = \frac{D}{r} \frac{\partial}{\partial r} \left(r \frac{\partial N}{\partial t} \right) \tag{8-19}$$

where N is the volume density of electrons at time t and distance r from the axis and D is the ionic diffusion coefficient in square meters per second. One particular solution of Eq. (8-19) has the form

$$N = \frac{1}{A(t + k)} \epsilon^{-[r^2/B(t+k)]}$$

where A, B, and k are constants. Direct substitution in Eq. (8-19) shows immediately that $B = 4D$. The constant A may be found from the condition that the total number of electrons in an infinite cross-sectional slice of unit thickness must equal q at all times. The number in an annular ring of radius r is $2\pi r N \, dr = \pi N d(r^2)$, and hence

$$q = \int_0^\infty \frac{\pi}{A(t + k)} \epsilon^{-[r^2/4D(t+k)]} d(r^2) = \frac{4\pi D}{A}$$

Thus the volume density may be expressed as

$$N(r,t) = \frac{q}{\pi(4Dt + r_0^2)} \epsilon^{-[r^2/(4Dt+r_0^2)]} \tag{8-20}$$

where the constant $4Dk$ is replaced by r_0^2, the square of the initial radius of the trail.

The diffusion coefficient D increases roughly exponentially with height in the meteor region. It may depend significantly on local atmospheric conditions and show daily and seasonal variations. Murray (1959) emphasizes that the great scatter of the observational data suggests that caution should be exercised in applying the results. Perhaps the most reliable determination of D is to be found in the work of Greenhow and Neufeld (1955). Their results may be summarized, for the region between $H = 80$ km and $H = 110$ km, by the relation

$$\log_{10} D = 0.067H - 5.6 \qquad (8\text{-}21)$$

where D is in square meters per second and H in kilometers. (See the Appendix for a discussion of D and other atmospheric parameters.) The decrease of both D and r_0 as the meteor descends should be taken into account in a more sophisticated treatment.

After the creation of the trail, we determine the echo amplitude by summing up the individual amplitude vectors from the electrons throughout the ionized cylinder. The time scale is now measured in tenths of seconds rather than in hundredths of seconds as in the discussion of the diffraction echo during the creative process. In the previous sections we considered that the cylinder radius was negligible in comparison with the wavelength. We now have to take account of the radial distribution of electrons, defined by Eq. (8-20), since there will be destructive interference effects between the electrons in any given cross section of the cylinder. Herlofson (1951), Eshleman (1955), and Brysk (1958), among others, have carried out this integration with varying degrees of generality. This is really a three-dimensional problem, but the essential answer can be obtained by considering the phase effects in a cross section near t_0 where the echo is strongest.

An annular ring of radial width dr is drawn about the trail axis in the cross-sectional plane (see Fig. 8-5). Throughout this ring the electron density is uniform. The amplitude of the echo signal from all electrons in this ring will be

$$dA = 2Nr\, dr \int_0^\pi \sin\left(2\pi ft - \frac{4\pi r}{\lambda}\cos\theta\right) d\theta$$

where the phase angle $(4\pi r/\lambda)\cos\theta$ of the electrons in the element $r\, dr\, d\theta$ is referred to a datum plane of zero phase, PP', which is drawn normal to the line of sight of the far distant radar station. Let us expand the integrand above. Then, since

$$\int_0^\pi \cos\left(\frac{4\pi r}{\lambda}\cos\theta\right) d\theta = \pi J_0\left(\frac{4\pi r}{\lambda}\right)$$

and the corresponding integral of the sine function is zero, we have

$$dA = 2\pi N J_0\left(\frac{4\pi r}{\lambda}\right) r\, dr \sin 2\pi ft$$

This amplitude is less than that which would be obtained if all the electrons were concentrated at the trail axis. The resultant phase angle is always zero for any ring, though, and so we may omit the r-f term and add up the amplitude contributions from all the rings. The ratio of the total scattered amplitude from the diffusing electrons to the total amplitude which would be obtained if all the electrons were in phase at the trail axis is

$$\frac{A}{A_0} = \frac{2\pi \int_0^\infty N J_0(4\pi r/\lambda) r \, dr}{2\pi \int_0^\infty N r \, dr} \tag{8-22}$$

In Eq. (8-22) we substitute the value of N given by Eq. (8-20). The denominator, of course, is equal to q. The numerator is a little more

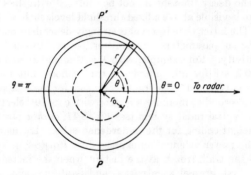

FIG. 8-5. Cross section of ionized trail near t_0 point.

difficult to evaluate* but it has been done in several texts (cf. G. N. Watson's "Theory of Bessel Functions," Cambridge University Press, New York, 1952, p. 393, or "Formulas and Theorems for the Special Functions of Mathematical Physics" by W. Magnus and F. Oberkettinger, Chelsea Publishing Company, New York, 1949, p. 35). When the integration is carried out, Eq. (8-22) becomes

$$\frac{P_R(t)}{P_R(0)} = \left(\frac{A}{A_0}\right)^2 = \epsilon^{-(32\pi^2 Dt/\lambda^2)} \epsilon^{-(8\pi^2 r_0^2/\lambda^2)} \tag{8-23}$$

where $P_R(0)$ is given by Eq. (8-7), after the meteor has passed t_0. This shows that the received power $P_R(t)$ is immediately reduced by an initial factor $\exp(-8\pi^2 r_0^2/\lambda^2)$ because of the finite initial width of the trail.

---

* The do-it-yourself reader might like to try this for his own satisfaction. One of several ways is to expand the Bessel function $J_0(4\pi r/\lambda)$ in its power series and then to integrate term by term, which results in the power series for the exponential.

The echo power subsequently decays according to the time-varying diffusion factor.

The *echo-amplitude decay time* T_{un} (or decay-time constant) for the *underdense* trail is defined as the time taken for $P_R(t)$ to decay by a factor of ϵ^{-2}, or the time interval during which the echo power decreases by 8.7 db. We have, from Eq. (8-23),

$$T_{un} = \frac{\lambda^2}{16\pi^2 D} \qquad (8\text{-}24)$$

This means that the theoretical decay time is independent of all the equipment parameters except the wavelength. Furthermore, T_{un} is the same for all meteors at a given height, no matter what their line densities are—provided the densities do not exceed the limit for an underdense trail. The echo decay time should not be confused with the time during which the echo is visible above a fixed threshold level, such as the receiver noise level. The latter time interval is strongly dependent on both q and the other system parameters, transmitter power, antenna gain, and receiver sensitivity. For example, with $\lambda = 9$ m and $D = 3$ m²/sec, we have $T_{un} = 0.2$ sec for all underdense trail echoes, but the duration above receiver noise could range from nearly zero for the smallest detectable meteor to a second or more for a meteor with $q \simeq 10^{14}$ electrons/m, as recorded by a typical radar system (see Fig. 8-11, *dashed curves*).

8-6. The height ceiling for the underdense echo. Let us examine in more detail the power attenuation expressed by Eq. (8-23). Figure 8-6 is a model of the trail, frozen at the instant when the meteor head has traversed the first Fresnel zone past t_0 and is at the point defined by $+\tau_F = (R_0\lambda/2)^{1/2}V$. At this place and time the effective trail radius is just the r_0 appropriate to the height. At the same moment, but at any point farther back up the trail, the effective radius will be $(r_0^2 + 4Dt)^{1/2}$, where t is measured backward from the point $+\tau_F$. In Fig. 8-6, the fixed r_0 cone is shown as the dashed line. The expanding diffusion cone is shown as the solid envelope. We now make two assumptions which are susceptible of more rigorous verification than we propose to offer in this text. First, most of the echo signal comes from the first Fresnel zone—this is fairly obvious from an examination of the Cornu spiral, Fig. 8-3, or from Eq. (8-6). Second, the signal received from the whole trail will be approximately equal to that which would be received if the trail were to have the uniform diameter shown at the t_0 point on the diagram. The latter assumption can be verified by an involved numerical integration along and across the trail at all points.

The effective radius at the t_0 point, under the above conditions, is defined by Eq. (8-20) when $t = \tau_F = (R_0\lambda/2)^{1/2}/V$. The relative echo power may be found by taking logarithms of both sides of Eq. (8-23), after substituting this value of t.   We obtain

$$\log_{10} \frac{P_R(t)}{P_R(0)} = -0.4343 \times 32\pi^2 \frac{R_0^{1/2}D}{2^{1/2}\lambda^{3/2}V} - 0.4343 \times 8\pi^2 \left(\frac{r_0}{\lambda}\right)^2$$

or, multiplying by 10 to get the power loss in decibels,

$$\text{Loss in db} = 970 \frac{R_0^{1/2}D}{\lambda^{3/2}V} + 343 \left(\frac{r_0}{\lambda}\right)^2$$

which reduces to

$$\text{Loss in db} \simeq 3.8 \times 10^5 \frac{D}{\lambda^{3/2}V} + 3.4 \times 10^2 \left(\frac{r_0}{\lambda}\right)^2 \qquad (8\text{-}25)$$

when we select $R_0 = 1.5 \times 10^5$ m as a typical average value for the range.

In calculating the total loss we shall use Eq. (8-18) for r_0 and Eq. (8-21) for D.   We shall also take $V = 7 \times 10^4$ m/sec.   The contribution from

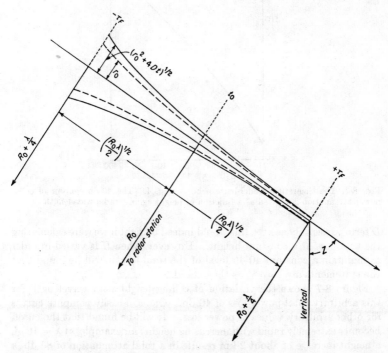

Fig. 8-6. Model of a meteor trail at time τ_F after t_0, where $\pm\tau_F = (R_0\lambda/2)^{1/2}/V$ defines one-half of the first Fresnel zone of the trail.   The initial radius is shown as the dashed line, while the effective radius due to diffusion is indicated by the solid-line envelope.

the D/V term would naturally be greater if we used a smaller value for V, but in evaluating an over-all ceiling, a large V value is more appropriate because high-velocity meteors ionize at greater heights than low-velocity meteors.   We shall set an arbitrary level of 40 db for the total power loss as delineating the limit for detection of underdense-type echoes.   For this particular value of the total power loss we find that the r_0 term dominates for wavelengths longer than 10 m, while the contribution from the D term becomes more important for shorter wavelengths.   A casual glance at Eq. (8-25) might suggest that these statements should be interchanged, since the contribution from the r_0 term varies as λ^{-2} while that from the

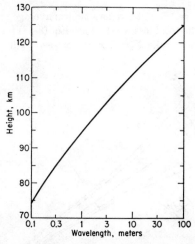

FIG. 8-7. The theoretical underdense echo ceiling, I.   The 40-db contour of echo-power attenuation is plotted as a function of height against radio wavelength.

D term varies only as $\lambda^{-3/2}$: this would indeed be right if we were calculating the total loss at a constant height.   However, when H is varied in order to maintain a constant 40-db level of the total loss, it will be found that the statements are correct as they stand.

Figure 8-7 shows the variation of ceiling height with wavelength for this arbitrary total power loss of 40 db.   One can easily compute curves for other arbitrary values of power loss.   It will be found that the cutoff becomes extremely rapid with increasing height: for example, at $\lambda = 10$ m, a height increase of about 2 km results in a total attenuation of 80 db, a further increase of 2 km produces a total loss of 160 db, and so on.

Figure 8-7 should be used with considerable reservation, especially since the absolute heights depend on the adopted model of the atmosphere.

For example, a two-to-one variation in ρ_a or MFP will change the heights by 4 km or so. The Appendix tables show that the present uncertainties in the atmospheric parameters are at least of this order. Furthermore, the ceiling will go up or down with diurnal and annual variations as well as with latitude variations in the parameters. Nevertheless, Fig. 8-7 may be regarded as indicative of the cutoff ceiling to be expected for different wavelengths. The level of 110 km for $\lambda = 9.2$ m is in reasonably good agreement with the observational evidence obtained at Ottawa.

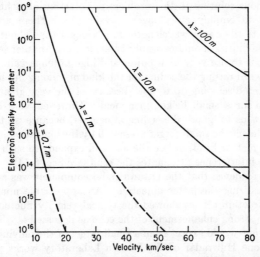

Fig. 8-8. The theoretical underdense echo ceiling, II. The area under a selected wavelength curve shows the range of meteor sizes and velocities for which the attenuation at the point of maximum ionization is equal to or less than 40 db.

It should be emphasized that the ceiling defined here applies to underdense-type echoes. As we shall see in Sec. 8-9, under certain conditions an overdense trail can yield an underdense-type echo, which subjects it to the underdense echo ceiling limitation, but only when those conditions apply.

We may combine the curve of Fig. 8-7 with those in Fig. 7-1 to determine the ceiling conditions for the point of maximum ionization on the trail. In Fig. 8-8, the region below a given wavelength curve shows the combinations of line densities and velocities which may be detected at that wavelength, assuming that a loss of 40 db or less is tolerable at the point of maximum ionization. For example, for $\lambda = 10$ m the graph suggests that a cutoff occurs for $V > 75$ km/sec for underdense trails with $q = 10^{14}$, the nominal crossover point between underdense and overdense trails. Some meteors in this category will still be detected at points on their trails below the maximum ionization points, but their number will naturally be fewer than the true number. It would appear, therefore, that a strong selection principle is operating to reduce the sensitivity of radio equipment to faint underdense meteors of high velocity. For $V = 40$ km/sec, tenth-magnitude meteors ($q = 10^{12}$) are well under the ceiling, and should be easily detectable with a typical 10-m radar.

One obvious solution to this problem of detecting faint high-velocity meteors is to employ still longer wavelengths. There are practical limitations to the use of wavelengths much longer than about 20 m, say, but the possibilities should certainly be explored. Another solution, not so obvious, is to use very high power and high antenna gain. This will do little toward raising the ceiling for the kind of echoing mechanism that we have been discussing up to now, because of the very great additional attenuation for a small height increment. However, very high power should allow us to ignore the ceiling altogether, because we then should be able to detect the small target presented by the ionization immediately behind the meteor head, before the ion trail expands to such a size that destructive interference attenuates the echo (see Sec. 8-14).

There is evidence that the Ottawa radio equipment was actually not far from realizing the latter objective. An appreciable number of the weaker diffraction echoes showed the typical velocity fluctuations prior to t_0 but no strong enhancement of the echo as it passed t_0. This behavior is what one would expect from a small target of the moving-ball type. The Millstone Hill radar of the Lincoln Laboratory works on a wavelength of 68 cm and hence should detect practically no underdense trails at all, according to Figs. 7-1 and 8-8. However, through the brute force provided by a peak power of 500 kw and an antenna gain of 37 db, the equipment has detected underdense trail echoes by virtue of this extremely short-trail, or moving-ball, effect. Dr. M. Loewenthal of Lincoln Laboratory, who has carried out some unpublished work on backscatter meteor echoes with this powerful radar, plans to apply the system to the study of forward-scatter meteor echoes. A combination of high power, high antenna gain, and moderately long wavelength should open new vistas to the meteor astronomer.

A third solution to the faint, fast meteor problem is to separate the transmitter and the receiver by distances of the order of 1,000 km. This will be discussed in Chap. 9.

Before we leave this section, let us see what happens as the meteor head in Fig. 8-6 moves on past successive Fresnel zones. We may write $\tau = s/V = x(R_0\lambda)^{1/2}/2V$ in the notation used in Sec. 8-1. Hence the

D term in Eq. (8-25) may be modified to read $3.8 \times 10^{5}(xD)/(2^{1/2}\lambda^{3/2}V)$. This represents a continuous decrease in echo power as the meteor moves away from t_0. If D is so small as to be negligible, we obtain the well-known prototype of the diffraction echo (Fig. 8-9, curve A). As the D/V term becomes dominant, the effect is to cause the envelope of the post-t_0 oscillations to approach the zero-power-level axis (see curve B).

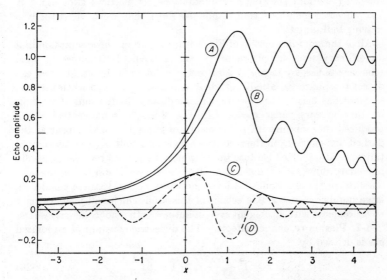

FIG. 8-9. Calculated amplitude-time curves of diffraction echoes from underdense trails. *Curve A*, no diffusion attenuation, incoherent radar echo; *curve B*, moderate diffusion attenuation, incoherent radar echo; *curve C*, severe diffusion attenuation, incoherent radar echo; *curve D*, same as for *curve C*, except that coherent detection is used, which brings out the phase variations of the meteor echo.

If the D/V term is large enough, the post-t_0 amplitude oscillations disappear altogether (see curve C), leaving only a smooth rise and fall in signal level at the t_0 point.

The reasons for these effects may be readily understood in qualitative terms from an examination of the Cornu spiral (Fig. 8-3). If there is no attenuation, the base of the amplitude vector remains anchored at the $x_1 = -\infty$ point, in effect, and its tip follows the curve round to $x = +\infty$, producing curve A of Fig. 8-9. With some attenuation at every point, which increases with time, the effective trail length will be finite, and the x_1 point will move in the same direction as the meteor. The echo amplitude will be reduced steadily, but as long as the effective trail length exceeds two or three turns of the upper right-hand spiral the resultant amplitude will show a few fluctuations (curve B), though they will die out as the x_1 point enters the top right-hand spiral. Note particularly that the phase of the Fresnel oscillations is not shifted perceptibly with respect to t_0 (except in the immediate vicinity of t_0); hence no error occurs in the velocity measurements. Once the effective trail length becomes less than one turn of the spiral, the net amplitude will decrease slowly and smoothly without showing any fluctuations, as in curve C of Fig. 8-9. The effective length of trail is now so short that we have virtually a moving-ball target.

All of the solid-line curves of Fig. 8-9 are drawn on the assumption that an ordinary noncoherent radar system is used. If we inject a local reference phase, by means of a cw set or a coherent-pulse radar, we can detect the phase variations both before and after t_0, even when the trail segment has become so short that no amplitude fluctuations at all show on the ordinary radar record. In Fig. 8-9, the same meteor which produced the noncoherent radar record of curve C would appear as the dashed-line curve D on the record of a cw equipment. (Negative amplitudes are also plotted because the output of a coherent receiver is usually bipolar.) Since the peak echo amplitude of curves C and D is as much as one-fifth of the unattenuated level shown by curve A, there could be a large number of detectable echoes of this kind which will yield velocity measurements with a coherent system but not with a noncoherent system.

8-7. Plasma resonance effects. The dielectric constant of an ionized gas is defined by

$$\kappa = 1 - \frac{N\lambda^2}{\pi} r_e \simeq 1 - 81 \frac{N}{f^2} \qquad (8\text{-}26)$$

where N is the number of electrons per cubic meter, and the classical electron radius is $r_e = (\sigma_e/4\pi)^{1/2} = 2.8 \times 10^{-15}$ m. λ is the wavelength in meters of the incident radiation, and f is the corresponding frequency in cycles per second.

When an electrically neutral volume of ionized gas (a plasma) is subject to certain boundary conditions, the possibility arises that a resonant oscillation can be induced in the plasma under the influence of the incident radiation, owing to separation of the electrons and ions. In the case of the underdense meteor trail no resonance effects are to be expected if the incident electric vector is parallel to the trail axis, because the ionization is assumed to be both uniform and virtually infinite in length, and hence there are no suitable boundaries. When the electric vector is transverse to the trail, though, it acts across a density gradient. The ions and electrons are separated slightly and the resultant restoring force will induce resonant oscillations. The axial dielectric constant may be highly negative initially. It will increase toward unity as the trail expands. Kaiser and Closs (1952) have shown that when κ is of the order of -1, the underdense trail will resonate under transversely polarized excitation. The theoretical maximum enhancement of the transverse echo amplitude relative to the longitudinal amplitude is approximately a factor of two, if a Gaussian radial distribution of ionization is assumed. Collision dampening keeps the resonance from being more pronounced. The transverse and longitudinal reflection coefficients will quickly approach unity again as the trail expands to the order of $r = \lambda/2\pi$, owing to radiation dampening.

This resonance phenomenon was originally predicted by Herlofson (1948b), though his preliminary estimate of the magnitude of the effect was considerably larger than subsequent work proved correct. An early experimental investigation (McKinley, 1951c) showed that if the effect were present the ratio of transverse to longitudinal scattering amplitudes was unlikely to be greater than 4. The reality of the effect and the observational confirmation of the revised theoretical ratio of 2 were demonstrated at Jodrell Bank in a series of careful and ingenious experiments (Closs, Clegg, and Kaiser, 1953; Billam and Browne, 1956). Stanford has also investigated the phenomenon (van Valkenburg, 1954). The phase of the transverse echo vector undergoes a theoretical reversal of 180° as the trail passes through resonance, and this aspect was examined by Greenhow and Neufeld (1956b). The observed phase changes averaged about 40°, with few cases being as large as 180°. The resonance effect usually disappeared about 25 msec after the echo reached its peak amplitude.

As a source of error in velocity measurements, resonance can rarely be considered significant. Observations of decay times can be affected to some extent, if the polarization is not known, unless care is taken to measure the decay-time constant well down on the decay curve, after the resonance effect has disappeared.

8-8. Recombination and attachment. The electrons will eventually recombine with the positive ions to form neutral molecules or atoms. Some electrons may attach themselves to neutral molecules to create negative ions which, though charged, are like the positive ions in being too heavy to oscillate appreciably in the incident field, and hence their scattering coefficient is negligibly small. Both effects can be expected to contribute to the eventual dissipation of the meteor ionization, but the rates at which they operate should be examined to see if they are significant in comparison with diffusion and turbulence.

The differential diffusion equation may be modified to include the recombination effect by subtracting the term $\alpha_e N_e{}^2$ from the right-hand side of Eq. (8-19). Here, α_e is the electronic recombination coefficient, and N_e is used throughout in the equation to emphasize that the electron volume density is meant. We shall not go into the analysis here (Kaiser and Greenhow, 1953), since the observations of long-enduring (overdense) echoes have demonstrated that recombination can hardly be a significant factor. The recombination coefficient for meteoric ionization must be of the order of 10^{-16} m^3/sec, or even less, in contrast to the generally accepted value of 10^{-14} m^3/sec for ionization created at meteoric heights in the atmosphere by solar radiation. Recombination may be neglected in comparison with ambipolar diffusion effects for either underdense or overdense trails.

In considering attachment effects, we subtract a term $\beta_e N_e N_m$ from the right-hand side of Eq. (8-19), where N_m is the density of neutral molecules capable of forming negative ions. In addition, terms should be added for the eventual detachment of the electrons. In the interest of simplicity these terms may be omitted to obtain an upper limit to the effect, if not an exact solution. If we make the plausible assumption that $q = q_0 \exp(-\beta_e N_m t)$ the revised volume density becomes

$$N_e = \frac{q_0}{\pi(4Dt + r_0^2)} \epsilon^{-\{[r^2/(4Dt+r_0^2)]+\beta_e N_m t\}} \tag{8-27}$$

Molecular oxygen is probably the main constituent of the atmosphere involved in the creation of negative ions. The coefficient β_e is not well determined in this case, but, if $\beta_e N_m t < 1$, Kaiser has shown that the effects of attachment are negligible in the case of the underdense trail. They may also be ignored during the early history of the overdense trail, but as we shall see later, they probably do come into play to limit the very-long-duration echoes.

8-9. The transition from underdense to overdense trails. If the volume density of the electrons is large enough, secondary scattering from electron to electron becomes important. The electrons are no longer independent scatterers, the incident wave does not penetrate the column freely, and the dielectric constant κ is negative throughout an appreciable volume of the gas. These are the conditions for the overdense trail. The transition from underdense to overdense is not sharply delineated. The axial dielectric constant can be highly negative in the underdense trail, but this does not mean that total reflection necessarily occurs. The wave can still penetrate the narrow underdense column, despite the negative κ, though with some loss of strength. Even in metals of high conductivity there is always a certain "skin depth" of penetration of the incident wave, defined as the depth at which the amplitude of the electric vector has fallen to $1/\epsilon$ of the surface amplitude. The important difference between metals and low-density ionized gases is that the conductivity (as expressed in the wave equation) is real for metals and imaginary for ionized gases. In the latter case a cumulative phase angle is built up by the ray as it passes through the ionized region, since the phase velocity here is greater than the group velocity of light. The greater the density, the greater the total phase angle, relative to free-space propagation. The amount of phase angle which can be tolerated before we define the trail as overdense seems to be pretty much a matter of opinion.

By definition, the critical density N_c is that for which $\kappa = 0$ in Eq. (8-26). As the column expands there will be a critical radius r_c within which $\kappa \leq 0$. For some value of q which marks the transition between underdense and overdense trails this radius will bound a volume both large enough and dense enough to attenuate the wave by $1/\epsilon$. If we put $\kappa = 0$ and use Eq. (8-20) we have

$$N_c = \frac{\pi}{\lambda^2 r_e} = \frac{q}{\pi(4Dt + r_0{}^2)} \, \epsilon^{-[r_c{}^2/(4Dt+r_0{}^2)]} \tag{8-28}$$

Our interest in the problem begins at the moment the trail is created with an initial radius r_0; that is, $t = 0$ when $r = r_0$. The transitional value of q is found by setting $r_c{}^2 = 4Dt + r_0{}^2 = \lambda^2/4\pi^2$, whence

$$q_{tr} = \frac{\epsilon}{4r_e} \simeq 2.4 \times 10^{14} \text{ electrons/m} \tag{8-29}$$

This is in agreement with the expression derived by Kaiser and Closs (1952). The Stanford group (Manning and Eshleman, 1959), with slightly different but equally acceptable reasoning, define the transition point by

$$q_{tr} = \frac{1}{\pi r_e} \simeq 1.1 \times 10^{14} \text{ electrons/m} \tag{8-30}$$

Note that q_{tr} is a line density. A trail with a line density $q > q_{tr}$ is defined as an overdense trail, and it may normally be expected to yield the overdense-type echo described by Eqs. (8-34) and (8-35) of Sec. 8-10. However, if the wavelength is short or the height is great, the echo received from an overdense trail may be of the underdense type. This is because we are considering that the echo observations begin only after the trail has reached its initial radius, and under either of the above conditions the volume density on the trail axis, at the instant that r_0 is attained, may be below the requirements for an overdense-type echo.

The condition for an overdense-type echo to be obtained from an overdense trail is that the overdense echo duration T_{ov} [see Eq. (8-34) of Sec. 8-10] shall be greater than the time which would be taken for the trail to reach r_0, were ordinary diffusion the only factor involved (Manning, 1958). From Eqs. (8-34) and (8-30) we have

$$T_{ov} = \frac{q\lambda^2 r_e}{4\pi^2 D} = \frac{\lambda^2 q}{4\pi^3 D q_{tr}} \tag{8-31}$$

This is to be equal to or greater than the time $r_0^2/4D$ [cf. Eq. (8-28)]. Hence

$$q \geq \frac{\pi^2}{r_e}\left(\frac{r_0}{\lambda}\right)^2 = \pi^3\left(\frac{r_0}{\lambda}\right)^2 q_{tr} \qquad (8\text{-}32)$$

If the line density q is below the limiting value given by Eq. (8-32) only an underdense-type echo will be received, even though $q > q_{tr}$. The r_0 ceiling effect of Sec. 8-6 now comes into play, and this underdense-type echo will be attenuated accordingly. Figure 8-10 is a graphical representation of Eq. (8-32) where Eq. (8-18) has been used to establish the connection between H and r_0.

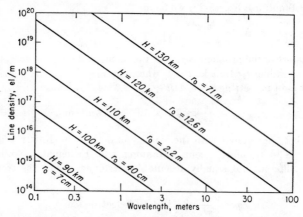

FIG. 8-10. The minimum line density required to produce an overdense-type echo, plotted against wavelength for selected values of H or r_0.

Various refinements to the approximate theory of this section have been proposed from time to time (for example, Brysk, 1959). The mathematical subtleties of some of these refinements put them beyond the scope of this book—furthermore, not all applied mathematicians in the field are agreed on their validity or usefulness.

8-10. The overdense trail. The basic conditions for the overdense trail and the threshold value of the line density have been discussed in the previous section. As the trail expands we define the effective trail radius as the boundary of the cylinder within which $\kappa < 0$. This radius follows immediately from Eq. (8-28).

$$r_c^2 = (4Dt + r_0^2) \log_\epsilon \frac{q}{\pi N_c (4Dt + r_0^2)}$$
$$= (4Dt + r_0^2) \log_\epsilon \frac{q\lambda^2 r_e}{\pi^2 (4Dt + r_0^2)} \qquad (8\text{-}33)$$

The radius grows to a maximum value $r_{c(\text{max})}^2$, which is found by differentiating Eq. (8-33) with respect to time and equating to zero. The square of the maximum radius is

$$r_{c(\text{max})}^2 = \frac{q}{\pi \epsilon N_c} = \frac{q \lambda^2 r_e}{\pi^2 \epsilon}$$

which is independent of r_0. (However, if $r_{c(\text{max})}$ should turn out to be less than r_0, an underdense-type echo only will be obtained after r_0 is reached.) This maximum occurs at time

$$t_{(\text{max})} = \frac{1}{4D\epsilon} \left(\frac{q}{\pi N_c} - r_0^2 \right)$$

The curve of r_c versus time is fairly flat at the maximum, but eventually the contraction accelerates rapidly. The trail becomes subcritical everywhere at a time T_{ov} (for *over*dense) which is determined by putting $r_c = 0$ in Eq. (8-28) (ignoring the obvious and trivial alternate solution $t = 0$). This gives us the *overdense echo duration*

$$T_{ov} = \frac{q}{4\pi N_c D} - \frac{r_0^2}{4D} \simeq \frac{q}{4\pi N_c D} = \frac{q \lambda^2 r_e}{4\pi^2 D} \qquad (8\text{-}34)$$

or
$$T_{ov} \simeq 7 \times 10^{-17} \frac{\lambda^2 q}{D} \qquad \text{sec}$$

for D in square meters per second, λ in meters, and q in electrons per meter. Except for trails at great heights, or trails for which the density just exceeds the transitional value, we have $q/\pi N_c \gg r_0^2$; hence the r_0 term is customarily omitted when discussing the typical overdense trail. The *echo duration* of the overdense trail, T_{ov}, should be clearly distinguished from T_{un}, the *decay time* of the underdense trail [Eq. (8-24)].

The equivalent echoing area of a long metallic column of radius $r \gg \lambda$ is $\sigma_{\text{cylinder}} = \pi R_0 r$ [Eq. (2-17)] for spherical waves incident upon it from a source at a perpendicular distance R_0. We may regard r_c as the equivalent reflecting boundary of the ionized column, though this is not strictly accurate because the wave will penetrate to some extent inside r_c before total refraction takes place. Furthermore, some refractive effects will be felt before the wave reaches r_c, which will be looked into later. For the moment let us consider that the maximum target area occurs when $r_c = r_{c(\text{max})}$. Thus $\pi R_0 r_{c(\text{max})} = R_0 \lambda (q r_e / \epsilon)^{1/2}$. The power flux incident upon the target is $P_T G / 4\pi R_0^2$. The echo-power flux will be attenuated by the same distance factor, $1/4\pi R_0^2$, when the wave returns to the station. The collecting area of the receiving antenna is $G\lambda^2/4\pi$. The echo power delivered to the receiver from the overdense trail is obtained by multiplying these four quantities:

$$P_R = \frac{P_T G^2}{64\pi^3\epsilon^{\frac{1}{2}}} \left(\frac{\lambda}{R_0}\right)^3 r_e^{\frac{1}{2}} q^{\frac{1}{2}}$$

$$= 1.6 \times 10^{-11} P_T G^2 \left(\frac{\lambda}{R_0}\right)^3 q^{\frac{1}{2}} \qquad \text{watts} \qquad (8\text{-}35)$$

Here, $P_R \sim q^{\frac{1}{2}}$, in contrast to the variation of P_R as q^2 in the underdense case [Eq. (8-7)]. Because the received power is relatively insensitive to line density in Eq. (8-35), it is often better to use Eq. (8-34) to determine q for the overdense trail, provided that D is known. This has the further advantage that all of the equipment parameters except λ may be neglected to a first approximation. In passing, it may be noted that the echo power from the underdense trail equals that from the overdense trail when $1/q = r_e \epsilon^{\frac{1}{3}}(2\pi)^{\frac{2}{3}}$ or $q = 0.75 \times 10^{14}$ electrons/m, which could be said to define yet another nominal value for q_{tr} (Hines and Forsyth, 1957).

In the above discussion the reader will have noticed that we began with a fully fledged overdense trail and skipped the formative stages. If we were to go back to the beginning of the trail history, we ought to arrive at expressions for the diffraction echo which are similar to those deduced in Secs. 8-2 and 8-3—for velocity-measuring purposes they should be effectively the same, in order to conform with observation. An analysis of the formative stage of the overdense trail would not really be redundant, since a different scattering mechanism is involved, but it is very difficult to handle and has not yet been done for the general case. Particular solutions for line densities near q_{tr} have been obtained, but only by long and tedious numerical integrations (Kaiser and Closs, 1952; Keitel, 1955).

Let us now examine the time variations of the overdense echo beginning at the moment r_0 is reached [note that Eq. (8-35) gives only the maximum echo level]. The echo power at any moment will be proportional to r_c, and the time variation of r_c may be found from Eq. (8-33). In Fig. 8-11 the solid curves show the overdense P_R versus time for a number of representative values of q. For convenience we have selected the following typical radar parameters: $P_T = 10^5$ watts, $G^2 = 10$, $\lambda = 10$ m, $R = 150$ km, and receiver noise level 10^{-14} watt. Logarithmic scales are used, after the example of Greenhow (1952a), to keep the diagram within reasonable bounds. All the curves are computed for $H = 93$ km for which $r_{0(ion)} = 12$ cm [Eq. (8-18)] and $D = 4$ m^2/sec [Eq. (8-21)]. Theoretically, the initial echo powers from the majority of the overdense trails will lie within a very narrow range—between 35 and 40 db above noise in this case. Few of them should increase more than 10 db during their lifetimes. The logarithmic time scale exaggerates the sharp decrease in echo strength as the echo terminates, but even on a linear scale it would be evident that the echo rapidly drops below noise. When the axial volume density falls below the critical value, the power level decreases according to the underdense decay curve (see dashed curve for $q = 2 \times 10^{14}$). For long durations this correction to the echo duration is entirely negligible.

In practice, the very-long-duration echoes do not appear either to last as long as the solid-line curves of Fig. 8-11 would suggest, nor do

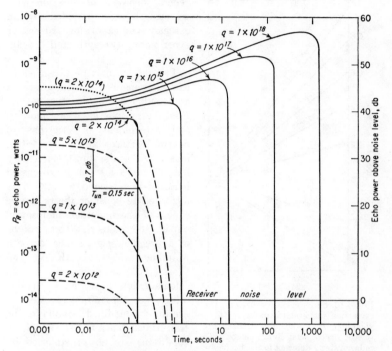

FIG. 8-11. Theoretical variation of echo power with time, based on typical radar parameters as outlined in the text. A diffusion coefficient of 4 m²/sec is assumed; for other values of D multiply the time scale by $4/D$. *Solid curves,* overdense trails; *dashed curves,* underdense trails; *dotted curve,* hypothetical underdense curve for $q = 2 \times 10^{14}$.

they drop off so rapidly. Suppose we were to look at the same meteor with two radar systems which differ in sensitivity by x db, where $x = 10 \log_{10} P_R(2) - 10 \log_{10} P_R(1)$. Here, $P_R(1)$ and $P_R(2)$ are the respective echo powers given by Eq. (8-35). The observed echo durations $T(1)$ and $T(2)$ can be connected by an empirical relation, deduced from simultaneous observations made with a 200-kw radar and a 100-watt radar (McKinley, 1953a). This is shown graphically in Fig. 8-12, where the ordinate represents the correction to be added to $\log_{10} T(1)$ to yield $\log_{10} T(2)$. The graph is at best an empirical approximation—the implications that a 940-sec-duration echo will be the same duration on any wavelength and that no longer durations ever occur are not really correct—the lines probably should approach the axis asymptotically.

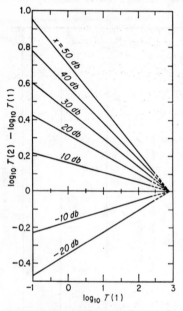

FIG. 8-12. Empirical curves showing the correction to be added to $\log_{10} T(1)$ to yield $\log_{10} T(2)$, when $T(1)$ and $T(2)$ are the observed echo durations on two radar systems differing in sensitivity by x db.

Independent confirmation of this general behavior of duration with wavelength was provided by an extensive series of forward-scatter experiments (Forsyth and Vogan, 1956).

Two reasons may be advanced for the difference between the observed and predicted echo-duration curves. First, atmospheric wind motions and attachment of electrons to neutral particles are both effective in shortening the durations of very long echoes—this will be discussed in Sec. 8-12. Second, we have so far neglected to consider the refractive effects of the underdense ionization outside the radius r_c. These can be of appreciable significance, as both Manning (1953) and Kaiser and Closs (1952) have pointed out. To calculate this effect we take the line integral of the refractive index to arrive at a modified formula for the transitional density. The boundary conditions are now established by the time of variation of r_c and the density gradient outside r_c and not by an arbitrary selection of a tolerable phase angle—we have to accept the total phase angle as it is actually computed at a given instant.

This calculation is not easy, and Manning has carried it out by a form of numerical integration. To summarize his results we may say that the maximum echo power received from the overdense trail will be 70 per cent of the power given by the overdense formula, Eq. (8-35). This quantitative correction to the echo power may not seem of great practical importance in view of the many ill-determined variables which can affect the observed power level much more seriously. From the philosophical viewpoint, though, it makes the story more complete. Furthermore,

Manning showed that the maximum radius is reached more quickly when refraction is considered, and dies away more slowly, though vanishing at the same time as before [Eq. (8-34)]. This means that the observed durations will depend more on the system sensitivity. Refraction outside the r_c radius can be rather more important in the case of oblique incidence (forward-scatter), when both direction and amplitude are affected.

Let us return for a moment to Fig. 8-11 to discuss the dashed curves. These are plotted for selected q's, using the underdense trail formulas, Eqs. (8-7) and (8-23). The radar parameters are the same as the ones adopted above for the overdense echoes. In Eq. (8-23) the initial attenuation due to the term $\exp(-8\pi^2 r_0^2/\lambda^2)$ is negligible here if we assume $r_0 = 12$ cm. The decay time, computed from Eq. (8-24) to be $T_{un} = 0.15$ sec, may also be found from any of the dashed curves by marking off an ordinate interval of 8.7 db anywhere on the curve and measuring the corresponding time interval. The minimum detectable signal, with our particular radar, should be obtained from a meteor with q slightly less than 2×10^{12} electrons/m, which corresponds roughly to a visual magnitude of $+10$.

As we remarked in Sec. 8-9, under certain conditions involving great echo heights or short radio wavelengths only an underdense-type echo can be obtained from an overdense trail (if we assume that our observation begins at the moment r_0 is reached). In Fig. 8-11 the dotted part of the hypothetical underdense echo curve for $q = 2 \times 10^{14}$ electrons/m is not observed. If, from our observation of the decay-type echo represented by the dashed part of this curve, we were to assume that the trail was underdense, we would underestimate the true value of q unless we were able to extrapolate the curve backward along the dotted line. The effect is to lop the top off the assumed echo curve (Forsyth, 1958). If we recognize the echo as due to an overdense trail, the correct value of q can be obtained from the overdense-echo formula. In practice, wind motions and other effects can greatly confuse the issue—in the broad transitional region many echoes of one type can successfully masquerade as members of the other group.

8-11. Enduring echo phenomena. The fading effects observed in long-enduring echoes from overdense trails are explicable in terms of interference between the waves scattered from two or more major echoing points on the trail. Two different mechanisms have been proposed to account for the creation of these discrete scattering centers, either of which can be fitted equally well to the majority of the observations. In certain selected examples, though, it is clear that the smooth-trail "glint" theory (Ellyett, 1950; Greenhow, 1952a; Manning, 1959c) is more appropriate. In other cases the glint theory will not explain observations which the rough-trail "blob" theory (McKinley and Millman, 1949a;

McNamara and McKinley, 1959) can account for quite readily. We shall now examine these two basic hypotheses in qualitative terms.

The glint theory assumes that the ionization is produced continuously and smoothly along the trail. The linear density of electrons rises to a maximum and then decreases, according to the theoretical ionization curve (Sec. 7-6). Wind shears in the upper atmosphere distort the trail more and more as time goes on (see Fig. 8-13). Whenever the tangent to a curved section of the trail becomes normal to the line of sight, an increase in echo power will be obtained from the immediate neighborhood of that point. In effect, a secondary R_0 point has been created on the trail, on either side of which a new first Fresnel zone is formed. The curvature of the trail shortens the zone lengths. Manning (1959c) has

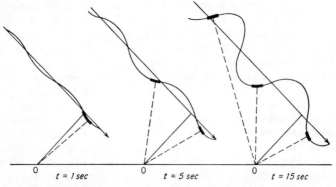

$t = 1\,sec$ $t = 5\,sec$ $t = 15\,sec$

FIG. 8-13. The glint theory, showing how additional reflecting points appear on the trail as distortion progresses.

computed the theoretical delay in the times of appearance of echoes from various parts of the trail. Figure 8-14, *solid curve*, shows this theoretical delay in terms of α, the elongation from the radiant ($\alpha = 0$ is the radiant point; $\alpha = 90°$ is the t_0 point). This delay is roughly proportional to $|\cos \alpha|$, though statistical allowance should be made for the observed fact that wind shears are greater at higher heights. Superposed on Fig. 8-14 are the mean observed delays obtained from visual-radar correlations done many years ago at Ottawa (McKinley and Millman, 1949a). The agreement with Manning's theoretical curve is very good, in view of the wide spread in the original experimental data. For example, in the interval $0 < \alpha < 40°$, the observed delays ranged from zero to over 30 sec—the value of 10 sec shown in Fig. 8-14 is a purely nominal mean.

The blob theory has as its fundamental postulate the requirement that the ionization is not created smoothly and continuously along the trail.

The trail is rough in the sense that the line density of ionization varies significantly over relatively short distances along the path (see Fig. 8-15). As time goes on, the less dense portions become underdense and little or no echo power is received from them. The denser portions grow in size

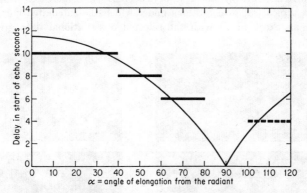

FIG. 8-14. Theoretical and observed delays in the appearance of the echo in terms of α, the elongation of the given point on the trail with respect to the meteor radiant. *Solid curve,* the glint theory (*after Manning,* 1959c); *horizontal lines,* observed delays for selected visual-radar correlations.

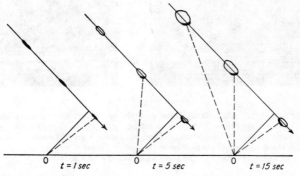

FIG. 8-15. The blob theory, showing how additional targets appear on the trail as the more densely ionized parts grow in volume due to diffusion.

as the electrons diffuse. The ratio of the radius to the length of a given segment increases until ultimately the blob may approach roughly spherical proportions, while remaining overdense. The effective echoing area of a blob at any time will be proportional to the product of the principal radii of curvature at the point where the line of sight intersects the critical density surface. For a given blob at any instant this product will be greatest if $\alpha = 90°$ and least if the blob is viewed end-on at $\alpha = 0°$. On this theory the delay in the appearance of the echo is also roughly proportional to $|\cos \alpha|$.

A further factor enters, though, because the rate of growth of the blob target increases with D, and D always decreases as α increases. One can select a typical set of conditions under which the calculated curve will display an excellent fit with the selected observational data given in

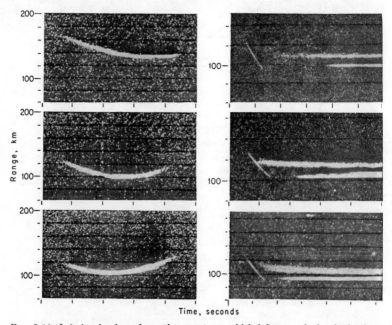

FIG. 8-16. *Left,* head echoes from three meteors which left no enduring ionization; *right,* head echoes from three meteors—enduring ionization has appeared in each case, at two or more quasi-stationary ranges, and with delays up to two or three seconds. (Note that these are single-station records of six *different* meteors, not three-station records of two meteors, despite the seeming similarity to Fig. 4-8.)

Fig. 8-14. One may also choose another set of conditions which will actually show a marked increase in delay as α approaches $90°$. To take an extreme case consider a meteor coming nearly head-on to the station from a radiant high in the sky. The diffusion coefficient will decrease by one or two orders of magnitude as the meteor falls, but α will not increase very much, and the diffusion factor will overrule the $\cos \alpha$ factor. This prediction is in agreement with many of the observational records (see Fig. 8-16, *right*). These illustrations show that meteors in the visual range—not necessarily the brighter ones only—can produce enduring echoes at points on the trail far removed from the t_0 point. The delays are often far too short to be explained by the glint theory. In many cases there may be no measurable delay at all relative to the head echo (see Fig. 8-17). The discrete echoing areas have been formed nearly instantaneously. The discreteness of the echoing sources follows from the assumption of an initially rough trail.

In the above discussion we have tacitly assumed, first, that the glint theory was based on a smooth trail and relied on wind shears alone to produce the glints, and second, that the blob theory demanded a rough trail but needed no wind shears. However, in both cases the restrictions are unnecessary. The smooth trail is not really essential to the glint theory, and the inclusion of wind shears will improve rather than spoil the blob theory. The fragmentation hypothesis, which states that meteoroids break up into many fine particles as they encounter the air resistance, is additional evidence for suggesting that the majority of meteor trails are rough, in the visual range of meteor sizes at least. This is probably the most important cause, though other physical processes may also be visualized to account for the initial roughness of meteor trail ionization, such as rotation of a nonspherical meteoroid—this could lead to a regularly repeated variation along the path which is apparent in many of the individual records.

The equivalent echoing areas of the *curved* glint segment and of the blob are both of the same form, namely, $\pi r_1 r_2$ (Sec. 2-10), and are both of the same order of magnitude. In neither case has the echo much depth in range: practically all of the echo is received from a small area of that part of the surface facing the line of sight, no matter what the shape of the rest of the body may be. As to the variation of echo delay time with wavelength, we may note that the critical radius increases with wavelength [Eq. (8-33)]. Either the glint segment or the blob will therefore appear as a larger target on a longer wavelength, and should therefore return a detectable echo sooner—which is in accord with the observations. Occasionally, a radar echo will change fairly rapidly and continuously in range as the glint point follows the convolutions of the trails. However, most of the discrete enduring echoes show no change of range at all, other than a small translational motion which can be attributed to ordinary wind drifts. Furthermore, many discrete echoes show no aspect sensitivity (Fig. 8-17), although they appear immediately after the passage of the meteor. This behavior is somewhat easier to explain if the trail ionization varies markedly along its length.

Analysis of echo fading rates with cw or long-pulse radar equipments shows that on the average a delay of 0.4 sec occurs before fading begins, that is, before a second reflecting center is formed. The spectrum of the

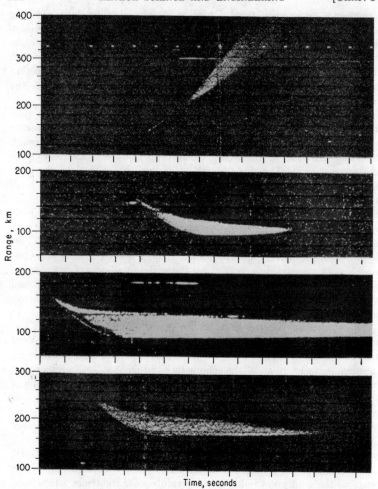

FIG. 8-17. Radar echoes from meteors. In each case the enduring ionization is practically continuous from all parts of the trail. The echo duration at any point of the trail is dependent both on the height and the rate of production of ionization at that point.

fading frequencies becomes more complicated as additional centers come into play. Finally, as the echoes die away from the parts at either end of the trail, the spectrum narrows down again to a single component. On the average, the longest echo endurance for a 40-km/sec meteor will be found at a height of 93 km. Above this height, diffusion quickly thins the ionization to underdense values while at lower altitudes some other processes, probably turbulence and attachment, act to shorten the duration. One can interpret the fading spectra in terms of turbulent conditions in the upper atmosphere. We shall not pursue this particular line of research further here because the meteor evidence, although important, is only a small part of all the available data in the field of ionospheric motions.

To sum up, we may say that neither theory alone is sufficient to explain all the phenomena adequately. If we combine the wind-shear action with the rough-trail hypothesis, a satisfactory compromise is reached which can cope, in qualitative terms at least, with all the observational evidence advanced so far.

8-12. Echo duration limited by attachment. Because of the initial aspect sensitivity of most meteor trails it is difficult to get a clear conception, from single-station observations at least, of the variation in line density of ionization along the entire trail. Exceptions to this general statement may be found in certain radar-echo records like Figs. 8-17 and 8-18. The implication of these records is strong that we have obtained here a fairly realistic picture of the typical variation of echo duration at every point on the trail, free of any aspect-sensitivity considerations. Figure 8-19 is a height-duration plot of the three-station meteor echo shown in Fig. 4-8. The observed duration at any height level is probably independent of the viewing aspect in this case too.

The problem arises in interpreting the echo duration at any given point in terms of the initial ionization produced there. For example, Fig. 8-18 shows a steadily increasing echo duration as the height along the path decreased. This can quite clearly be attributed both to the increasing rate of production of ions and to the decreasing value of D as the meteor descended. At some height a maximum duration was attained, below which the duration rapidly fell off to zero, but in the example given this cutoff cannot be due to a decrease in the rate of production of ionization. The head echo continued to be very strong, and it is unlikely that the point of maximum ionization was reached much before the meteor arrived at t_0, which is well below the height where any appreciable duration of the echo can be perceived. Some other physical process must be operating to reduce the echo duration so severely. The same "floor" effect is noticed in the photographic evidence of meteor trains (see Sec. 5-8).

Diffusion at heights below about 90 km is so slow that it cannot be considered as an effective agent. If we relied on diffusion alone to limit the echo duration we would find, for example, that Eq. (8-34) predicts a duration of over 3 hr on a 10-m radar for a -5 magnitude meteor moving at 40 km/sec. This is based on the assumption that the maximum duration would occur at the height of maximum ionization, which in this case is about 80 km (Fig. 7-1). In practice, though, the average observed duration of the same meteor would be more like 5 min, and the observed height of the maximum echo endurance would be about 93 km.

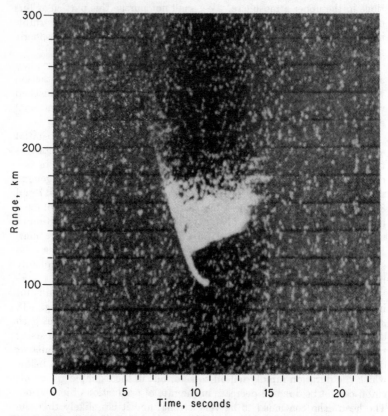

FIG. 8-18. A radar echo from a meteor which has passed right through the meteoric region before burning up. Note also the enhanced noise spots which appear on the record at all ranges while the enduring ionization persists. This effect is discussed in Sec. 10-1.

Recombination of the positive ions and the electrons has received serious consideration but has been rejected as a plausible cause. As Manning and Eshleman (1959) put it, recombination has been demonstrated to have negligible effect during the early history of the trail, and since the time constant of the recombination process increases with the age of the trail, it may therefore be considered entirely negligible during the later history.

Turbulence in the atmosphere will in time stir up the trail and redistribute the ionization. Greenhow and Neufeld (1959a) find that the turbulence is distinctly anisotropic; the vertical scale of the large eddies is roughly 7 km and the horizontal extent is about 150 km. [Large-scale motions of this order of size may be due to internal gravity waves in the upper atmosphere rather than to turbulence, according to Hines (1959).] The size of the smallest eddies is approximately 50 m. Even a smooth-trail model should eventually become rough by this process. The echo durations will be decreased and the dependence of duration on λ^2 will no longer hold. It has been noted from simultaneous observations made on two wavelengths (Greenhow, 1952a; McKinley, 1953b) that $T \sim \lambda^2$ for

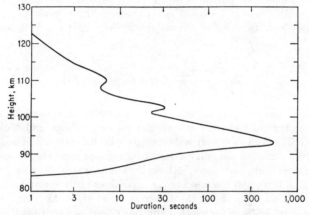

Fig. 8-19. Profile of echo height versus duration, for the three-station meteor echo of Fig. 4-8.

trails with electron densities not greatly in excess of the transitional density, but that the power of λ approaches unity for very-long-duration echoes. The theory of atmospheric turbulence, which is based only in part on the meteor observations, is undergoing continuous revision, and the discussions have occasionally been rather controversial (Booker, 1956, 1958; Booker and Cohen, 1956; Manning and Eshleman, 1957, 1958; Manning, 1959b, 1959c; Greenhow and Neufeld, 1959a, 1959b; Rao, 1959; Rao and Armstrong, 1958; and others). In one series of papers on the mechanics of turbulence and its effect on meteor echoes (included in the list above) both protagonists in the debate cited the same Ottawa observations (McKinley, 1953a, 1954b) in support of their widely differing viewpoints—which left the originator of the data both confused and complimented. Fluid dynamics is too involved a subject to be treated adequately in this book, and we shall not enlarge on its applications here.

The interested reader will find that accepted theories of comparatively recent vintage are being subjected to drastic overhaul in the current literature.

Attachment of the electrons to neutral atoms or molecules has just recently been put forward again as a process which seems quite capable of controlling the durations of very long echoes without greatly affecting the shorter echoes (Davis, Greenhow, and Hall, 1959a, 1959b). We have already obtained the echo duration T_D, based on diffusion alone, by putting $r_c = 0$ in Eq. (8-28). That is, $N_c = q/4\pi D T_D$, since we may neglect the r_0 term for long-duration echoes. Similarly, the duration T_A, which would be observed in the presence of both attachment and diffusion, is found by putting $t = T_A$ and $r = 0$ in Eq. (8-27). Thus, $N_c = (q/4\pi D T_A) \exp(-\beta_e N_m T_A)$. Equating these expressions, since the same limiting value of critical density is involved in both cases, we have

$$T_D = T_A \epsilon^{\beta_e N_m T_A}$$

or

$$\beta_e N_m = \frac{2.303}{T_A} (\log_{10} T_D - \log_{10} T_A) \qquad (8\text{-}36)$$

Next, let us examine the echo-duration correlation with visual magnitude for Perseid meteors observed at Ottawa (Millman and McKinley, 1956). The data show very wide spreads in both duration and magnitude —a given duration class may extend over eight or more magnitudes, or a given magnitude class may include durations which vary as much as 1,000:1. If we plot the mean of the logarithms of the durations for each magnitude class, we obtain the dashed curve of Fig. 8-20. Or, if we plot the mean magnitudes for selected duration classes, we arrive at the dotted curve of Fig. 8-20. Obviously, the true relation lies somewhere between these extremes. Empirical error functions have been evolved, based on the observed distributions. With these error functions, corrections have been computed for each of the points shown on Fig. 8-20. The corrected points (not shown) lie very closely about the solid straight line marked "Diffusion," over the magnitude range -3 to $+5$. For the brighter magnitudes the error functions become less reliable because of the scarcity of data. It is obvious, though, that the true curve must dip downward from the straight line and lie between the dotted and dashed curves as M becomes more negative. Even over the magnitude range -3 to $+5$ there is no assurance that the analytical procedure has not masked some small but real deviations from the calculated straight line.

We have computed values of $\log_{10} T_A$ for selected values of $\beta_e N_m$ in Eq. (8-36), taking the $\log_{10} T_D$ values from the extrapolated straight line. The most reasonable fit appears to result when $\beta_e N_m = 0.006$. This is shown in Fig. 8-20 as the solid curved marked "Attachment." Davis,

Greenhow, and Hall employed the Ottawa data somewhat differently to arrive at a value of $\beta_e N_m$ between 0.015 and 0.025. We are inclined to favor a value not exceeding 0.01. If $\beta_e N_m$ is greater than this, the theoretical maximum duration approaches a limit of 200 or 300 sec. Five-minute echoes are not uncommon at $\lambda = 10$ m. A few have been

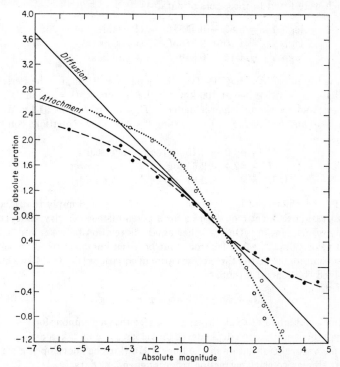

FIG. 8-20. Correlation between echo duration and magnitude of 1,404 Perseid meteors. *Solid circles and dashed line,* mean of log durations in given magnitude classes; *open circles and dotted line,* mean of magnitudes in given log duration classes. The straight line marked "Diffusion" is the best fit to the data over $-3 \leq M \leq 5$. The curve marked "Attachment" has been computed as described in the text.

observed with durations of 30 min or longer; they have not occurred often, it is true, though the frequency of their appearance was not at variance with the statistical expectation of extremely bright fireballs (McKinley and Millman, 1953; McKinley, 1954b). During daylight a photodetachment process may operate to decrease β_e. If so, the enhanced ultraviolet radiation that causes a sudden ionospheric disturbance might further lengthen the durations.

8-13. The radio magnitude relation.   In addition to the data on the Perseids ($V = 60$ km/sec) given in the previous section, the Ottawa observations included similar information on 256 Geminids ($V = 36$ km/sec) and on 1,420 nonshower meteors whose average velocity was taken to be about 45 km/sec.   The equations below represent the three lines which were fitted to these sets of data.

$$\log_{10} T_D = 0.87 - 0.406M \qquad \text{(Perseids, Fig. 8-20)}$$
$$\log_{10} T_D = 1.10 - 0.378M \qquad \text{(nonshower)} \qquad \text{(8-37)}$$
$$\log_{10} T_D = 1.15 - 0.349M \qquad \text{(Geminids)}$$

In the formula $T_D = 7 \times 10^{-17} \lambda^2 q / D$, we put $\lambda = 9.2$ m; for the Perseids we have $D = 13$ m²/sec at 100 km; for the Geminids, $D = 3.2$ m²/sec at 91 km; and for the nonshower meteors, $D = 5.0$ m²/sec at 94 km [from Fig. 5-10 and Eq. (8-21)].   Eliminating T_D, the above equations convert to

$$M_r = 40.0 - 2.45 \log_{10} q \qquad \text{(Perseids)}$$
$$M_r = 42.4 - 2.65 \log_{10} q \qquad \text{(nonshower)} \qquad \text{(8-38)}$$
$$M_r = 45.5 - 2.87 \log_{10} q \qquad \text{(Geminids)}$$

If the coefficient of $\log_{10} q$ were exactly 2.5, it would imply that a constant ratio exists between I and q for a given meteor velocity, independently of magnitude.   On the other hand the relation between ionization and velocity may well differ from that between luminosity and velocity. As a compromise to the three observational equations [Eq. (8-38)] we have evolved the general formula

$$M_r = 36 - 2.5 \log_{10} q + 2.5 \log_{10} V \qquad \text{(8-39)}$$

which is not a bad fit to all three, if we agree that a common slope of 2.5 is acceptable and that the dependence on velocity can be taken care of by a simple vertical translation of the lines.   Hawkins has developed a somewhat similar velocity correction from independent data.

Purely as a pragmatic expedient, and with even less physical justification than we invoked in producing Eq. (8-39), it happens that a very good fit can be obtained for all the lines of Eq. (8-38) by means of the simple expression

$$M_r = \frac{71 - 4.4 \log_{10} q}{\log_{10} V}$$

This we shall not dignify with an equation number.

We note that the three empirical lines in Eq. (8-38) are reasonably well satisfied by $q = 10^{16}$ when $M = 0$.   This gives us the link between magnitude and ionization of which we have made frequent use.   The simplified form of the radio magnitude equation which we first introduced in

Chap. 2 then follows immediately:

$$M_r = 40 - 2.5 \log_{10} q \qquad (2\text{-}3)$$

which is fairly satisfactory for $-2 \leq M_r \leq 5$ and average meteor velocities. Equation (8-39) reduces to Eq. (2-3) when $V = 40$ km/sec.

A connection between τ_q and τ_I may be deduced from Eq. (8-39).
First, by dividing Eqs. (7-3) and (7-6) we have $I \sim qV\tau_I/\tau_q$. From Eq.
(2-2) $M \sim -2.5 \log_{10} I \sim -2.5[\log_{10} q + \log_{10} (V\tau_I/\tau_q)]$. Comparing this
with the observational Eq. (8-39), we obtain $\log_{10} V \sim -\log_{10} (V\tau_I/\tau_q)$,
or $\tau_q \sim V^2\tau_I$.

Although the differences in the slopes of the observational relations
between M and q are small, they are probably quite real, and we have no
justification for forcing them into a common mold other than simplicity
and convenience. From Fig. 5-11 we have concluded that $H = 93$ km
represents the height of maximum echo duration which would be observed
if a meteor were to produce ionization at a constant rate all along its path.
Above 93 km diffusion is the controlling factor, and below 93 km attachment is possibly the chief agency reducing the durations. The duration
of a fifth-magnitude Perseid meteor will therefore be less than that of a
fifth-magnitude Geminid meteor, because the maximum ionization of the
Perseid occurs at 106 km and that of the Geminid at slightly more than
95 km (Fig. 7-1). On the other hand, a -5th-magnitude Perseid
(q_{max} at 89 km) will have a longer duration than a -5th-magnitude
Geminid (q_{max} at 79 km). Therefore the slope of the Perseid line of Eq.
(8-37) should indeed be steeper than that of the Geminid line.

We can easily calculate how far the point of maximum echo duration
will lie below the height of maximum ionization, in the region above
93 km where diffusion alone need be considered. From Eq. (8-34),
$T/T_{(max)} = qD_{(max)}/q_{max}D = q\rho_a/q_{max}\rho_{a(max)}$, if we tentatively assume
$D \sim 1/\rho_a$. Thus, from Eq. (7-29) we have

$$\frac{T}{T_{(max)}} = \frac{9}{4}\left(\frac{\rho_a}{\rho_{a(max)}}\right)^2\left(1 - \frac{\rho_a}{3\rho_{a(max)}}\right)^2 \qquad (8\text{-}40)$$

If we differentiate T with respect to ρ_a and equate to zero, we obtain
immediately $\rho_a = 1.5\rho_{a(max)}$ for the density at the height of maximum
duration T_m. At this point $q = (^{27}\!/_{32})q_{max}$ and $T_m = (^{81}\!/_{64})T_{(max)}$. In
terms of height we have $0.075(H_{(max)} - H) = \log_{10} 1.5$, or $H_{(max)} -$
$H \simeq 2.3$ km. The height of the longest echo will therefore be 2 or 3 km
below the height of maximum ionization (this will vary with the scale
height adopted). However, this constant differential cannot hold as
$H_{(max)}$ approaches 93 km. At heights where diffusion alone is operative
we should multiply the q's deduced from the observed T_m's by the factor
$^{32}\!/_{27}$ to obtain q_{max} values, for truer correlation with the visual magnitude
estimates. This multiplying factor will approach unity at 93 km, and

below this height it will increase again in some manner, though for entirely different reasons.   In a qualitative sense this could be interpreted in terms of rotation of the M versus $\log_{10} q$ lines: the amount of rotation would depend on the pivotal point, which in turn depends on the velocity. It would not require much ingenuity to juggle the corrections arising from this *ad hoc* logic to yield an ideal straight line to fit all meteor sizes and velocities.   The practical virtue of such a procedure is dubious and the theoretical validity is weak.   The true relation between M and $\log_{10} q$ is not likely to be represented by an exact straight line, even over the range $-3 \leq M \leq 5$.   Until more information becomes available, though, one may use the simple formula [Eq. (2-3)] as a fair working tool, or the one with the velocity correction [Eq. (8-39)] if more precision is needed.   (The reader may use the unnumbered M versus $\log_{10} q$ formula at his own risk!)

In deriving Eq. (8-40) we assumed tentatively that $D \sim 1/\rho_a$, whence $T/T_{(max)} = q \rho_a / q_{max} \rho_{a(max)}$.   From Eq. (7-24), $\rho_{a(max)} \sim q_{max}^{1/3}$; so

$$\frac{T}{T_{(max)}} = \frac{q^{4/3}}{q_{max}^{4/3}} \tag{8-41}$$

In practice (see Appendix for an explanation) we have adopted a slightly larger effective scale height for the diffusion equation ($H_D = 0.434/0.067 = 6.5$ km) than for the other atmospheric parameters ($H = 0.434/0.075 = 5.8$ km).   Hence, in our empirical relation, the power of q will be slightly less than $4/3$.   In fact, combining Eqs. (7-27), (8-21), and (8-34) we have

$$\log_{10} T_{(max)} = 1.30 \log_{10} q_{max} - 3.3 \log_{10} V - 2 \log_{10} \lambda - 16.0 \tag{8-42}$$

$\text{Log}_{10} T_m$ is obtained by adding $\log_{10} (81/64)$ to Eq. (8-42).   Assuming $\log_{10} q \sim \log_{10} I \sim -0.4M$ one might think that the slopes of all the lines of Eq. (8-37) should be $-1.30 \times 0.4 = -0.52$, which they are not. We would therefore be no further ahead if we used Eq. (8-42) as the intermediary between Eqs. (8-37) and (8-38), although the presence of the $\log_{10} V$ term in Eq. (8-42) helps to rationalize the empirical inclusion of $\log_{10} V$ in Eq. (8-39).   The basic observational data should be regarded as authoritative, but the necessary processing of the data for comparison with theory is itself an interpretative procedure which involves theoretical considerations and subjective opinions.   The problem is intriguing and will bear further examination, both from the experimental and the theoretical viewpoints.

8-14. The head echo.   The integral of the field vector given in Eq. (8-3) is quite general and applies all along the trail.   In Sec. 8-1 we were interested only in the portion near t_0, and hence we were able to carry out the integration by making an approximation for R which is valid only near t_0.   The increase in echo strength as the meteor nears t_0 is due to the increasing length of each new Fresnel zone and not to the decrease in R, which is negligible. Going to the other extreme, where the meteor is approaching directly toward the station, the converse situation exists: each Fresnel zone is the same length, namely $\lambda/4$, and any over-all increase in echo power will be due chiefly to the decrease in range, if we assume a constant q. In this case we may write R for s in Eq. (8-3). When R is large, the net amplitude due to any two adjoining Fresnel zones is very close to zero. In effect, the last zone to be formed will largely determine the instantaneous magnitude and phase of the total amplitude vector A_R. We therefore need integrate the phase angle $4\pi R/\lambda$ only over the distance $\lambda/4$. Over this small interval the range factor in ΔP_R may be considered constant.

$$A_R(\text{end-on}) = (2\mathbf{r}\,\Delta P_R)^{1/2} \cdot q \cdot \frac{1}{2} \int_0^{\lambda/4} \sin\left(2\pi ft - \frac{4\pi R}{\lambda}\right) dR$$

whence

$$P_R(\text{end-on}) = \frac{A_R{}^2}{2\mathbf{r}} = \Delta P_R \frac{\lambda^2}{16\pi^2}\, q^2 \qquad (8\text{-}43)$$

For any other trail orientation the echo signal will increase smoothly from this limiting asymptotic value to the maximum value obtained when the meteor passes t_0. The analysis above is equally valid for meteors receding from the station, and if the radar range resolution is adequate, both the approaching and receding echoes will be separable from the strong echo at t_0. If our end-on trail were rotated 90° so that it crossed the line of sight at range R (with the meteor head well past t_0), the echo power would be $P_R(\text{normal}) = \Delta P_R R\lambda q^2/2$, from Eq. (8-6). The ratio of these powers is

$$\frac{P_R(\text{end-on})}{P_R(\text{normal})} = \frac{\lambda}{8\pi^2 R} \qquad (8\text{-}44)$$

When $\lambda = 10$ m and $R = 150$ km, the power level of the end-on echo will be more than 60 db below $P_R(\text{normal})$. Although weak, these echoes are easily detectable with conventional cw meteor systems. In addition to the stronger echoes which change pitch rapidly near t_0, many fainter Doppler whistles of nearly constant pitch can be recorded from meteors far from the t_0 point.

A diffraction echo will thus be obtained from every trail as it is being formed, no matter what the trail orientations may be, but the intensity will fall off rapidly on either side of t_0. Browne and Kaiser (1953) suggested that this simple extension of the diffraction theory to points remote from t_0 would account for the head echoes which are observed on range-time radar records. The major objection to this is that the observed variation in intensity of the head echoes is usually very much less than that predicted by the diffraction theory (McKinley, 1955). The brighter the meteor, the less the variation in strength as the meteor passes t_0. These echoes probably come from highly overdense trails. It has been suggested (McKinley and Millman, 1949a) that the transient head echo is received from a large cloud of ionization which accompanies the meteor head. The echo from such a moving-ball target will be relatively independent of aspect. For very bright meteors the diffraction echo may be negligible in comparison with the moving-ball echo, even near t_0. Occasionally, interference effects are observed near t_0 (see Fig. 4-9b) which support the thesis that these two types of echoing mechanism do exist together. Some typical head echoes are shown in Fig. 8-21; others appear in Figs. 8-16 and 8-17.

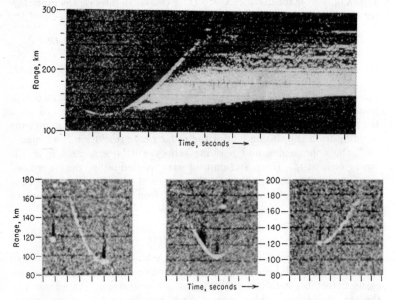

FIG. 8-21. Meteoric head echoes.

It has been difficult to visualize a reasonable physical process which will account not only for the creation of a large ionized cloud around the meteor head but also for its necessarily rapid dissipation, since another striking feature of the head echo is that, as a type, it shows little or no measurable duration at any point of the path. Shock waves have been proposed as a possible ionizing agent, though the theory encounters some problems where the air density is very low—head echoes are observed as high as 130 km. The complete lack of aspect sensitivity of the true head echo (it seems not to matter whether the meteor is approaching or receding from the observer) might be hard to explain in view of the probable conical outline of the ionization created by the shock-wave front.

Another suggestion was offered some time ago (McKinley and Millman, 1949a) that ultraviolet light from the meteor head could ionize the air particles at a considerable distance from the meteor. This was criticized partly on the grounds that the amount of available uv energy seemed inadequate, and partly because the estimated values of the recombination or attachment coefficients of any of the known atmospheric particles were too small to allow for the rapid disappearance of the echo. Cook and Hawkins (1960) have recently concluded that neither objection may be insuperable. According to them, the ionizing radiation from a meteor of magnitude -5 is of the order of 10^7 watts, and the spherical volume thus ionized can have a critical density radius of several hundred meters. Bialecke and Dougal (1958) have shown that molecular nitrogen ions have a recombination coefficient of 9×10^{-13} m^3/sec at meteoric heights. Although this value for N_2^+ is considerably larger than earlier work had indicated to be possible, it is nevertheless too small for the present purpose and therefore seems to rule out N_2^+ as the major constituent of the ionized ball. A recombination coefficient of the order of 2×10^{-11} m^3/sec is needed to account for the rapid disappearance of the echo, and Cook and Hawkins are of the opinion that the dissociative recombination coefficient of photo-ionized molecular oxygen may meet the requirements adequately. Other questions remain, though, such as a predicted decrease in diameter of the ionized ball as the meteor falls. Owing to the increasing air density the absorption of the uv light should occur within a smaller volume as the height decreases. It may be that this effect is counterbalanced by the increasing light output prior to the point of maximum light. Much more work must be done before a final conclusion can be reached about the validity of the uv light hypothesis.

The term "head echo," as used in this book, is intended to apply to the bright-meteor phenomenon we have just been discussing, where the head-echo amplitude does not vary much along the path. In the broadest sense, of course, every meteor is capable of producing a diffraction-type echo continuously as it moves along its path, though at points remote from t_0 this echo is usually below the level of detection. When D and r_0 are both very large, as is the case for very faint, fast meteors, the first few meters of trail behind the meteor head may be the only part of the trail from which we can hope to get an echo at all. These echoes are also of the moving-ball type, similar to the bright-meteor head echoes, but the mechanism of their production is clearly different. At the t_0 point their power levels may be 30 to 50 db below the maximum echo power which would be expected if the effects of D and r_0 were negligible. These attenuations may seem large, but they can be overcome by quite practical and not prohibitively expensive increases in transmitter power and antenna gain.

CHAPTER 9

Forward-scatter from Meteor Trails

One of the most intriguing scientific aspects of oblique scattering from meteor trails is that, by placing transmitter and receiver several hundred kilometers apart, one may observe considerably fainter and higher meteors than when the same equipment is concentrated at one spot on the earth's surface. True, more sophisticated methods are required to take full advantage of this very desirable raising of the underdense trail ceiling. The ellipsoidal geometry of forward-scatter introduces ambiguities in the measurement of some of the parameters of the meteor, which can be overcome only by deploying additional observing equipment over the countryside. Despite the complexities this challenge to the experimenter's ingenuity is not going unanswered. Methods of measuring spatial position, trail orientation, and meteor velocity are now being developed. If successful, they should greatly expand our present observational limits. Fortunately, these particular difficulties are no handicap in the practical application of forward-scatter to radio communications, although some other problems do come up. Engineered systems for point-to-point communication via meteor trails are now being put into commercial and military service in several countries. Some examples of these equipments will be examined later in this chapter.

We shall first develop the modifications and extensions of the backscatter theory which are needed to cover the forward-scatter situation. In the previous chapter we might have worked out a generalized theory, from which the backscatter and forward-scatter results could be deduced as special cases. The degree of appreciation of such a broad attack would probably vary greatly with the mathematical background of the reader. The particular plan we have elected to follow, in this as in the earlier chapters, has been hopefully designed to take him painlessly through some of the more prickly mathematical thickets without unduly obscuring his view of the forest of physical evidence.

9-1. Forward-scatter from the underdense trail. We will not need to rework the theory of Chap. 8 from first principles, as an examination of the forward-scatter geometry suggests that only three relatively simple

236

mechanical modifications are required to adapt the backscatter theory to the oblique-incidence case.

The first adjustment is to reinsert the $\sin^2 \gamma$ term in the pattern of the scattering cross section of the trail electron. In three dimensions the amplitude pattern of the electron reradiating as a Hertzian dipole is a circle rotated about a tangent—a tight toroid, or a holeless doughnut. There is no scattered field in either direction along the dipole axis, this axis being coincident with the incident electric vector. The expression for the power received from a single electron given in Eq. (8-1) will therefore read

$$\Delta P_R = \frac{P_T G_T G_R \sigma_e \sin^2 \gamma}{64\pi^3 R_1{}^2 R_2{}^2} \tag{9-1}$$

where R_1 is the range from the transmitter to the trail and R_2 the distance from the trail to the receiver. The transmitting and receiving antenna gains may not be identical and so are separated in Eq. (9-1).

The major lobe of the backscatter reradiation pattern of a meteor trail lies in the plane which contains the line of sight and which is also normal to the trail axis. This pattern will be a circle if the electric vector of the incident radiation is parallel to the trail axis, or it will be a figure of eight if the electric vector is perpendicular to the trail. The general condition for forward scattering is that the angle between the incident ray and the trail should equal the angle between the reflected ray and the trail. Reflected rays satisfying this condition will lie on a cone with the same axis as the trail. The dipole-pattern factor will attenuate the power level in certain directions along the cone, depending on the trail orientation, incident polarization, and the spatial geometry. The use of circularly polarized waves would smooth out this effect, though at the expense of an average power loss of 3 db over the power attainable with the optimum linear polarization.

It will be noted from Eq. (8-6) that the equivalent backscatter echoing area of an underdense trail is $\sigma_e q^2$ multiplied by $R_0 \lambda / 2$. The last quantity is the square of the length of half the first Fresnel zone. In our second modification to the backscatter theory we shall assume that the new equivalent echoing area will be $\sigma_e q^2 \sin^2 \gamma$ times the square of half the first Fresnel zone for forward-scatter. This half length f must be found in terms of wavelength and the geometrical parameters. The center of the first Fresnel zone (the t_0 point) will be at the point of tangency of the trail and an ellipsoid of revolution (i.e., a prolate spheroid) whose foci are at the transmitter and receiver. Figure 9-1 outlines the pertinent geometry. The transmitter T, receiver R, and the point of tangency are in one plane called the *plane of propagation*. The meteor trail lies in the tangent plane which is at right angles to the propagation plane. It is a property of the prolate spheroid that the bisector of the angle 2ϕ between R_1 and R_2 is normal to the tangent plane. The angle 2ϕ is termed the forward-scatter angle. Let the meteor trail assume any arbitrary orientation in the tangent plane, defined by β, the angle between the trail and the plane of propagation. Next, draw the paths R_1' and R_2' to one end of the first Fresnel zone, indicated by the segment f on the diagram. The angle ω between f and R_1 is the supplement of the angle between f and R_2, as can be seen by reflecting the rays R_2 and R_2' in the tangent plane. Note also that $\cos \omega = \sin \phi \cos \beta$.

In the triangle with sides R_1, R_1', f, we have

$$(R_1')^2 = R_1^2 + f^2 - 2R_1 f \cos \omega = (R_1 - f \cos \omega)^2 + f^2 \sin^2 \omega$$

Similarly, $(R_2')^2 = (R_2 + f \cos \omega)^2 + f^2 \sin^2 \omega$. Since $f^2 \sin^2 \omega$ is small by comparison with $(R_1 - f \cos \omega)^2$ or $(R_2 + f \cos \omega)^2$ we may approxi-

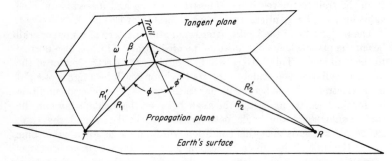

FIG. 9-1. The geometry of forward-scatter involved in the calculation of f, the length of one-half of the first Fresnel zone.

mate to the square roots as follows:

$$R_1' + R_2' = R_1 + R_2 + \frac{f^2 \sin^2 \omega}{2} \left(\frac{1}{R_1 - f \cos \omega} + \frac{1}{R_2 + f \cos \omega} \right)$$

Only at this stage are we able to neglect $f \cos \omega$ in comparison with either R_1 or R_2.

The condition for f to be one-half of the first Fresnel zone is

$$R_1' + R_2' = R_1 + R_2 + \frac{\lambda}{2}$$

It follows directly that

$$f = \left[\frac{\lambda R_1 R_2}{(R_1 + R_2)(1 - \sin^2 \phi \cos^2 \beta)} \right]^{\frac{1}{2}} \tag{9-2}$$

The final modification to the earlier theory arises when we are summing up the phase differences between the waves scattered from electrons in different parts of the trail, as in Sec. 8-5.   In place of the single datum plane of zero phase (Fig. 8-5) we now have two planes.   The datum plane normal to the incident ray is shown as MM' in Fig. 9-2 and the plane for the emergent ray as NN'.   The net phase angle (for the ray drawn) is

$$\frac{2\pi}{\lambda}(a + b) = \frac{2\pi}{\lambda} r \left[\sin\left(\frac{\pi}{2} - \phi - \theta\right) + \sin\left(\frac{\pi}{2} - \phi + \theta\right) \right]$$

$$= \frac{4\pi}{\lambda} r \cos\theta \cos\phi$$

The right-hand side is a maximum at $\theta = 0$ or π and is zero at $\theta = \pi/2$ or $3\pi/2$.   For comparison, the dashed line on Fig. 9-2 shows the length of the backscatter path, referred to the plane PP', for which the phase angle

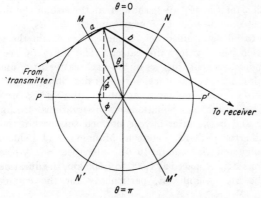

FIG. 9-2. The geometry for the calculation of the phase of the wave scattered from a trail electron.

is $(4\pi/\lambda)r \cos\theta$.   This shows that we need only to include the factor $\cos\phi$ to convert the backscatter analysis to the forward-scatter case.   In effect, λ has now become $\lambda \sec\phi$.   Incidentally, to simplify the diagram, Fig. 9-2 was drawn with the trail perpendicular to the plane of propagation, but the conclusion is general and applies to any trail orientation.

To sum up, the power delivered to the receiver after the meteor trail is formed is

$$P_R = \frac{P_T G_T G_R \lambda^3 \sigma_e}{64\pi^3} \frac{q^2 \sin^2\gamma}{(R_1 R_2)(R_1 + R_2)(1 - \sin^2\phi \cos^2\beta)}$$

$$= 5 \times 10^{-32} \frac{P_T G_T G_R \lambda^3 q^2 \sin^2\gamma}{(R_1 R_2)(R_1 + R_2)(1 - \sin^2\phi \cos^2\beta)} \quad \text{watts} \quad (9\text{-}3)$$

This reduces to Eq. (8-7) for the backscatter case, when $R_1 = R_2$, $\phi = 0°$, $\beta = 90°$, and $\gamma = 90°$.

Substitution of $\lambda \sec \phi$ for λ in Eq. (8-23) leads to

$$\frac{P_R(t)}{P_R(0)} = \epsilon^{-(32\pi^2 Dt/\lambda^2 \sec^2 \phi)} \epsilon^{-(8\pi^2 r_0^2/\lambda^2 \sec^2 \phi)} \qquad (9\text{-}4)$$

and the power attenuation of the echo (for $R_1 = R_2 = 150$ km) is

$$\text{Loss in db} \simeq 3.8 \times 10^5 \frac{D}{(\lambda \sec \phi)^{3/2} V} + 3.4 \times 10^2 \left(\frac{r_0}{\lambda \sec \phi}\right)^2 \qquad (9\text{-}5)$$

Equation (8-24) for the echo *decay time* becomes

$$T_{un} = \frac{\lambda^2 \sec^2 \phi}{16\pi^2 D} \qquad (9\text{-}6)$$

Some very interesting conclusions may be drawn from these relations. The expression for f in Eq. (9-2) shows that the size of the first (or any other) Fresnel zone depends on four parameters, R_1, R_2, ϕ, and β, all of which have to be determined before one can entertain the thought of measuring velocities by forward-scatter. The diffraction-echo fluctuations are indeed present, just as in the backscatter case, and it is not difficult to produce the analytical formulas describing them. Of more immediate importance is the fact that substituting $\lambda \sec \phi$ for λ increases the decay time by $\sec^2 \phi$. Simultaneous observations of echoes by forward-scatter and backscatter have confirmed this within the limits of experimental error (Villard, Peterson, Manning, and Eshleman, 1953, 1956; McKinley and McNamara, 1956). Since $\sec^2 \phi$ may be as great as 25 or more for stations spaced at 1,000 to 1,500 km, the duration enhancement can be very significant, particularly for the communications application.

When $\beta = 90°$ the forward-scatter echo power from a given meteor will at least be equal to that obtained from a backscatter radar at a range $R = [(R_1 R_2)(R_1 + R_2)/2]^{1/3}$. When $\beta = 0°$ the lengths of the Fresnel zones increase as $\sec \phi$, with a corresponding increase in echo power of $\sec^2 \phi$. This power increase tends to be counteracted by the attenuation due to the increase in the ranges, which goes hand in hand with the increase in ϕ.

The meteor scientist will appreciate the very significant increase in the height of the underdense trail ceiling which is implied by Eq. (9-5). To see what this means quantitatively let us choose $\sec \phi = 3$ as a very conservative estimate of the average value of $\sec \phi$ for typical forward-scatter systems. If we go back to Fig. 8-7 and multiply the wavelength scale by three, we see that the ceiling is raised by about 7 km. According to Fig. 8-8, the 40-db cutoff for $\lambda = 10$ m and $V = 75$ km/sec will be shifted from $q \simeq 10^{14}$ to $q \simeq 3 \times 10^{12}$. The theoretical limit of detectability for meteors of a given velocity is therefore increased by about four magnitudes. The system sensitivity must also be sufficient to detect the smaller meteors, of course, but the 40-db increase required to extend the sensitivity of our typical 10-m radar (on which the curves of Fig. 8-11 are based) from the tenth to the fifteenth magnitude is well within practical engineering capabilities. In fact, the Stanford group (Gallagher, 1958) and the National Bureau of Standards (Bowles, 1958) have already gone beyond this.

The meteor astronomer still awaits the development of suitable forward-scatter instrumentation for the determination of individual radiants and velocities of these very faint meteors. In the meantime he can carry out statistical studies of shower and nonshower rates, though the interpretation of these observations in terms of hypothetical distributions of meteors over the celestial sphere is not made easy by the unavoidable ambiguities of the simple techniques (Hines, 1955, 1958; Forsyth, Hines, and Vogan, 1955; Bain, 1960). There are so many unknown parameters that the data can be adjusted to fit a wide variety of possible distributions—which would amuse the shades of Schiaparelli and von Niessl! The meteor-communications engineer can hardly be expected to delay his work until a comprehensive description of the orbital distributions of faint meteors becomes available, however useful this would be in predicting the performance of his links. (It may even turn out that the very faint meteor distributions do not repeat predictably.) For him the proof of the pudding lies not in the mystery of its ingredients but in the nourishment it imparts. He can set up his radio circuits and accumulate quite easily all the propagational information that is both necessary and sufficient for the development of his systems.

9-2. Forward-scatter from the overdense trail. A satisfactory theory of the echoing properties of the overdense trail has not been worked out for the general forward-scatter case, although the formulas of the back-scatter model—itself not very well determined in several respects—have been converted to the oblique-incidence situation through a judicious admixture of analogy, analysis, and intuition (Hines and Forsyth, 1957; Forsyth, 1958). Manning (1959a) has used geometrical ray-tracing theory to investigate in a semiquantitative manner the effects of refraction outside the critical density radius. Attempts by Keitel (1955) to obtain exact solutions through the application of the wave theory of physical optics were limited to a few special cases. Kaiser and Closs (1952) and Herlofson (1951) laid some of the groundwork for this difficult task, and their approximate solutions agreed reasonably well with the precise calculations of Keitel's electronic computer. Eshleman's early work in this field has been used freely by a number of investigators, though he did not get around to publishing much of it in referable form until six years later (Eshleman, 1955).

The heuristic conversion of the backscatter equations to the forward-scatter case is essentially accomplished through the f and $\lambda \sec \phi$ factors of the previous section. The maximum equivalent echoing area of the critical-radius cylinder will now be $2f^2(qr_e/\epsilon)^{1/2}$ by analogy with the development in Sec. 8-10. Thus we may write

$$P_R = \frac{P_T G_T G_R \lambda^3 r_e^{1/2}}{32\pi^3 \epsilon^{1/2}} \frac{q^{1/2} \sin^2 \gamma}{(R_1 R_2)(R_1 + R_2)(1 - \sin^2 \phi \cos^2 \beta)}$$
$$= 3.2 \times 10^{-11} \frac{P_T G_T G_R \lambda^3 \sin^2 \gamma}{(R_1 R_2)(R_1 + R_2)(1 - \sin^2 \phi \cos^2 \beta)} q^{1/2} \quad (9\text{-}7)$$

In practice, for the overdense trail it is found that the signal power falls off less rapidly than $\sin^2 \gamma$ as γ departs from 90°. This is partly because of the mechanics of reflection at the virtually metallic surface of the critical-radius cylinder, and partly because the scattered polarization tends to become random as the trail ages and breaks up into blobs or glints.

When λ is replaced by $\lambda \sec \phi$, we obtain the forward-scatter echo duration

$$T_{ov} \simeq \frac{qr_e \lambda^2 \sec^2 \phi}{4\pi^2 D} = 7 \times 10^{-17} \frac{q\lambda^2 \sec^2 \phi}{D} \quad \text{sec} \quad (9\text{-}8)$$

We may carry over the philosophy, expressed in Sec. 8-10, that an acceptable definition of the transitional line density is given by that value of q which equates the underdense and overdense echo powers. From Eqs. (9-3) and (9-7) we obtain $q_{tr} = 0.75 \times 10^{14}$ electrons/m, which is identical to the backscatter case (Hines and Forsyth, 1957).

Manning (1959a) has pointed out that these simple developments have not included the refractive effects of the electrons outside the critical radius. He has tackled this recalcitrant problem with the aid of a ray-tracing technique which was an extension of his earlier treatment of the backscatter trail, mentioned in Sec. 8-10. Manning finds marked deviations from the elementary forward-scattering cone of the underdense trail. After a few seconds, though, the overdense trail can no longer be considered an ideal cylinder. The blob-glint theory shows that the scattering pattern must broaden rapidly. The observational evidence (see Fig. 9-3) demonstrates that echoes with durations of 20 sec or longer become substantially omnidirectional.

An important feature of Manning's analysis is the deduction that the forward echo duration from even the ideal simple model should no longer bear the constant ratio $\sec^2 \phi$ to the backscatter duration which Eq. (9-8) implies it should hold. Depending on the orientation of the trail Manning finds that a $\sec^m \phi$ law may be adopted, with $m \simeq 0.3$ for $\beta = 90°$, up to a maximum of $m = 2$ for $\beta = 0°$. The conclusions are assumed to apply from the moment of formation of the trail.

An experimental investigation of the dependence of the exponent m in $\sec^m \phi$ was undertaken by means of simultaneous backscatter and forward-scatter observations (McKinley and McNamara, 1956). Pulses of 300-kw peak power were transmitted on 33 Mc/sec at Ottawa, and

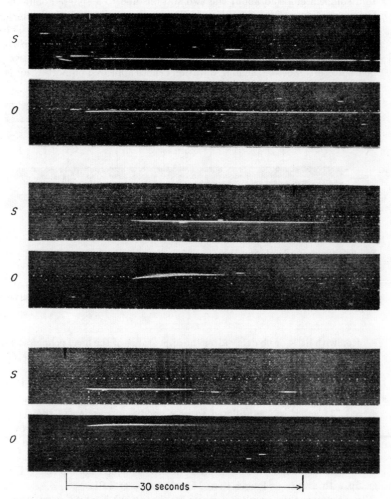

FIG. 9-3. Simultaneous records of meteor echoes obtained by backscatter at Ottawa (O), and by forward-scatter at Scarboro (S), 338 km distant from Ottawa.

meteoric echoes were recorded simultaneously on identical receiving equipments at Ottawa and at Scarboro (near Toronto), 338 km distant. Figure 9-3 shows some of the two-station records. Relatively few underdense trail echoes were simultaneously observed in comparison with the total number of such echoes seen at either station, which is a natural consequence of the condition that the underdense trail should be tangent both to a confocal ellipsoid about the two stations and to a sphere about the Ottawa station. A large fraction of the overdense echoes showed coincidences, the percentage increasing with the durations of the echoes. The Stanford group has confirmed this observation in an independent experiment (Villard, Peterson, Manning, and Eshleman, 1956). In the Ottawa-Scarboro test, most of the long-duration echoes appeared on both records

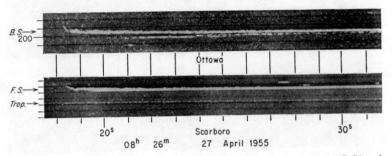

FIG. 9-4. A meteor echo observed simultaneously at Ottawa by backscatter (B.S.) and at Scarboro by forward-scatter (F.S.). The echo marked *Trop.* is the direct tropospheric wave between the Ottawa transmitter and the Scarboro receiver. The measured delay between the meteor echo and the direct wave, together with the Ottawa radar range, fixes the position of the meteor on the curve of intersection of an ellipsoid and a sphere.

—often with little or no delay after the appearance of the head echo associated with the passage of the meteor (see Fig. 9-4). From the geometry it was possible to compute sec ϕ with reasonable accuracy for every meteor. The exponent m was found from the ratio of the forward-scatter and backscatter duration. The underdense-echo class yielded the value $m = 1.73$, which was considered to be a good confirmation of the theoretical value $m = 2$, in view of the probable contamination of this group by an appreciable number of slightly overdense echoes. A value of $m = 1.13$ was obtained for the overdense-echo group as a whole, which comprised all echoes with backscatter duration in excess of 3.5 sec. The group with durations longer than 15 sec gave $m = 1.01$.

In discussing these results we may note that the blob-glint theory, when applied to overdense meteor echoes, does not necessarily demand that m

should be less than 2 at the beginning of the echo, but it does require m to approach unity as the trail ages (Eshleman, 1955). The theory proposed here by Manning (1959a) stresses that the value of m is mainly a function of the trail orientation β, while this is not a predominant factor in the blob-glint hypothesis. The Ottawa-Scarboro experiment was not designed to measure β for every meteor. If this were done, say, by means of a backscatter radar at the mid-point of the path, it should be possible to determine if there is a significant variation of m with β (McNamara and McKinley, 1959). An examination of the individual echo records of the original experiment does suggest that the β parameter may be important in some and not in others. Until further work is done we cannot decide the question. In the meantime, whatever may be the reasons, we do have the indisputable observational evidence that the duration enhancement of forward-scatter echoes from overdense trails is less than the factor $\sec^2 \phi$ which would be predicted from the elementary model.

9-3. Principles of intermittent communication via meteor trails. For purposes of this discussion we shall divide the meteor population into three loosely defined groups. The first comprises the myriad of very faint meteors, of tenth to fifteenth magnitude and perhaps fainter, that are detectable near the noise level of a moderately powerful forward-scatter system. These echoes, which overlap in time to form practically a continuum, play a very important role in high-power ionospheric-scatter communication. This function will be examined in more detail in Sec. 9-7. The individual echoes in this group are too weak to support the intermittent type of low-power communication we are about to consider now. At the other extreme are the meteors of fifth magnitude and brighter which create overdense trails. These meteors are relatively few in number—typical rates may run from 10 to 100 hr^{-1}—but their long durations tend to counterbalance their low rates. The effect of the long-duration echoes on meteor communication is usually beneficial though sometimes not. It is the intermediate group of meteors, beginning around the tenth magnitude and extending somewhat into the visual meteor range, which plays the major role in low-power meteor systems.

As was pointed out earlier, in order to support reflection of a signal between points A and B, an underdense trail should be tangent to one of a family of prolate spheroids having A and B as foci. The hourly rates of suitably oriented trails are dependent on the geographical disposition of A and B, on the system sensitivity, and on the distribution of meteor radiants and their activity. The useful integrated duration time of such trails is usually a small fraction of the total time: typical values of this fraction, or duty cycle, run from 0.01 to 0.1. Means must therefore be devised first to determine when suitable trails are available and second to transmit intelligence only during the usable durations of those trails.

The first of these aims is achieved by the closed-loop technique. A transmitter T_A and a receiver R_A are located at point A. Similar apparatus, T_B and R_B, are placed at point B. T_A and R_B operate on one frequency, and T_B and R_A are tuned to another frequency which differs enough from the first to permit simultaneous transmission and reception at each end of the link. So far, this arrangement does not differ from the usual point-to-point system where a direct line-of-sight path or a conventional ionospheric path is available. To find out when a suitable trail comes into existence, T_A continuously transmits an unmodulated carrier (for identification the carrier may be modulated by a tone or a code group). Reception of this carrier by R_B indicates that a suitable path has been established. The output of R_B turns on T_B and the wave from T_B travels to point A via the same meteor trail. The loop is now closed; both stations have learned that a suitable path exists, and either or both may proceed to send messages until the loop is broken by fading of the signal. The second object, to transmit intelligence only while a path exists, may be accomplished by storing the information temporarily, on magnetic tape, for example. When the loop is closed, the tape is started and run at high speed while the signal strength is above a predetermined level. The tape is then shut off to await the next closing of the loop. The transmission of a complete message may require many meteor trails occurring at random intervals.

An aptly descriptive name for the closed-loop type of low-power intermittent meteor communication was proposed by scientists of the Defence Research Board, at Ottawa, who demonstrated the first system in June, 1953 (Forsyth, Vogan, Hansen, and Hines, 1957). They called it JANET, after Janus, the Roman god of the doorway who looked both ways at once. The Stanford group, whose earlier work in forward-scatter-meteor propagation (one-way) was given full credit for inspiring the Ottawa experiments, have leaned toward the term "meteor-burst" system. The closed-loop and low-power features are not implicit in this description—open-loop ionospheric-scatter systems also depend to a great extent on the meteor bursts of countless small meteors. However, as a generic term "meteor burst" has the virtues of being expressible in lower-case letters and of being fairly readily understood by nonspecialists. Incidentally, in this connection the word "burst" applies to the sudden increase in the diffraction signal as the meteor crosses t_0 and not to any physical bursting of the meteor along its path. The visual and photographic observers have always used "burst" in the latter sense, meaning a sudden flare due to disintegration of the meteor. It should be unnecessary to add that the "burst" reflection is part and parcel of the whole diffraction echo and not a separate entity as some of the literature seems to suggest.

Naturally, it would be highly desirable to be able to predict the system performance for any time of day or year and for any physical disposition of the stations. We might start by attempting to derive a forward-scatter probability function similar to the $P(Z)$ function discussed in Sec. 5-3. In backscatter geometry, meteors from a radiant at a zenith angle Z will be detected at an elevation angle Z, on a bearing 180° from the azimuth of the radiant. A plan position of density distribution of numbers of backscatter echoes, due to a uniform radiant distribution, may therefore be obtained directly from Fig. 5-6 by projecting the $P(Z)$ values (in discrete steps for convenience in plotting) on a horizontal plane 100 km above the station (see Fig. 9-5a). A similar plot, with some radial displacement, will be obtained for the density of echo durations. A nonuniform radiant distribution will alter this picture. A concentration of radiants in the south, for example, will produce a concentration of meteor echoes in the north, as in Fig. 9-5b, but because of the spherical symmetry (omnidirectional antenna) the observed radar rates will still depend only on the zenith angles of the radiants. This statement will no longer be true if we separate transmitter and receiver, even if each station continues to use an omnidirectional antenna.

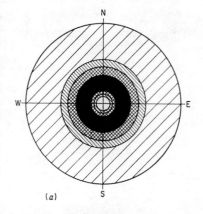

(a)

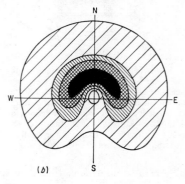

(b)

FIG. 9-5. (a) The relative number density of backscatter echoes, projected on a horizontal plane at a height of 100 km above the station; (b) the effect of a concentration of radiants south of the station's zenith.

Figure 9-6a is a similar qualitative representation of the number density of echoes detectable by forward-scatter, again assuming a uniform radiant distribution (Villard, Eshleman, Manning, and Peterson, 1955). The concentration near the stations is partly because the range

attenuation [Eq. (9-7)] is less for these meteors than for trails near the
mid-point.   The orientation of the trail is also a factor which is evident
particularly in the low-density region about the line between the two
stations—the density per unit area of nearly horizontal trails is very low.

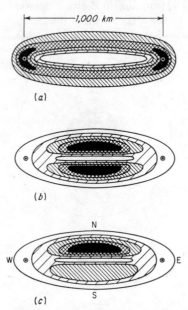

(a)

(b)

(c)

FIG. 9-6. (a) The relative number density
of forward-scatter echoes, projected on a
horizontal plane at a height of 100 km
above the stations; (b) the relative duration density of forward-scatter echoes for
a uniform radiant distribution; (c) the
relative duration density for a radiant
distribution concentrated in the south.

We may now take each meteor
represented in Fig. 9-6a and multiply its backscatter echo duration
by $\sec^2 \phi$ to obtain the plot of echo-
duration density shown in Fig. 9-6b.
The influence of the $\sec^2 \phi$ factor
is very marked; the maximum-
density areas have shifted from near
the stations to two "hot spots"
located halfway between the stations, on either side of the mid-point.
Obviously, to take full advantage
of this one should use antennas of
moderately high directivity and
aim them at one or the other of the
hot spots (or at both by means
of split-beam antennas) rather
than focus them on the mid-point
where there are few suitably oriented meteors.

The effect of a concentration of
radiants in the south is indicated
in Fig. 9-6c. This situation is
characteristic of an east-west path
in the Northern Hemisphere
around 0600 local time. For a
north-south path, at the same time
of day, the duration-density areas
would be symmetrically disposed
about the center line, though displaced toward the northern station.
For optimum efficiency in a practical system it would therefore be advis-
able to use steerable antennas to take advantage of the shifting hot spots
(Eshleman and Mlodnosky, 1957).

It is clear that we are not likely to be able to specify a simple probability
function for the general forward-scatter situation. Given the specific
geographical locations of the stations, the system parameters, and the
radiant distribution, one can compute the performance. Until the
radiant distribution of meteors as faint as the tenth magnitude becomes
known for any time of the day or year, the pragmatic approach seems

best. That is, several experimental links are set up, with various spacings and orientations, and the observational data accumulated over a year or more (Forsyth and Vogan, 1955; Montgomery and Sugar, 1957; Meeks and James, 1957; Vincent, Wolfram, Sifford, Jaye, and Peterson, 1957b). From such data a reasonably good estimate can be made of the performance to be expected in a given practical situation. It is not a simple process to deduce the radiant distribution from the observed rates, nor does it usually lead to unambiguous results acceptable to the meteor astronomer.

9-4. Information capacity of forward-scatter communication systems.
There are a number of factors to be considered in connection with the forward-scatter technique which have not been discussed in the earlier chapters because their effects on backscatter observations have not been very important. The theoretical and observational relations between integrated echo power, integrated echo duration, and radio wavelength are of great practical interest in forward-scatter. Absorption in the ionosphere and other environmental phenomena which are scarcely noticeable in backscatter work can influence forward-scatter propagation most markedly. In designing practical communication systems, the engineer's ingenuity must be brought to bear to devise suitable compromises between bandwidth, type of modulation, trigger level, and a variety of other parameters in order to cope with the unpredictable and highly variable characteristics of the meteor signal.

It has been shown that the hourly rate of backscatter echoes is proportional to the square root of the power sensitivity of the system (McKinley, 1951c). If we select an arbitrary minimum value of q as a reference level, the number of trails per hour with density q and higher is therefore

$$N \sim \frac{P_T{}^{\frac{1}{2}}G\lambda^{\frac{3}{2}}}{P_R{}^{\frac{1}{2}}} \tag{9-9}$$

The integrated duration of these echoes is $\Sigma N_i T_i$, where N_i is the number of echoes with duration T_i. In practice, the integrated backscatter duration can be evaluated directly from the radar range-time records, since the range resolution permits the analyst to make due allowance for overlapping of echoes in time whenever such overlapping becomes significant. We now define the *duty cycle F* as the fraction of the total observing time during which at least one echo is visible above an arbitrary power level; that is, $F = (\Sigma N_i T_i)/\mathbf{T}$ where $\mathbf{T}$ is the observing period. Where overlapping of echoes is appreciable and has not been allowed for in the reduction process, the true duty cycle may be taken to be approximately equal to $1 - \exp(-F)$. The uncorrected F values can exceed unity, but the true value can never quite reach unity.

Let us vary the wavelength while keeping the other parameters constant in Eq. (9-9). If we assume $T \sim \lambda^2$, we have

$$F \sim N\lambda^2 \sim \lambda^{7/2} \qquad (9\text{-}10)$$

From backscatter experiments the exponent of λ was shown to lie between 3.36 and 3.64 (McKinley, 1954b), which is reasonable confirmation of the theoretical value in Eq. (9-10).

If we allow one or more of the other system parameters to vary also, we may write

$$F \sim \frac{P_T{}^{1/2}G}{P_R{}^{1/2}} \lambda^{7/2} \qquad (9\text{-}11)$$

This means that the system sensitivity should vary inversely as λ^7 if we wish to keep the duty cycle constant. If P_T is a variable, it follows that $P_T \sim \lambda^{-7}$. If P_R is taken as the variable it is implied that the fraction of the total time during which echoes are present above a given power level should be directly proportional to λ^7 (Villard, Eshleman, Manning, and Peterson, 1955).

Observations have shown that the exponent of P_T/P_R in Eq. (9-11) should be somewhat greater than 0.5. For convenience, let us tentatively label this exponent k. Backscatter data suggest as a minimum value $k = 0.56$ (McKinley, 1954b), whence $P_R \sim \lambda^{3.5/0.56} = \lambda^{6.3}$. Forward-scatter experiments have yielded still higher values, ranging from $k = 0.57$ to 0.96 (Forsyth and Vogan, 1955; Campbell and Hines, 1957). From these data the power dependence is found to vary between $\lambda^{6.2}$ and $\lambda^{3.6}$. The decrease in the exponent of λ may be attributed to the influence of overdense trails. This has been borne out further by recent work done by J. C. Blair of the National Bureau of Standards. He found that λ^5 represented the performance of a high-power scatter system during periods when meteor activity was high, compared to λ^8 when few strong meteor signals were present. In theory, if we adopt $T \sim \lambda$ for very-long-duration echoes (Sec. 8-10), we have $F \sim \lambda^{5/2}$, whence $P_R \sim \lambda^5$.

In a practical circuit one attempts to operate at a threshold signal level which bears a fixed ratio to the ambient noise level. This noise level is usually determined by cosmic noise, which has been found to vary about as $\lambda^{2.3}$ (Sec. 2-8). If the receiver bandwidth is B, the threshold power level will then be proportional to $B\lambda^{2.3}$, which quantity replaces P_R in Eqs. (9-9) and (9-11). Let us also write the empirical k in place of the exponent of P_T and P_R in these equations. The duty cycle under these conditions becomes

$$F \sim \left(\frac{P_T G^2}{B\lambda^{2.3}}\right)^k \lambda^{3.5} \qquad (9\text{-}12)$$

The average rate W at which information is transferred is proportional to the duty cycle multiplied by the bandwidth. Thus,

$$W \sim FB \sim P_T^k G^{2k} B^{(1-k)} \lambda^{(3.5-2.3k)} \qquad (9\text{-}13)$$

Since $k < 1$, it follows that the information capacity of the system is increased by making B large, despite the decrease in duty cycle which necessarily occurs at the same time. A practical restraint on increasing the bandwidth indefinitely is determined by the length of time one is willing to wait between transmissions. Forsyth has suggested that one might vary the bandwidth and the signaling rate in proportion to the power received from each individual trail to make the most efficient use of the meteoric medium.

The diffraction-echo fluctuations due to the moving meteor do not cause any trouble because they have usually died out by the time the loop is closed and signaling started. Theoretically, all systems of modulation should be equally effective in meteor communications, though the current state of the engineering art may give one method a temporary ascendancy

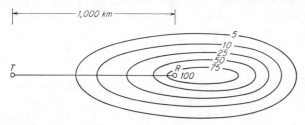

FIG. 9-7. Relative levels of information which might be intercepted by an independent receiver in the vicinity of the meteor scatter system.

over another. Frequency or phase modulation might be thought the most suitable in view of the rapid amplitude variation of the meteor signals. However, amplitude modulation has been used very successfully, either double-side band (Davis, Gladys, Lang, Luke, and Taylor, 1957) or single-side band (Vincent, Wolfram, Sifford, Jaye, and Peterson, 1957a). The bandwidths for teletype transmission extend up to 3 kc with these systems, and the signaling rates run up to 2,700 wpm or more. Transmitter output powers are usually of the order of 1 kw and antenna gains perhaps 10 db. The maximum distance between stations is limited to about 2,200 km, both by the earth's curvature and by the amount of antenna gain that is feasible at low elevations (Vincent, Wolfram, Sifford, Jaye, and Peterson, 1957b).

A certain amount of privacy is obtained in meteor communications by virtue of the directional characteristics of the reflections from underdense trails. Contours are shown in Fig. 9-7 of the relative level of information which could be intercepted by an unauthorized receiver located in the vicinity of one of the stations (Forsyth, Vogan, Hansen, and Hines, 1957). Some protection from jamming transmitters or other interfering sources is also afforded. The presence of the overdense trails tends to spoil this privacy, because their scattering patterns are very broad. While few in number, compared to the underdense trails, their contribution to the integrated echo duration can be as much or more than that of the underdense trails. If the system loop is deliberately opened one second, say, after a meteor signal has closed it, regardless of the strength or the eventual duration of that signal, one may reduce this omnidirectional scatter at the expense of a substantially decreased duty cycle.

9-5. Environmental effects. During the period 1952 to 1956, when the forward-scatter systems were first being tested, it was found that the onset of an SID (sudden ionospheric disturbance) had little or no effect on the meteoric signal. The SID is a daytime absorption phenomenon caused by a sudden increase of ionization in the upper atmosphere, which in turn is due to abnormal ultraviolet radiation from a solar flare. Worldwide h-f communications are sometimes interrupted for periods of a few minutes to a few hours when an SID occurs. The meteor-scatter links operate on frequencies in the vhf band well above the maximum usable frequencies for ordinary h-f propagation and are much less vulnerable to SID effects.

Besides its other attractive features, the comparative immunity of the JANET-type system to ordinary SIDs greatly intrigued the potential military and commercial users, particularly for use in high latitudes where conventional h-f circuits are more susceptible to trouble. However, it happened that all of the tests in this developmental period had been carried out south of the auroral zone. Furthermore, we were in the trough of the sunspot cycle at the time, and auroral activity was low. Some of the rosy optimism about the Far North application was rather rudely dampened when, in 1958, the peak of the sunspot cycle brought greatly enhanced auroral activity and severe absorptive effects.

In early July, 1958, a JANET 40-Mc/sec circuit was set up between Edmonton, Alberta, and Yellowknife, in the Northwest Territories, specifically to check out the performance in the auroral zone (Crysdale, 1960). Three days after it went into operation an intense polar-cap blackout on July 7 rendered it unusable for several hours. A polar-cap blackout, so called because its effects on radio communication are greatest from the auroral zones to the poles, is caused by a really gigantic flare on the sun—a 3+ flare in the solar astronomer's terminology. As if just to emphasize the point, three more 3+ flares occurred during August, 1958. In each case the ensuing hours were periods of complete radio silence in the auroral and polar regions, not only for the JANET system but also for high-power ionospheric-scatter equipments and conventional h-f stations.

This was a pretty rugged environmental test to be imposed on the new system in the first few days of its northern trials, particularly as it is estimated that not more than seven or eight 3+ flares occurred in all of 1958, a year of most intense solar activity!

The initial reaction of disappointment was followed by the realization that this early encounter with the worst conditions that are ever likely to occur may have avoided a good deal of trouble later. The prospective customers, who wanted to use the system in the north, naturally adopted a wait-and-see attitude, while the designers hastened back to their drawing boards.

The polar-cap blackout can be overcome by a shift to higher frequencies. To see this, let us look briefly at the nature of the polar-blackout absorption. One of the best instruments for evaluating the ionospheric absorption of vhf waves is the riometer. This is nothing more than a sensitive receiver, operating on a fixed frequency f_A (30 Mc/sec is a commonly used frequency), which records cosmic-noise signals from a broad cone overhead. During the most severe polar blackout the attenuation of cosmic noise on its one-way, nearly vertical path through the ionosphere may exceed 10 db, though it very rarely reaches 15 db. We assume that the major part of this attenuation occurs below the meteoric region (some recent evidence suggests that it may be as low as 50 km at times). We may then calculate the absorption loss incurred along any oblique path passing twice through this region, from the formula

$$\text{Loss in db} \simeq 2A_V \left(\frac{f_A}{f}\right)^2 \sec \phi \tag{9-14}$$

where A_V is the riometer value of the vertical absorption in decibels and f is the frequency used on the oblique path. Equation (9-14) shows that when A_V reaches 10 db on 30 Mc/sec, as it can easily do after a 3+ flare, the absorption attenuation on a 40-Mc/sec circuit between two stations 1,000 km apart (sec $\phi \simeq 4.5$) will amount to 50 db. Small wonder that the 40-Mc/sec link was put out of operation! On the other hand, a similar circuit working on 100 Mc/sec should suffer only 8 db loss during the same blackout conditions (Crysdale, 1960). Tests are now in progress on both 40 Mc/sec and 100 Mc/sec between Goose Bay, Newfoundland, and Ottawa, to find out if this prediction will be verified experimentally. The duty cycle falls off rapidly with increasing frequency, and it remains to be seen if practical low-power systems can be built to work at frequencies of 100 Mc/sec and higher. Recent high-power experiments on 200 Mc/sec over a 1,300-km path have shown the possibilities to be encouraging (Heritage, Weisbrod, and Fay, 1960). The individual echo durations were naturally quite short, but the duty cycle was as high as 20 per cent at times.

A certain amount of absorption may also accompany severe auroral activity, and though it can be almost as strong as the polar-cap-blackout absorption, it is not nearly as sustained. Considerably more important than the absorption effects are the multipath signals which are scattered from the ionized regions associated with the aurora. The extremely rapid power fluctuations caused by this nonmeteoric type of propagation will introduce serious message errors in a system designed to suit meteor signals only. Increasing the frequency does not help because the frequency dependence is roughly the same for both—after all, auroral targets are analogous to meteors in that they are presumed to consist of lines of ionization created by high-speed particles ejected by the sun. Since we cannot easily ignore the contribution from the auroral mode of propagation, it behooves us to devise ways and means of utilizing it to advantage in meteor-scatter systems. Some steps toward this end are being taken: one of the most promising is the incorporation of sophisticated error-correcting techniques in the data-handling part of the system. As the duty cycle generally is greater during times when auroral signals are present, it seems likely that satisfactory information rates may still be obtained, even though a fair fraction of the time may be occupied by the redundancy involved in reading back and correcting errors.

There are several other modes of propagation which can occasionally intrude adversely. One of them appears to be backscatter from the ground at great distances, received via the ionosphere. For example, a ray from the transmitter may pass through the meteoric region and be refracted by a higher ionospheric layer (the F region) to the ground. The ground-reflected signal may follow another path via the F region to the receiver. The delays between the meteor signal and the ground-scatter signal can amount to 20 or 30 msec, and this unwanted signal can create errors in the transmissions. Error-correcting techniques may be of some help. A move to higher frequencies would also reduce the ground scatter. The relatively large delays suggest that a slow FM technique might be fairly effective against this type of interference. For example, if the transmitter frequency were varied in a saw-tooth fashion (or in discrete steps) where the period of the saw-tooth waveform was just longer than the delay of the ground scatter, the receiver (which would be tracking the transmitter frequency) could reject the off-frequency ground echoes.

From this brief discussion the reader will no doubt conclude that nature in her worst moods can be very devastating in this as in other fields. The applied scientist and the design engineer must work unceasingly to circumvent her, or if they cannot ward off the slings and arrows of outrageous fortune, they must seize them and turn them to their own advantage. The inevitable result seems to be that the practical embodiment of a beautifully simple original concept soon becomes hedged in by a fearsome array of complex gadgetry. In this respect, though, the meteor-scatter system is no worse, if no better, off than any other modern mode of communication, and the evolutionary process often does much to advance man's knowledge in rather unexpected areas. Quite possibly the inventors and users of fire and smoke signals were forced into operational research on the frequency of incidence of fog and rain, thereby establishing the science of meteorology.

Even in high latitudes, though, these abnormal environmental effects are either infrequent or can be overcome. They are much less troublesome over the equatorial and temperate zones of the earth's surface. Meteor-scatter systems are now in production and are entering service in several countries because they offer features which complement rather than supplant the characteristics of other types of radio communications. Certain circumstances even favor meteor-scatter for air-to-ground communications, despite the intermittent nature of the contact and the complex ancillary equipment which must be carried.

9-6. Meteor-scatter equipments. Fully engineered meteor-scatter equipments have been produced by industrial firms both in Canada and the United States. The following brief description of some features of these systems is intended to cover only a few high lights for the information of the reader who may not be versed in communication techniques. The expert will find in the referenced papers much more detail than we can provide in this book—the highly specialized terminology of communications engineering would alone take several pages to explain to the uninitiated.

The JANET equipment, of which a number have been supplied to government agencies in Canada, England, Holland, and the United States, is a typical representative of the closed-loop systems (Davis, Gladys, Lang, Luke, and Taylor, 1957). It is designed to accept and discharge information continuously at the standard teletype rate of 60 wpm. Since the average duty cycle is about 5 per cent, transmission over the radio links must take place at twenty times this rate, or roughly 1,200 to 1,300 wpm, to maintain the steady flow. To do this, temporary storage must be provided for the incoming and outgoing information. The perforated paper tape accumulated in the input store is "read" electronically and converted to a suitable code for radio transmission. At the receiving end the snatches of coded messages are applied to high-speed magnetic tape. The tape is then read continuously, at a lower speed, into a teleprinter which produces typed text.

In the quiet periods when no meteor path is available, each JANET transmitter emits an unmodulated carrier on different frequencies, f_1 and f_2, spaced about 1 to 2 Mc/sec apart in the band 40 to 50 Mc/sec. Figure 9-8 is a block diagram of one terminal of the JANET system; the other

terminal is identical except that frequencies f_1 and f_2 are reversed.   The
incoming carrier level in each receiver is compared with the ambient noise
level in sidebands outside those required for intelligence.   When the
carrier levels rise to a predetermined value, the master gate controls are
actuated at each end.   These open both the input gates and the receiver
gates to permit synchronizing signals from one station to pass to the other.
After synchronization has been achieved the output gates are opened, and
the transmission of messages begins in either or both directions.   Transmission is stopped when the carrier level drops below threshold, the output store is filled, or a "stop-code" signal is received.

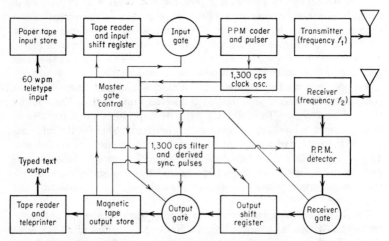

FIG. 9-8. Simplified block diagram of one terminal of a JANET system.   Heavy lines
show the flow of information; light lines indicate the control paths.

During a transmission, the teletype paper tape is removed from the
input store by means of a fast-acting stop-and-start drive mechanism.
The standard 5-digit teletype code is read into the input shift register,
passed through the open input gate, and converted into a two-position
PPM code (pulse position modulation).   This PPM is applied to the
carrier as amplitude-modulated pulses, which have a cosine-squared waveform to minimize unwanted higher sidebands.   The 1,300-cps clock
oscillator superposes a synchronizing tone on the PPM.   At the receiver,
this 1,300-cps tone is filtered out and subdivided to provide the necessary
timing and synchronizing pulses.

The output of the PPM detector goes through the receiver gate into the
output shift register.   When the system is synchronized and the output
gate is opened, the shift-register output is applied to the magnetic tape

on five parallel tracks.   In effect, the PPM code has been converted back to teletype code at this stage.   The accumulated tape is drawn continuously from the output store, put through a special tape reader, and finally printed out by a conventional teleprinter.

The five racks which house the data-handling portion of one terminal of the JANET 204-B system are shown in Fig. 9-9.   The detail of the magnetic-tape rate-changing equipment appears on Fig. 9-10.   This unit is the heart of the output store; it records the incoming information intermittently at high speed and reads it out continuously at low speed.   Figure 9-11 is a view of the antennas.

FIG. 9-9. Data-handling equipment of JANET 204-B system.   (*Courtesy of G. W. L. Davis, Ferranti-Packard Electric, Ltd., Toronto.*)

In broad outline, the experimental equipment built by the National Bureau of Standards (Carpenter and Ochs, 1957) was similar to the JANET apparatus.   It provided duplex teletype channels with 60 wpm input and output, and the high-speed part of the system operated at 2,400 wpm or more.

The meteor-scatter system designed by the Stanford Research Institute was also similar in operating principle to JANET, though there were many differences in detail (Vincent, Wolfram, Sifford, Jaye, and Peterson, 1957a).   For example, over the radio link the intelligence was transmitted in a binary code by switching back and forth from one to the other of two closely spaced carrier frequencies.   For convenience, a separate radio link was used for control purposes in the early experimental setup. Two kinds of output storage were available, the high- and low-speed-magnetic-tape method, and a magnetic-core storage wherein the informa-

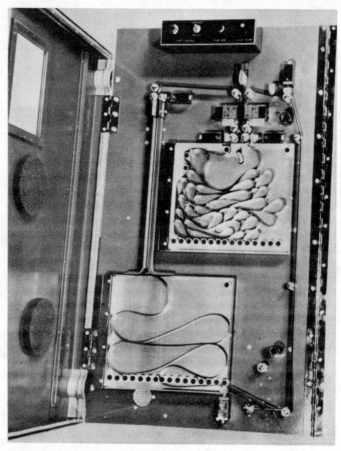

FIG. 9-10. Magnetic-tape rate-changing equipment.   (*Courtesy of G. W. L. Davis, Ferranti-Packard Electric, Ltd., Toronto.*)

tion was stored in magnetic-core matrices and read out at slow speed into a standard teleprinter.

Voice transmission was also accomplished with the Stanford system. Figure 9-12 illustrates the one-way arrangement for doing this.   Recording was done at normal speed on a continuous loop of magnetic tape.

FIG. 9-11. JANET antenna system.   (*Courtesy of G. W. L. Davis, Ferranti-Packard Electric, Ltd., Toronto.*)

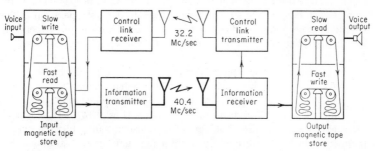

FIG. 9-12. The Stanford arrangement for transmitting speech via meteor trails. (*Vincent, Wolfram, Sifford, Jaye, and Peterson, 1957a.*)

The slack in the tape was stored in bins on either side of the high-speed read-out head.   On command from the link control the voice signal was read out at five times normal speed and used to modulate a single-side band transmitter.   The process was reversed at the receiving end.   Good quality voice communication was obtained with 20-kc/sec bandwidth over the high-speed part of the circuit.

Facsimile pictures have been successfully transmitted over a 1,450-km path via meteor trails (Bliss, Wagner, and Wickizer, 1957). Two frames per second were sent, each with a resolution of 67 picture elements per inch, which required a bandwidth of 27 kc. The early experimental arrangement did not use a closed loop; the pictures were repeated until one or more complete ones got through. The results were sufficiently encouraging to warrant further development.

An air-to-ground meteoric-scatter system has been developed as a cooperative project between the Wright Air Development Center and the Hughes Aircraft Company. This has some special features well worth mentioning (Hannum, Evans, Chambers, and Otten, 1960). In the first place it is not solely a meteor-scatter system. Other modes of propagation, such as auroral ionization and sporadic E, can be turned to advantage as well. This is partly because both links operate on the same frequency, which avoids the lack of correlation and reciprocity that sometimes occurs with two-frequency operation when modes other than the meteoric one appear. More important, perhaps, the error-correcting technique incorporated in the system ensures that garbled parts of the message will be checked and corrected or repeated until correctly received.

The ground transmitter probes the medium continuously with a short-pulse code while the aircraft transmitter is silent. On reception of the ground signal, via a meteor trail or other path, the airborne transmitter replies on the same frequency, either to send back a message or to invite the ground station to send its traffic. Time-sharing of groups of pulses from either end of the link permits single-frequency operation. This results in some delay, because it is not possible to transmit while receiving, but higher effective transmission rates (2,700 wpm) help to offset the delay.

The radio link in the Hughes system employs a type of frequency shift keying which may be better described as dual-channel amplitude modulation, something like the Stanford system. Both the airborne and ground transmitters have 10-kw peak pulse capacity (Fig. 9-13). It is scarcely practical to provide directivity in the airborne antenna, but the over-all loop gain can be maintained by using a high-gain ground antenna (Fig. 9-14) which should be kept pointed in the general direction of the aircraft.

9-7. High-power ionospheric scatter. In 1951 an historic experiment was performed to test the theory that scattering from ionospheric turbulence in the lower E region could support a weak but continuous signal at vhf frequencies over distances well beyond the line of sight (Bailey and seven others, 1952). A cw transmitter at Cedar Rapids, Iowa, radiated 25 kw on 49.8 Mc/sec. The receiver was located at Sterling, Virginia, 1,245 km away. From each terminal, antennas with gains of 18 db were directed to the mid-point of the path so that their patterns overlapped roughly at the 100-km level. The experiment was a success: a weak level

Fig. 9-13. Airborne 10-kw 50-Mc/sec power amplifier. (*Courtesy of L. C. Parode, Hughes Aircraft Company, Los Angeles.*)

of signal was maintained day in and day out. Superposed on the weak signal were numerous strong spikes which were obviously due to echoes from meteors. There was never any question about the meteoric contribution to the total signal level in those cases where the individual meteor echoes could be identified. In fact, the continued operation of this circuit did much to aid forward-scatter research on meteors, since the larger meteoric signals were detectable well off to either side of the path

Fig. 9-14. Forty-eight-element ground antenna. (*Courtesy of L. C. Parode, Hughes Aircraft Company, Los Angeles.*)

between the stations.   However, it was not so easy to resolve the relative contributions of meteoric and other forms of ionization to the continuous background signal level.

This weak signal showed diurnal variations that were similar in broad outline to the typical backscatter records of meteor echoes which were available at that time.   There were discrepancies, though, such as a relatively higher daytime level and smaller swings between maxima and minima of the scatter signal, which were significant enough to suggest that small meteors could neither be the sole agency nor even an important one.   This conclusion was given added weight by some early measurements of the heights from which the scattering occurred; an observed daytime level of 70 km appeared to be well below the normal meteor levels.

Later developments corrected some of these earlier impressions.   The daytime scattering heights were revised upward to around 80 km through more accurate measurements.   The lack of close agreement between the diurnal curves for the scatter signal and the backscatter meteor echoes was resolved by the Stanford and Ottawa workers who brought out a point which we discussed in Sec. 9-3, namely, that a given radiant distribution will yield forward-scatter daily-rate curves which depend strongly on the geometry and which can differ markedly from the usual curves obtained by backscatter radar.   In particular, the forward-scatter meteor results showed higher midafternoon rates and a smaller ratio of maximum-to-minimum rates (compare curves B and D, Fig. 5-4).   Other experiments demonstrated that the innumerable faint meteors could provide (not necessarily that they did provide) the continuum of scattering centers required to support the weak scatter signal (Villard, Eshleman, Manning, and Peterson, 1955; Forsyth and Vogan, 1955; McKinley, 1954b).

The antennas in the Cedar Rapids–Sterling tests were beamed directly above the mid-point of the path because scattering from ionospheric turbulence would favor this on-path propagation.   On the other hand, meteoric propagation would tend to be off path, via either of the two hot spots of Fig. 9-6b.   The gain of the antennas in the vicinity of these hot spots was appreciably lower than the gain at the mid-point, and in this way the original arrangement discriminated against the meteoric component.   The relative contribution of each mode to the total signal might have been determined by steering the antennas rapidly from the center point to either side, but this was difficult to do.   Instead, two additional receiving stations were set up on either side of Sterling with high-gain antennas beamed at the mid-point of the original path (Pineo, 1958).   This meant that the central region illuminated by the transmitter became the southern hot spot for the receiver north of Sterling, and vice versa, while the Sterling receiver continued to provide on-path records for com-

parison.   The results are shown in Fig. 9-15, where the signal gain of each
of the off-path links is plotted relative to that of the on-path link.   The
crosshatched areas, during which the off-path gain was positive, show
that for most of the day the meteor signal predominated.

The weight of the evidence seems to be that the bulk of the weak scatter
signal is made up of the contribution of very faint meteors, perhaps as
faint as fifteenth magnitude, but that during part of the daytime an additional agent is certainly present, probably photo-ionization coupled with
increased turbulence, which becomes effective in the afternoon when

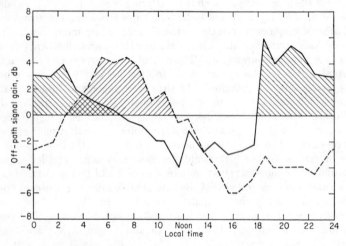

FIG. 9-15. The variation with time of the signal gain of the two off-path receivers
relative to zero db for the on-path receiver.   The solid curve refers to the path utilizing
the southern hot spot and the dashed curve applies to the northern hot spot.   The
extent of the shaded area shows that the meteor signal predominated during all but
the afternoon hours (*after Manning and Eshleman, 1959, based on data by Pineo, 1958*).

meteor activity is at a low ebb.   The interesting possibility remains that
meteor-trail ionization might be enhanced or prolonged by the solar radiation process too.   As was pointed out in Sec. 8-12, photo-ionization may
reduce the attachment coefficient and increase the duration of the meteor
echo.   This would apply to the longer echoes mainly, which tend to scatter omnidirectionally; hence the effect would be observed on path as much
if not more than off path.   Both photo-ionization and photodetachment
are enhanced during a normal SID, and so either mechanism could
account for the observed increase in the weak scatter signal during an
SID.

If the increase in photo-ionization is great enough and occurs sufficiently low in the atmosphere, the signal level will decrease rather than rise, owing to absorption setting in.   The catastrophic polar-cap blackout cuts off the high-power ionospheric-scatter circuits just as effectively as it severs the low-power closed-loop links.   The obvious solution is the same as the one advocated for the meteor system, namely, to move to a much higher frequency, but it may be difficult to implement.

CHAPTER 10

Other Effects of Meteors

Several interesting associations between meteors and other physical phenomena have been suggested, which vary in their degree of plausibility. For example, it seems reasonable that a meteor which produces copious radiation on optical frequencies should also emit energy on radio frequencies. The question is whether or not the amount of radio noise is significant or even observable. Auroral activity ties in closely with geomagnetic fluctuations: perhaps the magnetometers react also to the passage of a bright meteor. Much of this book has been devoted to the thesis that meteors create ionization in the upper atmosphere. Do they generate enough to contribute appreciably to the ambient level of E-region ionization?

No one denies that the amount of rainfall fluctuates widely from day to day, nor is the marked variability of meteor rates in much dispute. Meteoric dust should be about the right size to serve as nuclei on which raindrops may form. Whether or not one believes in a direct correlation between rainfall and the incidence of meteors seems to depend on one's faith, not only in the accuracy and adequacy of the observational data in both fields but also in the mechanics of the difficult statistical analyses required to establish or disprove a connection.

The space traveler is not likely to doubt the reality of his meteoric environment—these miniature planets of the sun will have a very literal impact on his activities. We shall send him abroad armed with the best information that we can provide about his chance of survival in a space filled with flying particles. At the moment, in comparison with radiation hazards and the basic technological difficulties of life in a space vehicle, the likelihood of disaster from meteoric collisions seems acceptably small, though not entirely negligible. However, the data on which the probabilities are based have been obtained almost entirely from earth-bound observations. The pioneer astronauts may have to find out the hard way whether or not interplanetary hazards exist in the form of vast meteoric streams which have not yet swung within our ken.

10-1. Radio-noise emission from meteors. An examination of the Ottawa range-time meteor records has revealed a few isolated cases, such as Fig. 8-18, in which the normal character of the background noise became significantly different when the echo appeared. The highly speculative suggestion that this might be due to radio noise emitted by the ionized trail was hedged by the thought that the cause was much more likely to be reflections, via the meteor trail, of man-made or other sources of electrical noise (McKinley and Millman, 1949a).

A meteor trail is a plasma of electrons and ions with boundaries and gradients, which under certain circumstances will resonate coherently under the influence of an applied field. Whether or not the meteoric plasma can also radiate incoherently at h-f and vhf frequencies is a moot point. The plasma of a fluorescent lamp can and does radiate radio noise —in fact, the fluorescent lamp has been used as a standard source of microwave noise. The effect in the meteor trail is plausible, but it is difficult to determine if it is measurable or separable from reflections. From time to time radio-noise radiations have been reported from auroral ionization, which is similar in some respects to meteoric ionization. Here, the difficulty of separating direct emissions and reflected signals is again present, and not all observers are agreed on the reality of the electrical noise from the aurora. (The reality of *acoustical* noise from the aurora has also been the subject of considerable debate, often more heated than scientific!)

A series of experiments designed to shed further light on this question has been described by Hawkins (1958b). Three sensitive receivers were used with high-gain antennas on 30, 218, and 475 Mc/sec respectively. No transmitters were involved—the correlation of noise pulses with meteors was done entirely with the aid of simultaneous visual or photographic observations. At 218 Mc/sec, no noise signals were associated with the 26 meteors of magnitude 4 and brighter that occurred in the antenna beam during the observing period. At 475 Mc/sec, 3 out of 36 meteors in the beam showed noise bursts of 3 db above the ambient level, and 7 of 43 meteors which occurred outside the beam also yielded noise pulses. Twenty of the 37 meteors observed at 30 Mc/sec appeared to give observable signals, one of them being 15 db above ambient noise.

Hawkins interpreted the observations on 475 Mc/sec as demonstrating that the level of spurious correlation was of the same order as, if not higher than, the level which could be attributed to meteors within the coverage of the antenna beam. The 30-Mc/sec data were clouded by the presence of extraneous reflections, either via the meteor trail or the ionosphere, and Hawkins considered that the possibility of true noise emission at this frequency was not entirely ruled out. On the whole, though, he was inclined to believe that the results showed that meteors in the magnitude range -1 to 4 do not emit appreciable radio noise. This appears to set an upper limit of about 10^{-18} for the efficiency of conversion of the original kinetic energy of the meteor into electromagnetic radiation in a bandwidth of 1 cps. However, this does not exclude the possibility that meteors in the fireball range may radiate detectable radio noise.

10-2. Geomagnetic effects of meteors. Bumba (1955) has suggested that there may be a direct correlation between meteoric and magnetic activity; his view is based on a comparison of certain synoptic variations in the earth's magnetic field over a 48-year period with the occurrence of the stronger annual meteor showers. His data were interpreted to indicate that the magnetic index increased significantly at the peak of a shower and then dropped below normal about three days later. As Bumba himself pointed out, the results are far from conclusive, though well worthy of further investigation. Furthermore, the analysis dealt with both meteors and magnetic activity in gross, as it were, and shed no light on a possible connection between individual meteors and local fluctuations.

Kalashnikov (1949, 1952), in Russia, developed instrumentation for the purpose of detecting magnetic effects from showers and from individual meteors. He used large coils, 100 to 300 m in diameter, coupled to a moving-coil galvanometer. The limiting sensitivity of the apparatus was given as 4×10^{-8} oersted. An increase in the rate of magnetic pulses was observed to correspond to the expected peaks of the Leonid, Geminid, Quadrantid, and Perseid showers. During the Perseid shower of 1950, 49 out of 169 meteors observed visually were coincident within ± 1 sec with a magnetic pulse.

Hawkins (1958a) undertook to repeat the experiment at Sacramento Peak in New Mexico. One of his equipments consisted of three small orthogonal magnetometer coils, each coupled to a low-noise amplifier and recorder. Later, a large coil was added to the apparatus to increase the sensitivity which, in the limit, was about 2×10^{-8} oersted. Hawkins found that the percentage of coincidence (within ± 1 sec) between meteors and magnetic pulses was no greater than one would expect if there were no correlation at all between the two types of events. The actual percentage of coincidences in both the Russian and American observations was about the same, around 35 per cent. Hawkins pointed out that the sensitivity of the New Mexico equipment was limited only by the ambient variations in the background level of the earth's field, while Kalashnikov's published records did not show conclusively that his apparatus had attained this limit. Furthermore, a positive correlation with the Leonid shower seems open to question because few Leonids have appeared in any year since the 1931–1935 period.

Jenkins, Phillips, and Maple (1960) have tentatively suggested a connection between certain meteor showers and the fluctuations of geomagnetic activity observed with a recording magnetometer. Several tuned filters were used to cover the range 1 to 50 cps, but correlations were observed mainly with the output of the lowest frequency band, centered on 1.5 cps. Some correlation was noticeable for the band centered at 2.75 cps, but none was found for frequencies higher than 5 cps. The authors state that these are only preliminary deductions, as a vast amount of data has yet to be analysed.

We can only say that much more work should be done on this problem to reach a definitive answer. If we had to express an opinion it would be that meteors taken singly probably do not create measurable magnetic effects, though strong showers may show some correlation with magnetic activity. The ordinary daily variation of meteor rates should have as great an effect as most showers would, but so far this does not appear to have been examined. It is difficult to produce a theoretical explanation of the magnetic effects of either individual meteors or showers that is compatible with our present knowledge of meteoric processes in the upper atmosphere.

10-3. Meteoric contribution to E-region ionization. The ambient ionization in the E region of the ionosphere, roughly 100 to 120 km high, is almost 10^{11} electrons/m³ during a midsummer day. Photo-ionization by solar radiation and recombination are the major processes involved, though not the only ones. During the night the level of ionization drops to about 10^{10} electrons/m³, which is much too high to be accounted for as a residue of daytime photo-ionization. Meteoric ionization undoubtedly contributes something to the ambient level. Suppose that the total meteoric contribution is Q electrons/(m³)(sec). If N_e is the volume density of electrons at any moment, we have (see Sec. 8-8)

$$\frac{dN_e}{dt} = Q - \alpha_e N_e^2 \qquad (10\text{-}1)$$

and for equilibrium,

$$N_e = \left(\frac{Q}{\alpha_e}\right)^{1/2} \qquad (10\text{-}2)$$

The accepted value of α_e is 10^{-14} m³/sec for the recombination of electrons and atmospheric ions in the E region. The value of the recombination coefficient for electrons and meteoric ions is not known, but it is estimated to be considerably smaller, perhaps of the order of 10^{-16} m³/sec. The appropriate value of Q to use in Eq. (10-2) is even more uncertain. We can, however, arrive at a crude estimate for Q by adopting a value for the total meteoric mass entering the earth's atmosphere in 24 hr. We assume first that meteors fainter than the fifteenth magnitude do not create appreciable ionization. From Fig. 5-8, a conservative estimate of the total mass of meteors of fifteenth magnitude and brighter is about 10^7 g per day over the earth (using the Hawkins and Upton graph based on $m = 1$ g for $M_v = 0$). This guess may easily be wrong by an order of magnitude. The number of atoms in the total mass is

$$\frac{10^7 \times 6 \times 10^{23}}{30} = 2 \times 10^{29}$$

if the material is stony with an average atomic weight of 30. We shall assume an ionizing efficiency of 0.1 (see Sec. 7-3). The volume of the whole region between the heights of 100 and 120 km is

$$2 \times 10^4 \times 5 \times 10^{14} = 10^{19} \text{ m}^3$$

Hence

$$Q = \frac{2 \times 10^{28}}{10^{19} \times 8.64 \times 10^4} \simeq 2 \times 10^4 \text{ electrons/(m}^3\text{)(sec)}$$

With $\alpha_e = 10^{-14}$ and the above value of Q, Eq. (10-2) gives $N_e \simeq 10^9$ electrons/m³, which is only an order of magnitude below the normal nighttime density. The smaller and more probable value suggested for the meteoric recombination coefficient yields $N_e \simeq 10^{10}$ electrons/m³. This implies that the meteoric contribution might well be capable of maintaining the nighttime level. The very large uncertainties involved in this rough order of magnitude calculation should caution one against too ready an acceptance of the idea.

Dubin (1955) found $Q \simeq 2 \times 10^7$ electrons/(m³)(sec) on the assumption that the vast mass of micrometeorites also contributes to the ionization, which does not seem very probable. From this we obtain $N_e \simeq 5 \times 10^{10}$ when $\alpha_e = 10^{-14}$, or $N_e \simeq 5 \times 10^{11}$ for $\alpha_e = 10^{-16}$—values which appear to be on the high side. Kaiser (1955b) has concluded that $Q = 2 \times 10^2$ electrons/(m³)(sec) from a more direct assessment of the total ionization. This leads to $N_e \simeq 10^8$ or 10^9, depending on which value of α_e is used. The latter density is not far below the ambient nighttime level. Kaiser himself suggested that $\alpha_e \simeq 10^{-17}$ was not incompatible with meteor-trail measurements; this yields $N_e \simeq 5 \times 10^9$. Nicolet (1955), in a discussion of the various possible atomic processes in the upper atmosphere, agreed that the meteoric influx was the most likely source of the ionization needed to maintain the nighttime level in the E region, but he pointed out that we simply do not have enough information yet to evaluate the situation quantitatively.

One would expect that an abnormal increase in meteoric activity would raise the ambient ionization enough to test the hypothesis. The tremendous Giacobinid shower of 1946 did create a reflection layer which lasted for several hours on a frequency of 3.5 Mc/sec (Pierce, 1947). However, opinion has been divided on the question of whether the well-known annual showers are responsible for some forms of sporadic E-region ionization. Pineo (1950), and other observers too, have found little correlation between shower activity and the incidence of sporadic-E clouds. On the other hand, Lovell (1948, 1957) considers that there is little doubt that some forms of sporadic E are caused by meteors, particularly in the middle and high latitudes. Some recent work in India (Kotadia, 1958) suggests that even in low latitudes there may be a positive correlation. Sporadic E takes on a variety of forms and it is unlikely that any one agency can account for all of them. Meteoric activity does seem to explain some of the types quite well. For other manifestations of sporadic E none of the current theories are completely satisfactory.

Meteors may also be expected to contribute to the ionization in the upper part of the D region, around 90 km, though only the larger ones will penetrate to this level. In broad terms this would restrict the possibilities to the naked-eye range of magnitudes. The stronger showers should therefore have relatively more effect at D-region levels than in the E region.

10-4. Meteors and rainfall. From a study of many years of rainfall records Bowen (1953) came to the conclusion that there was a marked tendency for heavy falls of rain to occur on certain days of the year. This pattern appeared to be repeated year after year, at places widespread over the earth's surface and in both Northern and Southern Hemispheres. Bowen suggested that the cause must be extraterrestrial because of its world-wide effect. He thought that the agent was most likely to be meteoric since meteor showers are the only known extraterrestrial phenomena which occur year after year on the same dates. There is a phase lag of some 29 to 31 days in Bowen's correlations. That is, the statistics can be interpreted to show there is a tendency for heavy rainfall to occur about 30 days after the peak of a prominent meteor shower (Bowen, 1956a, 1956b, 1957a,b).

It has been shown experimentally that small particles in the lower atmosphere can stimulate precipitation. In some circumstances their presence is necessary before condensation can begin at all. These particles, of the order of a few microns in diameter, serve as nuclei for the condensation of water or ice crystals. Micrometeorites, which are slowed up in the upper atmosphere without burning up, are of the right order of size to provide the nuclei. Whether or not they are the right kind of material is another matter—not all substances will act as condensation nuclei, even though the particle sizes are suitable. The velocity of free fall from 100 to 10 km will vary greatly with the size of the particle. For particles in the size range 1 to 10 μ the estimated times of fall extend from 20 to 50 days. This ignores the effects of vertical air motions and large-scale turbulence which could well be controlling factors. Nevertheless, there is a persuasive physical plausibility to Bowen's theory.

The reality of the heavy world-wide rainfalls on certain dates, repetitive each year, is a question for the meteorologists to answer, and no easy one either. This problem is an internal exercise in statistical analysis; that is, it need not be related to meteors or anything else. For years, meteorologists have been divided on the issue, some finding evidence of periodicity and others not. Recent results from a computing-machine analysis of rainfall data were reported to the April, 1960, meeting of the American Meteorological Society by Glenn W. Brier. He found that there was a strong tendency for precipitation anomalies, both high and low levels of rainfall, to occur on specific calendar dates, though he did not suggest that there was any proven connection between his findings and meteoric activity. Dmitriev and Chili (1958) have done a similar analysis of weather data, including the correlation with meteor showers. They go further than Brier and agree with Bowen that a statistical connection with meteors may exist. The connection seems so convincing to Kvíz (1960) that he suggests its adoption as a primary postulate. He would then seek new evidence which would permit a reconciliation with current meteoric and meteorological conceptions.

As a tentative working hypothesis let us accept the proposition that rainfalls do repeat on certain calendar dates. We could furthermore accept as a fact that pronounced rainfall peaks occur 30 days after the Orionid, Geminid, Ursid, and Quadrantid showers, as proposed by Bowen. However, it happens that these particular streams have radiants well north of the celestial equator (see Table 6-1), the Ursids and Quadrantids in particular, and their effect at Sydney, Australia, should scarcely be more than the day-to-day variations in the normal nonshower rate (Millman, 1954b; Whipple and Hawkins, 1956). Bowen (1956a) has associated a six-year periodicity in the late December rainfall records with the Bielids, which have a nominal orbital period of six years (Table 6-2). The difficulty is that very few Bielids at all have been seen during this century. In contrast, the last great Bielid shower in 1872 was followed 30 days later by a minimum not a maximum in the rainfall record. The two really spectacular displays of the twentieth century, the Giacobinid showers of 1933 and 1946, should have precipitated torrential rains everywhere a month later, but no abnormalities were evident.

We are in no position to dispute the internal consistency of the meteorological data. We may point out, though, that the broad and amorphous character of the rate maxima of many meteor showers (see Table 6-1) lends a certain flexibility to the cross correlation between the two sets of data. In two or three striking instances of great meteor showers, where it should have been possible to demonstrate an unequivocal connection, none was apparent. We are forced to conclude that meteors in the incandescent range should have little or no effect on the weather.

The amount of meteoric material brought in by the major annual showers is but a small fraction of the total amount introduced by all meteors brighter than fifteenth magnitude. This total mass influx, which may amount to 10^4 kg per day over the earth, is mainly dissipated as atoms in the upper atmosphere, and relatively little survives in the form of macroscopic particles. The spherules reported by Landsberg (1947) and Hodge and Wildt (1958) may be in part the residue of ordinary meteors (see Sec. 5-5). On the other hand, micrometeorites and dust particles do survive as solid bodies without much loss by ablation, and furthermore their total mass influx probably outweighs the total of the entire range of incandescent meteors by two orders of magnitude.

Micrometeorites may indeed be capable of acting as nuclei, but are they present in significant numbers in the well-known showers? The size distribution in the Geminid and Perseid streams is such that the peak ratio of shower to nonshower meteors may be 3 to 1 at the visual limit of fifth magnitude, and only about 1 to 1 at the tenth magnitude, as observed at both limits by radar. The implication is clear that the smaller meteors have been weeded out of the streams (see Secs. 6-2 and 6-5). This means that it is extremely unlikely that the trend in this ratio will reverse as we go to still finer particles. Yet there seems no other way by which we could explain the supposed correlation between rainfall and the visual showers than to assume that the micrometeoritic content of these showers is not only high but that it has the same spatial and temporal distribution as the visible meteors. Even the younger streams like the Giacobinids do not appear to contain such swarms of very fine particles. The meteor astronomer finds it very difficult to visualize any mechanism whereby the smallest particles can be retained in very close association with the largest ones, while the ones of intermediate size are dissipated.

We feel that the old Scottish verdict "Not proven," is the fairest answer we can give at this time, meaning that the prosecution has managed to sow a few seeds of doubt but has failed to prove the case to the majority. Much more convincing evidence on both sides of the question will have to be assembled before a future jury can be expected to return a clear-cut verdict either way.

A word on noctilucent clouds may not be out of place here. These clouds are similar in appearance to cirrus or cirro-stratus clouds of the troposphere, but they occur very high in the atmosphere at the 80- to 90-km level. They are visible only by reflected sunlight when the sun is from 10 to 18° below the horizon, and hence they are best observed in summertime and in the high latitudes. Vestine (1934), from an examination of observations from many sources made over a period of fifty years, has concluded that the agency responsible for the clouds is extraterrestrial in origin and is most likely meteoric dust. Other writers at that time ascribed the clouds to ice crystals, though in those days the temperature at 82 km was thought to be around 300°K, which seemed too high for crystal formation.   The current estimate of a temperature in the neighbourhood of 170°K at this height (see Appendix) has revived the ice crystal theory, which is further reinforced by the presence of quantities of micrometeorites and meteoric dust which may possibly serve as the necessary condensation nuclei.   As we go up in the atmosphere, we find that above 40 km the only region where the total pressure exceeds the saturated water vapor pressure is in the neighbourhood of the temperature minimum near 82 km (Giovanelli, 1954).   Because of the low temperature the condensation must take place as ice crystals.   The crystals eventually evaporate when they fall out of the height region conducive to their formation.

Bowen suggested that there was a direct connection between Vestine's records of noctilucent clouds and the early Jodrell Bank radio observations of the summer meteor showers, both of which showed peak incidences in June and July.   Whipple and Hawkins pointed out that revised data from Jodrell Bank indicated that the correlation was not good. However, the hypothesis that the noctilucent clouds are caused by an influx of micrometeorites and meteoric dust is not necessarily denied. Extensive observations of these clouds have been made during the International Geophysical Year and these should lead to a better understanding of the phenomenon.

10-5. Meteors and space travel.   The space traveler of the future will need some assessment of the potential risk of damage or disaster due to meteoric impacts on his ship.   Although not the only one to have investigated the problem, Whipple (1952, 1958) has made the most exhaustive study, and the development here is based in rather broad outline on his work.

Penetration of the skin of the vehicle by even a small meteoroid would release the air inside very quickly, and death would result unless the hole were patched in short order.   We begin the discussion therefore by determining the resistance of the skin to meteoric impacts.   Whipple has developed a quasi-empirical formula which connects the depth of penetration d (in centimeters) with the kinetic energy E (in ergs) of the incident meteoroid, as follows:

$$E = \frac{\pi \rho \zeta}{9} d^3 \tag{10-3}$$

or $$\log_{10} E \simeq 3 \log_{10} d + 10.0 \tag{10-4}$$

if we assume that the skin is made of aluminum, with a density $\rho = 2.7$ g/cm^3 and a heat of fusion $\zeta = 1.1 \times 10^{10}$ ergs/g.

Next, to calculate the energy we use Eq. (5-15) for the mass m_M of a meteor of magnitude M.   In this equation the constant k is the mass of a zero-magnitude meteor. We shall carry k through the computations because opinion varies as to its value. For convenience, we shall retain the magnitude scale of meteor sizes: a meteoroid of magnitude M is a term which simply defines the size of an object which would produce a meteor of magnitude M if it were to enter the earth's atmosphere. If we adopt 40 km/sec as an average for the relative velocities of the vehicle and parti- cle, we have for the energy in ergs of a meteoroid of magnitude M,

$$E_M \simeq k \times 10^{13} \times 10^{-0.40M} \qquad (10\text{-}5)$$

Equations (10-4) and (10-5) combine to yield M_P, the magnitude of the smallest meteoroid which will just penetrate the skin:

$$M_P = 2.5 \log_{10} k - 7.5 \log_{10} d + 7.5 \qquad (10\text{-}6)$$

We wish to determine the rate at which meteoroids of this size and larger may be expected to strike the vehicle. Figure 5-3 shows three similar relations between the total number of meteors, incident on the whole earth in 24 hr, and limiting magnitude. Here we shall adopt the Hawkins and Upton relation, which is $\log_{10} N_M = 0.537M - 13.45$, in terms of the daily number passing through an area of 1 cm^2. Suppose that our space vehicle has an effective area of S cm^2. The number of meteors of magnitude M and brighter which strike it each day is given by

$$\log_{10} N_M = 0.537M + \log_{10} S - 13.45 \qquad (10\text{-}7)$$

If the vehicle is shielded by the earth—an earth satellite, for example— the effective area S will be one-half the geometrical area.

Substitution of M_P from Eq. (10-6) for M in Eq. (10-7) results in the total number $N_P(S)$ of meteoric particles which will penetrate the vehicle in 24 hr:

$$\log_{10} N_P(S) = 1.34 \log_{10} k + \log_{10} S - 4.0 \log_{10} d - 9.4 \qquad (10\text{-}8)$$

In order to evaluate some numerical examples we shall now adopt $k = 1$ g. Suppose that our space ship is covered with an aluminum skin $\frac{1}{8}$ in. thick (0.32 cm) and that its area is 10^6 cm^2, roughly that of a sphere 5.6 m in diameter. Equation (10-8) shows that we may expect 4×10^{-2} penetrating hits per day in an orbit about the sun not too far removed from the earth's orbit. In other words, we should need to apply a patch about once in every 25 days. From Eq. (10-6), $M_P = 11.25$ in this case, and the energy released by the particle is 3×10^8 ergs [Eq. (10-5) or (10-4)].

From time to time, Whipple has adopted different values of the parame- ters involved in this problem. In a recent publication (Whipple, 1958) he used $k = 25$ g and $V = 28$ km/sec down to $M = 7$, thence decreasing to $V = 15$ km/sec for all $M > 20$. He also employed a different value of r, the incremental ratio. It happens that for the particular example we have chosen Whipple's data give almost the same result, namely, that a serious leak in the ship might develop every three weeks on the average.

The chances of a major disaster will also concern our astronaut. Presumably the explosion of 100 g of TNT (roughly the amount contained in a hand grenade) within the cabin would blow the ship completely apart—at least the personnel within would have no further interest in patching the gaping holes that should certainly result. The heat energy released per gram of high explosive is in the neighborhood of 1,000 calories, so that our high explosive charge will produce about 4×10^{12} ergs of energy. From Eq. (10-5), this is the amount of kinetic energy available in a first-magnitude meteoroid moving at 40 km/sec. (Note that this meteoroid weighs only 0.4 g, contrasted with the equivalent 100 g of TNT.) The number of first-magnitude meteors encountering the ship in a day is about 10^{-7} [from Eq. (10-7)]. Using Whipple's heavier meteoroids, the same damage would result from a meteor slightly brighter than the fourth magnitude, and the daily probability is about 10^{-5}. In either case, the astronaut could figure on traveling all his life without encountering a catastrophe of this proportion.

We are in no position to evaluate the tolerable degree of damage which could be withstood, but it seems likely that meteors with ten times the minimal energy necessary for penetration would be extremely uncomfortable, if not fatal, to the crew. The daily probability of hits by such meteors ($M = 8.75$) is 1.8×10^{-3}, which implies an average immunity of a year and a half. Whipple has suggested that the effectiveness of a given thickness of shell could be increased tenfold or more by making it up of two skins with a space between. When a penetrating particle strikes the thinner outer skin, or "meteoric bumper," it literally explodes and sprays meteoric and skin particles and vapor over a wide area of the inside shell, which can therefore withstand the strain much better. Actually, to survive the sun's proton bombardment the crew would need a better shield than an eighth of an inch of aluminum. However, bumper or no bumper, and no matter how thick the shell, the ship would probably be written off entirely if it encountered a fast meteoroid weighing a pound or more.

Skill in navigation should also help to enhance the astronaut's chance of survival, though at the moment we can offer no charts and only a few general suggestions. Detection and avoidance of individual meteoroids appear to be entirely out of the question—the best the navigator can do is to avoid those regions in space where the density of this potent shrapnel is likely to be greatest. The region near the plane of the ecliptic is thought to be more densely populated with all sizes of meteoric material, and the asteroidal belt between Mars and Jupiter probably contains a higher proportion of the larger meteoroids.   Comet orbits and the orbits of known meteor streams should be shunned.   We know nothing about meteor streams which have not intersected the earth's orbit—there may be some surprises in store for the pioneer astronaut.

At the other extreme of sizes, micrometeorites and dust will pepper the ship continuously.   Whipple has calculated that this sandblasting effect is unlikely to cause serious wear and tear to the metallic skin, though after a year's exposure optical surfaces would suffer considerable abrasion. The magnitude of the meteoric sandblasting effect is about the same as the erosion caused by solar-proton sputtering, both being of the order of 10^{-13} g/(cm^2)(sec).

10-6. Artificial meteors.   In defining the scope of this book we stated at the outset that our attention would be focused on meteors both in the stricter sense of the word, that is, on the upper-atmospheric phenomena arising from the influx of solid particles, and also on the history of the particles before they enter our atmosphere.   Any mention of the survivors of the flight through the atmosphere has been confined largely to brief discussions of the smallest members, the micrometeorites and meteoric dust.   Field and laboratory studies of the larger meteorites form an important aspect of the subject as a whole, but it is an aspect which has little direct effect on the radio engineer's problems—furthermore, we would not feel competent to give it the thorough treatment it deserves.   Some mention should be made, though, of another phase of laboratory studies which could help our understanding of meteoric processes.

In spite of the increasing vigorous efforts by meteor scientists to explain meteoric phenomena in the natural environment of the upper atmosphere, many essential elements are still lacking in the formulation of a satisfactory over-all theory.   We need more information about the atomic and molecular cross sections for excitation, ionization, dissociation, recombination, and attachment, for energy levels up to 1,000 ev.   Controlled laboratory experiments offer the best hope for accurate quantitative determinations in this area.   The sputtering effects of high-energy protons on fine particles could be examined with a view to elucidating the effect of corpuscular radiation from the sun on the meteoric dust.

Some of the so-called constants of the physical theory of meteors, particularly Λ, β (the ionizing probability), τ_I, and τ_q, continue to elude the efforts of upper-air physicists to pin them down firmly.   It seems likely that better values for these may come from ballistic experiments with artificial meteors, such as those by Rinehart and his coworkers at Inyokern, California (1952) and also by the team at the University of Utah (Partridge and Harris, 1957; Davidson and Partridge, 1957; Hendricks, 1957).   These workers employed shaped charges to fire small pellets at velocities up to 5 km/sec. A light-gas gun may also be used to accelerate somewhat larger projectiles to velocities of the order of 7 km/sec (Bull, 1959). These speeds are somewhat short of the range of meteor velocities. Nevertheless, the progress made to date is most encouraging.

One can obtain a more realistic simulation by firing the artificial meteor from a rocket as it passes through the meteoric region. Two of the most ill-determined parameters of the meteor, its mass and density, can thus be eliminated from the set of unknowns which confronts the observer. Photographic and radio observations of these artificial meteors may be compared directly with the natural phenomena. One or two attempts have been made to eject pellets from rockets with some success. McCrosky (1959) has reported on photographic observations of artificial meteors fired from a rocket at a height of 79 km. The shaped-charge technique was used to eject aluminum particles of small but unknown sizes—roughly estimated to be about 25 μ in diameter, on the average. McCrosky determined the initial velocity of the particles to be 14.4 km/sec. The final velocity, after a life of 0.07 sec, was 12.6 km/sec. The use of a rocket-borne gas gun, or other method whereby a moderately large body of known shape, density, and mass can be ejected, should further improve this promising technique.

We have noticed that in a book of this nature it is not uncommon that the author should provide a summarizing epilogue which recapitulates the major theme with due emphasis on the importance of the tremendous strides which have been made in the field and on the clear-cut and definitive conclusions which have been reached. As the curtain falls he declaims a prognosis of future progress which reveals beckoning vistas to the fascinated acolyte. The résumé should naturally be couched in the most glowing terms, particularly for the benefit of the reader with detective-story training who, before making the plunge, habitually flips to the back of the book to see how the tale turns out.

It is with no small inner struggle that we have deliberately suppressed the temptation to indulge in a valedictory of pyrotechnical rhetoric. Rather, we have felt that it would be better to leave the reader with the sober thought that meteor research is not yet an exact science. The technological advances of the last decade or two have indeed helped greatly to extend our knowledge of these elusive particles, but most of the answers obtained so far should be regarded as semiquantitative at best and subject to major change and revision as new data are forthcoming and new theories evolved. Long a poor relation in the astronomical family, meteor studies have been accorded much more prominence in recent years, partly because of the bearing they have both on fundamental physical processes and on cosmological problems, and partly because of their practical interconnection with communications and space research Large-scale meteor programs are now under way in many laboratories and observatories throughout the world, which may be expected to yield masses of new information.   However, the era of individual effort is not past.   Despite the necessity for greater organization to cope with the increasingly complicated and expensive instrumentation of modern research, the flash of intuitive genius was never more needed to weld a coherent framework.

Appendix: Upper Atmosphere Data

The atmospheric gases are assumed to obey the perfect gas law (equation of state) given by $p_a = \rho_a RT/M = \rho_a g\mathbf{H}$. In these relations p_a = pressure, ρ_a = density, R = universal gas constant, T = absolute temperature, M = mean molecular weight, and g = acceleration due to gravity. The scale height, $\mathbf{H} = RT/Mg$, is a parameter which depends chiefly on the temperature and the degree of dissociation of the gas molecules at a given true height H. The value of g at height H may be found from the formula

$$g = g_0 \left(\frac{\mathbf{R}}{\mathbf{R} + H} \right)^2 \tag{A-1}$$

where g_0 is the sea-level value at the observer's latitude and $\mathbf{R}$ is the earth's radius. Adopted values are $g_0 = 9.807$ m/sec^2 and $\mathbf{R} = 6{,}357$ km.

The difference in pressure between two levels dH apart is equal to the weight of air per unit cross section contained between the levels. That is, $dp = -\rho_a g\, dH = -p_a\, dH/\mathbf{H}$. Integrating,

$$p_a = p_0 \epsilon^{-\int_0^H (dH/\mathbf{H})} \tag{A-2}$$

where p_0 is the sea-level pressure. In an isothermal homogeneous atmosphere $\mathbf{H}$ is a constant, and hence

$$p_a = p_0 \epsilon^{-H/\mathbf{H}} \quad \text{and} \quad \rho_a = \rho_0 \epsilon^{-H/\mathbf{H}} \tag{A-3}$$

A glance at Tables A-1 and A-2 will show that these equations should be applied over small height differences only, in the actual atmosphere. In the discussions in the main text we have assumed they apply to a first order of approximation over the meteoric range of heights in order to simplify the developments. The adopted relations are given in Eqs. (A-4) to (A-9). This procedure also has the virtue that, if significant revisions to the basic data should appear in the future, it would not be difficult for the interested reader to reevaluate the relations and to adjust the equations and figures in the main text accordingly.

Table A-1. ARDC Model Atmosphere, 1956

(1) H Height, km	(2) Temp., °K	(3) Molecular weight, g/mole	(4) H Scale height, km	(5) log pressure, newtons/m²	(6) log density, kg/m³	(7) log MFP, m	(8) log kinematic viscosity, m²/sec
0	288.2	28.97	8.43	+5.01	+0.09	−7.18	−4.84
10	223.3	28.97	6.56	+4.42	−0.38	−6.71	−4.45
20	216.7	28.97	6.38	+3.74	−1.05	−6.04	−3.80
30	231.2	28.97	6.83	+3.07	−1.75	−5.34	−3.08
40	260.9	28.97	7.73	+2.48	−2.40	−4.69	−2.38
50	282.7	28.97	8.40	+1.94	−2.97	−4.12	−1.79
60	257.6	28.97	7.68	+1.41	−3.46	−3.63	−1.33
70	219.3	28.97	6.56	+0.80	−4.00	−3.09	−0.84
75	200.3	28.97	6.00	+0.45	−4.30	−2.79	−0.57
80	196.9	28.97	5.91	+0.09	−4.66	−2.43	−0.22
85	196.9	28.97	5.92	−0.28	−5.03	−2.06	+0.15
90	196.9	28.96	5.93	−0.65	−5.40	−1.70	+0.52
95	199.3	27.56	6.32	−1.004	−5.78	−1.33	
100	207.0	26.48	6.84	−1.33	−6.15	−0.98	
105	217.0	25.82	7.36	−1.64	−6.48	−0.66	
110	228.1	25.39	7.89	−1.92	−6.80	−0.35	
115	239.9	25.07	8.41	−2.19	−7.09	−0.06	
120	252.2	24.84	8.94	−2.44	−7.37	+0.21	
130	284.9	24.51	10.27	−2.90	−7.89	+0.72	
140	362.7	24.28	13.23	−3.27	−8.37	+1.20	
150	440.0	24.13	16.20	−3.57	−8.75	+1.58	

Tables A-1 and A-2 list some directly and indirectly measured properties of the atmosphere. The data in Table A-1 have been abstracted (with permission) from the *ARDC Model Atmosphere, 1956** and those in Table A-2 were taken from the *ARDC Model Atmosphere, 1959*.† In the last four columns of the tables we list the common logarithms of the quantities for tabular convenience, since the quantities themselves change by several orders of magnitude. Column 8, kinematic viscosity, is terminated at 90 km, where the composition of the atmosphere is assumed to change. The empirical equations and assumptions used in computing the viscosity become unreliable above 90 km. The ambipolar diffusion

* Minzner, R. A., and Ripley, W. S., **1956,** Air Force Cambridge Research Center, AFCRC-TN-56-204, *The ARDC model atmosphere, 1956*.

† Minzner, R. A., Champion, K. S. W., and Pond, H. L., **1959,** Air Force Cambridge Research Center, AFCRC-TR-59-267, *The ARDC model atmosphere, 1959*.

Note: These United States government reports may be requested from the United States Department of Commerce, Office of Technical Services, Washington 25, D.C.

Table A-2. ARDC Model Atmosphere, 1959

(1) H Height, km	(2) Temp., °K	(3) Molecular weight, g/mole	(4) H Scale height, km	(5) log pressure, newtons/m²	(6) log density, kg/m³	(7) log MFP, m	(8) log kinematic viscosity, m²/sec
0	288	28.97	8.4	+5.01	+0.09	−7.18	−4.84
10	223	28.97	6.6	+4.42	−0.38	−6.71	−4.45
20	217	28.97	6.4	+3.74	−1.05	−6.04	−3.80
30	231	28.97	6.8	+3.08	−1.75	−5.34	−3.08
40	261	28.97	7.7	+2.48	−2.40	−4.69	−2.38
50	283	28.97	8.4	+1.94	−2.97	−4.12	−1.79
60	254	28.97	7.6	+1.41	−3.45	−3.64	−1.34
70	210	28.97	6.3	+0.78	−4.00	−3.09	−0.86
75	188	28.97	5.6	+0.41	−4.32	−2.77	−0.58
80	166	28.97	5.0	+0.004	−4.67	−2.42	−0.27
85	166	28.97	5.0	−0.43	−5.11	−1.98	+0.16
90	166	28.97	5.0	−0.87	−5.55	−1.54	+0.60
95	180	28.94	5.4	−1.29	−6.01	−1.09	
100	199	28.90	6.0	−1.67	−6.43	−0.66	
105	218	28.86	6.6	−2.01	−6.81	−0.28	
110	287	28.82	8.7	−2.31	−7.23	+0.13	
115	382	28.77	11.7	−2.52	−7.57	+0.47	
120	477	28.71	14.6	−2.69	−7.83	+0.74	
130	665	28.59	20.5	−2.94	−8.23	+1.13	
140	850	28.45	26.5	−3.12	−8.52	+1.42	
150	1031	28.27	32.4	−3.27	−8.75	+1.65	

coefficient D may usually be taken to be from 1.2 to 1.5 times the kinematic viscosity. However, in view of the uncertainty of the viscosity data, we have used the results of Greenhow and Neufeld (1955), which may be expressed as

$$\log_{10} D(\text{m}^2/\text{sec}) = 0.067H(\text{km}) - 5.6 \tag{A-4}$$

For our convenience in various theoretical computations throughout this book, we have adopted some simplified relations between density, pressure, mean free path (MFP), and height, applicable for $70 < H < 120$. These were obtained by plotting both the 1956 and 1959 logarithmic data for each quantity against height, and fitting a mean straight line to give approximately equal weights to both sets of data.

$$\log_{10} \rho_a(\text{kg/m}^3) = 1.3 - 0.075H(\text{km}) \tag{A-5}$$
$$\log_{10} p_a(\text{newton/m}^2) = 6.1 - 0.075H(\text{km}) \tag{A-6}$$
$$\log_{10} (\text{MFP}) (\text{m}) = -8.4 + 0.075H(\text{km}) \tag{A-7}$$

The coefficient of H corresponds to a mean scale height

$$H = \frac{0.434}{0.075} = 5.8 \text{ km}$$

which agrees closely with the tabulated H only near $H = 95$ km.

Two interconnecting relations are also useful.

$$\log_{10} p_a - \log_{10} \rho_a = 4.8 \qquad \text{(A-8)}$$
$$\log_{10} \rho_a + \log_{10} (\text{MFP}) = -7.1 \qquad \text{(A-9)}$$

In the interest of consistency it might be thought that the coefficient of H in the adopted diffusion equation, Eq. (A-4), should be the same as the coefficient used in Eqs. (A-5), (A-6), and (A-7). However, the effect of the earth's magnetic field at meteoric heights is to modify the electron-diffusion coefficient without affecting the coefficient for the positive ions. At 92 km the electrons and ions diffuse together in true ambipolar fashion. At higher levels the electrons will tend to diffuse more slowly than the ions, perhaps by as much as a factor of 2 (Weiss, 1955b; Huxley, 1952). Hence, there is both theoretical and observational support for our adoption of a seemingly inconsistent value for the coefficient of H in the diffusion equation. It is quite possible that the adopted coefficient of H in Eqs. (A-5), (A-6), and (A-7) may be too large anyway, but the wide divergence in the current observational data does not enable us to decide definitely. If a smaller value of this coefficient were to be selected (corresponding to a larger scale height), then the radio-echo ceilings calculated in Secs. 7-5 and 8-6 would be raised appreciably. In fact, if we were to carry out a point-by-point analysis using the increasing scale heights listed in the tables, the ceiling would turn out to be higher. The radio-echo ceilings which have been calculated from the simple formulas are therefore very conservative in the sense that they probably are lower limits.

The 1956 information is based on rocket flights made near White Sands, New Mexico, and the 1959 material stems chiefly from rocket flights made at Churchill, Manitoba. There are some very significant differences between the two tables; for example, the 1956 density at 100 km is about twice the 1959 density at the same height, and the temperatures and scale heights over this general height region also differ appreciably. The discrepancies may possibly be attributed to geographical or geomagnetic latitude differences (Churchill is in the auroral zone), or to diurnal and seasonal effects (Greenhow and Hall, 1960). The observational errors are still quite large in this field and much more information is needed. For the present, the data in the tables may be accepted as indicating the physical properties of the atmosphere to better than an order of magnitude at least; hopefully one may assume their validity within a factor of two or three.

Bibliography

Allen, C. W., **1946**, Mon. Not. Roy. Astron. Soc., *106*, 137–150, *The spectrum of the corona at the eclipse of 1940, October 1.*

Allen, E. W., **1948**, Proc. Inst. Radio Engrs., *36*, 346–352, *Reflections of very high frequency radio waves from meteoric ionization.*

Almond, Mary, **1951**, Mon. Not. Roy. Astron. Soc., *111*, 37–44, *The summer daytime meteor streams of 1949 and 1950. III: Computation of the orbits.*

Almond, Mary, Davies, J. G., and Lovell, A. C. B., **1951**, Mon. Not. Roy. Astron Soc., *111*, 585–608, *The velocity distribution of sporadic meteors. I.*

———, **1952**, Mon. Not. Roy. Astron. Soc., *112*, 21–39, *The velocity distribution of sporadic meteors. II.*

———, **1953**, Mon. Not. Roy. Astron. Soc., *113*, 411–427, *The velocity distribution of sporadic meteors. IV: Extension to magnitude +8 and final conclusions.*

Appleton, E. V., **1930**, Proc. Roy. Soc., *A126*, 542–569, *On some measurements of the equivalent height of the atmospheric ionized layer.*

Appleton, E. V., and Barnett, M. A. F., **1925**, Proc. Roy. Soc., *A109*, 621–641, *On some direct evidence for downward atmospheric reflection of electric rays.*

Appleton, E. V., and Naismith, R., **1947**, Proc. Phys. Soc., *59*, 461–473, *The radio detection of meteor trails and allied phenomena.*

Appleton, E. V., Naismith, R., and Ingram, L. J., **1937**, Phil. Trans. Roy. Soc., *236*, 191–259, *British radio observations during the second International Polar Year, 1932-33.*

Appleton, E. V., and Piddington, J. H., **1938**, Proc. Roy. Soc., *A164*, 467–476, *Reflection coefficients of ionospheric regions.*

Aspinall, A., Clegg, J. A., and Hawkins, G. S., **1951**, Phil. Mag., (7) *42*, 504–514, *A radio echo apparatus for the delineation of meteor radiants.*

Astapovich, I. S., **1935**, Astron. J. U.S.S.R., *12*, 60–100, *On the nature of telescopic meteors* (in Russian, with a summary in English).

———, **1958**, State Publishing House of Physical and Mathematical Literature, Moscow, 640 pp., *Meteoric phenomena in the earth's atmosphere* (in Russian)

Astavin-Razumin, D. L., **1958**, Bull. VAGO (29) (No. 22), 23–27 [VAGO = All-Union Astro-Geodetic Society], *An experiment in the observation of meteors by photoelectric methods* (in Russian).

Bailey, D. K., Bateman, R., Berkner, L. V., Booker, H. G., Montgomery, G. F., Purcell, E. M., Salisbury, W. W., and Wiesner, J. B., **1952**, Phys. Rev., *86*, 141–145, *A new kind of radio propagation at very high frequencies observable over long distances.*

Bain, W. C., **1960**, J. Atmos. Terr. Phys., *17*, 188–204, *The azimuth distribution of oblique reflections from meteor trails and its relation to meteor radiant distributions.*

Bateman, R., McNish, A. G., and Pineo, V. C., **1946**, Science, *104*, 434–435, *Radar observations during meteor showers 9 October 1946.*

Beard, D. B., **1959**, Astrophys. J., *129*, 496–506, *Interplanetary dust distribution.*

Berg, O. E., and Meredith, L. H., **1956**, J. Geophys. Res., *61*, 751–754, *Meteorite impacts to altitude of 103 kilometers.*

Bialecke, E. P., and Dougal, A. A., **1958**, J. Geophys. Res., *63*, 539–546, *Pressure and temperature variation of the electron-ion recombination coefficient in nitrogen.*

Billam, E. R., and Browne, I. C., **1956**, Proc. Phys. Soc., *B69*, 98–113, *Characteristics of radio echoes from meteor trails. IV: Polarization effects.*

Biot, E., **1846**, Paris, *Catalogue général des étoiles filantes et des autres météores observés en Chine pendant 24 siècles* (in French).

Blackett, P. M. S., and Lovell, A. C. B., **1941**, Proc. Roy. Soc., *A177*, 183–186, *Radio echoes and cosmic ray showers.*

Bliss, W. H., Wagner, R. J., and Wickizer, G. S., **1957**, Proc. Inst. Radio Engrs., *45*, 1734–1735, *Experimental facsimile communication utilizing intermittent meteor ionization.*

Booker, H. G., **1956**, J. Geophys. Res., *61*, 673–705, *Turbulence in the ionosphere with applications to meteor-trails, radio-star scintillation, auroral radar echoes, and other phenomena.*

——, **1958**, J. Geophys. Res., *63*, 97–107, *Concerning ionospheric turbulence at the meteoric level.*

Booker, H. G., and Cohen, R., **1956**, J. Geophys. Res., *61*, 707–733, *A theory of long-duration meteor-echoes based on atmospheric turbulence with experimental confirmation.*

Bowen, E. G., **1953**, Aust. J. Phys., *6*, 490–497, *The influence of meteoric dust on rainfall.*

——, **1956a**, J. Meteorology, *13*, 142–151, *The relation between rainfall and meteor showers.*

——, **1956b**, Tellus, *8*, 394–402, *A relation between meteor showers and the rainfall of November and December.*

——, **1957a**, Aust. J. Phys., *10*, 412–417, *Relation between meteor showers and the rainfall of August, September and October.*

——, **1957b**, Observatory, *77*, 99–102, *A prediction of a meteor orbital period.*

Bowles, K. L., **1958**, Phys. Rev. Letters, *1*, 454–455, *Observation of vertical-incidence scatter from the ionosphere at 41 Mc/sec.*

Breit, G., and Tuve, M. A., **1926**, Phys. Rev., *28*, 554–573, *A test of the existence of the conducting layer.*

Browne, I. C., **1958**, Jodrell Bank Ann., *1*, 245–254, *The effect of atmospheric wind shear on the distribution of meteor echo durations.*

Browne, I. C., Bullough, K., Evans, S., and Kaiser, T. R., **1956**, Proc. Phys. Soc., *B69*, 83–97, *Characteristics of radio echoes from meteor trails. II: The distribution of meteor magnitudes and masses.*

Browne, I. C., and Kaiser, T. R., **1953**, J. Atmos. Terr. Phys., *4*, 1–4, *The radio echo from the head of meteor trails.*

Brysk, H., **1958**, J. Geophys. Res., *63*, 693–716, *Electromagnetic scattering by low-density meteor trails.*

——, **1959**, Inst. Radio Engrs. Trans., *AP-7*, S330–S336, *Electromagnetic scattering by high-density meteor trails.*

Buddhue, J. D., **1950**, University of New Mexico Press, Albuquerque, 102 pp., *Meteoric dust.*

Bull, G. V., **1959**, Proc. 7th Anglo-American Aeronautical Conference, Inst. Aero. Sciences, 312–343, *Re-entry studies in free flight ranges.*

Bumba, V., **1955**, Bull. Astron. Inst. Czech., *6*, 1–5, *Influence of the strong meteor showers on the characteristic variation of geomagnetic activity* (in German).

Campbell, L. L., and Hines, C. O., **1957**, Proc. Inst. Radio Engrs., *45*, 1658–1660, *Bandwidth considerations in a JANET system.*

Carpenter, R. J., and Ochs, G. R., **1957**, Inst. Radio Engrs. Wescon Convention Record, *1*, (1), 283–293, *Experimental equipment for communication utilizing meteor bursts.*

Ceplecha, Zd., **1950**, Bull. Astron. Inst. Czech., *2* (No. 10), *On the visibility of meteors.*

———, **1958**, Publ. Czech. Acad. Sci. Astron. Inst., (No. 41), 313–328, (No. 42), 329–343, *Hourly rate of sporadic meteors, 1948 and 1949* and *The hourly rates of shower meteors.*

Ceplecha, Zd., Rajchl, J., and Sehnal, L., **1959**, Bull. Astron. Inst. Czech., *10* (No. 4), 147–148, *New Czechoslovak meteorite LUHY (or PRIBRAM) (in English).*

Chamanlal and Venkataraman, K., **1941**, Electrotechnics, *14*, 28–40 (a summary is given in Nature, **1942**, *149*, 416), *Whistling meteors—Doppler effect produced by meteors entering the ionosphere.*

Clegg, J. A., **1948**, Phil. Mag., (7) *39*, 577–594, *Determination of meteor radiants by observation of radio echoes from meteor trails.*

———, **1952**, Mon. Not. Roy. Astron. Soc., *112*, 399–413, *The velocity distribution of sporadic meteors. III: Calculation of the theoretical distributions.*

Clegg, J. A., and Davidson, I. A., **1950**, Phil. Mag., (7) *41*, 77–85, *A radio echo method for the measurement of the heights of the reflecting points of meteor trails.*

Clegg, J. A., Hughes, V. A., and Lovell, A. C. B., **1947**, Mon. Not. Roy. Astron. Soc., *107*, 369–378, *The daylight meteor streams of 1947 May–August.*

Closs, R. L., Clegg, J. A., and Kaiser, T. R., **1953**, Phil. Mag., (7) *44*, 313–324, *An experimental study of radio reflections from meteor trails.*

Cook, A. F., **1954**, Astrophys. J., *120*, 572–577, *The physical theory of meteors. VI: The light curve.*

———, **1955**, Spec. Supp. J. Atmos. Terr. Phys., *2*, 8–14, *The nature of meteoric radiation.*

Cook, A. F., and Hawkins, G. S., **1960**, Smith. Contr. to Astrophys., *5*, 1–7, *The meteoric head echo.*

Cook, A. F., and Millman, P. M., **1955**, Astrophys. J., *121*, 250–270, *Photometric analysis of a spectrogram of a Perseid meteor.*

Cottony, H. V., and Johler, J. R., **1952**, Proc. Inst. Radio Engrs., *40*, 1053–1060, *Cosmic radio noise intensities in the VHF band.*

Crysdale, J. H., **1960**, Inst. Radio Engrs. Trans., *CS-8*, 33–40, *Analysis of the performance of the Edmonton-Yellowknife Janet circuit.*

Davidson, R. A., and Partridge, W. S., **1957**, J. App. Phys., *28*, 1304–1308, *Time lag between high-speed pellets and the ionization in their trails.*

Davies, J. G., **1957**, Advances in Electronics and Electron Physics, *9*, 95–128, Academic Press, Inc., New York, *Radio observations of meteors.*

Davies, J. G., and Ellyett, C. D., **1949**, Phil. Mag., (7) *40*, 614–626, *The diffraction of radio waves from meteor trails and the measurement of meteor velocities.*

Davies, J. G., and Lovell, A. C. B., **1955**, Mon. Not. Roy. Astron. Soc., *115*, 23–31, *The Giacobinid meteor stream.*

Davis, G. W. L., Gladys, S. J., Lang, G. R., Luke, L. M., and Taylor, M. K., **1957**, Proc. Inst. Radio Engrs., *45*, 1666–1678, *The Canadian Janet system.*

Davis, J., Greenhow, J. S., and Hall, J. E., **1959a**, Proc. Roy. Soc., *A253*, 121–129, *Combined photographic and radio observations of meteors.*

———, **1959b**, Proc. Roy. Soc., *A253*, 130–139, *The effect of attachment on radio echo observations of meteors.*

Denning, W. F., **1899**, Mem. Roy. Astron. Soc., *53*, 203, *General catalogue of the radiant points of meteoric showers and of fireballs and shooting stars observed at more than one station.*

Dmitriev, A. A., and Chili, A. V., **1958**, Trudy Morskogo gidrofizrcheskogo instituta, *12*, 181–190, *On meteor showers and precipitation.*

Dubin, M., **1955**, Spec. Supp. J. Atmos. Terr. Phys., *2*, 111–118, *Meteor ionization in the E-region.*

———, **1960**, Planet. Space Sci., *2*, 121–129, *Meteoric dust measured from Explorer I.*

Eastwood, E., and Mercer, K. A., **1948**, Proc. Phys. Soc., *61*, 122–134, *A study of transient radar echoes from the ionosphere.*

Eckersley, T. L., **1932**, J. Inst. Elect. Engrs., *71*, 405–459, *Studies in radio transmission.*

———, **1937**, Nature, *140*, 846–847, *Irregular ionic clouds in the E-layer of the ionosphere.*

Elford, W. G., and Robertson, D. S., **1953**, J. Atmos. Terr. Phys., *4*, 271–284, *Measurements of winds in the upper atmosphere by means of drifting meteor trails. II.*

Ellyett, C. D., **1950**, Phil. Mag., (7) *41*, 694–700, *The influence of high altitude winds on meteor trail ionization.*

———, **1955**, Spec. Supp. J. Atmos. Terr. Phys., *2*, 198–199, *Radar-meteor research in New Zealand.*

Ellyett, C. D., and Davies, J. G., **1948**, Nature, *161*, 596–597, *Velocity of meteors measured by diffraction of radio waves from trails during formation.*

Ellyett, C. D., and Roth, K. W., **1955**, Aust. J. Phys., *8*, 390–401, *The radar determination of meteor showers in the Southern Hemisphere.*

Eshleman, V. R., **1953**, Inst. Radio Engrs. Trans., *AP-1*, 37–42, *The effect of radar wavelength on meteor echo rate.*

———, **1955**, Inst. Radio Engrs. Trans., *AP-3*, 32–39, *Theory of radio reflections from electron-ion clouds.*

———, **1957**, J. Atmos. Terr. Phys., *10*, 57–72, *The theoretical length distribution of ionized meteor trails.*

Eshleman, V. R., and Manning, L. A., **1954**, Proc. Inst. Radio Engrs., *42*, 530–536, *Radio communication by scattering from meteoric ionization.*

Eshleman, V. R., and Mlodnosky, R. F., **1957**, Proc. Inst. Radio Engrs., *45*, 1715–1723, *Directional characteristics of meteor propagation derived from radar measurements.*

Evans, S., **1954**, Mon. Not. Roy. Astron. Soc., *114*, 63–73, *Scale heights and pressures in the upper atmosphere from radio-echo observations of meteors.*

———, **1955**, Spec. Supp. J. Atmos. Terr. Phys., *2*, 86–91, *Atmospheric pressures and scale heights from radio echo observations of meteors.*

Evans, S., and Hall, J. E., **1955**, Spec. Supp. J. Atmos. Terr. Phys., *2*, 18–22, *Meteor ionizing and luminous efficiencies.*

Fedynsky, V. V., **1955**, Spec. Supp. J. Atmos. Terr. Phys., *2*, 188–192, *Meteor studies in the Soviet Union.*

Fielko, E. I., **1957**, Astron. J. U.S.S.R., *34*, 241–246 (in English in Soviet Astron., *1*, 235–240, 1958), *Distribution of meteoric radio echoes according to their duration.*

Flood, W. A., **1957**, J. Geophys. Res., *62*, 79–91, *Meteor echoes at ultra-high frequencies.*

Forsyth, P. A., **1958**, Canad. J. Phys., *36*, 1112–1124, *The forward-scattered radio signal from an overdense meteor trail.*

Forsyth, P. A., Hines, C. O., and Vogan, E. L., **1955**, Canad. J. Res., *33*, 600–606, *Diurnal variations in the number of shower meteors detected by the forward-scattering of radio waves. II:. Experiment.*

Forsyth, P. A., and Vogan, E. L., **1955**, Canad. J. Phys., *33*, 176–188, *Forward-scattering of radio waves by meteor trails.*

——, **1956,** Canad. J. Phys., *34*, 535–545, *The duration of forward-scattered signals from meteor trails.*

Forsyth, P. A., Vogan, E. L., Hansen, D. R., and Hines, C. O., **1957,** Proc. Inst. Radio Engrs., *45*, 1642–1657, *The principles of JANET—a meteor-burst communication system.*

Gallagher, P. B., **1958,** Proc. Inst. Radio Engrs., *46*, 89–92, *An antenna array for studies in meteor and radio astronomy at 13 meters.*

Gallagher, P. B., and Eshleman, V. R., **1960,** J. Geophys. Res., *65*, 1846–1847, *Sporadic shower properties of very small meteors.*

Galle, J. G., **1868,** Abhandl. Schles. Ges. f. vaterl. kultur., Abteilung f. naturwiss. Medicin, Breslau (in German).

Gill, J. C., and Davies, J. G., **1956,** Mon. Not. Roy. Astron. Soc., *116*, 105–113, *A radio echo method of meteor orbit determination.*

Giovanelli, R. G., **1954,** Aust. J. Phys., *7*, 641–648, *The attenuation of light by meteoric dust in the upper atmosphere.*

Greenhow, J. S., **1952a,** Proc. Phys. Soc., *65*, 169–181, *Characteristics of radio echoes from meteor trails. III: The behaviour of the electron trails after formation.*

——, **1952b,** J. Atmos. Terr. Phys., *2*, 282–291, *A radio-echo method for the investigation of atmospheric winds at altitudes of 80 to 100 km.*

——, **1954,** Phil. Mag., (7) *45*, 471–490, *Systematic wind measurements at altitudes of 80–100 km using radio echoes.*

Greenhow, J. S., and Hall, J. E., **1960,** J. Atmos. Terr. Phys., *18*, 203–214, *Diurnal variation of density and scale height in the upper atmosphere.*

Greenhow, J. S., and Neufeld, E. L., **1955,** J. Atmos. Terr. Phys., *6*, 133–140, *The diffusion of ionized meteor trails in the upper atmosphere.*

——, **1956a,** Phil. Mag., (8) *1*, 1157–1171, *The height variation of upper atmosphere winds.*

——, **1956b,** Proc. Phys. Soc., *B69*, 1069–1076, *Phase changes and resonance effects in radio-echoes from meteor trails.*

——, **1959a,** Proc. Phys. Soc., *74*, 1–9, *Measurements of turbulence in the upper atmosphere.*

——, **1959b,** J. Atmos. Terr. Phys., *16*, 384–392, *Turbulence at altitudes of 80–100 km and its effects on long-duration meteor echoes.*

Guth, V., and Ceplecha, Zd., **1958,** Publ. Czech. Acad. Sci. Astron. Inst., (No. 40), 305–312, *Hourly rates of sporadic meteors, 1947* (in English).

Halliday, I., **1957,** J. Roy. Astron. Soc. Can., *51*, 287–297, *The orbit and spectrum of a bright meteor.*

——, **1958a,** Astrophys. J., *127*, 245–252, *Meteor wakes and their spectra.*

——, **1958b,** Astrophys. J., *128*, 441–443, *Forbidden line of OI observed in meteor spectra.*

Hannum, A. J., Evans, G. L., Chambers, J. T., and Otten, K., **1960,** Inst. Radio Engrs. Trans., *CS-8*, 113–133, *Air-to-ground meteoric scatter communication system.*

Hawkins, G. S., **1956a,** Mon. Not. Roy. Astron. Soc., *116*, 92–104, *A radio echo survey of sporadic meteor radiants.*

——, **1956b,** Proc. Inst. Radio Engrs., *44*, 1192, *Radar echoes from meteor trails under conditions of severe diffusion.*

——, **1956c,** Astrophys. J., *124*, 311–313, *Meteor ionization and its dependence on velocity.*

——, **1958a,** J. Geophys. Res., *63*, 467–475, *A search for magnetic effects from meteors.*

——, **1958b,** Astrophys. J., *128*, 724–726, *A search for radio emission from meteors.*

Hawkins, G. S., and Howard, W. E., **1959,** Astrophys. J., *130*, 1003–1007, *Decay of light from a meteor train.*

Hawkins, G. S., and Southworth, R. B., **1958**, Smith. Contr. to Astrophys., *2*, 349–364, *The statistics of meteors in the earth's atmosphere.*

Hawkins, G. S., Southworth, R. B., and Stienon, F., **1959**, Astron. J., *64*, 183–188, *Recovery of the Andromedids.*

Hawkins, G. S., and Upton, E. K. L., **1958**, Astrophys. J., *128*, 727–735, *The influx rate of meteors in the earth's atmosphere.*

Hawkins, G. S., and Whipple, F. L., **1958**, Astron. J., *63*, 283–291, *The width of meteor trails.*

Heising, R. A., **1928**, Proc. Inst. Radio Engrs., *16*, 75–99, *Experiments and observations concerning the ionized regions of the atmosphere.*

Hendricks, C. D., **1957**, J. App. Phys., *28*, 1339–1341, *Ionization by ultra-speed pellets.*

Herbstreit, J. W., **1948**, Advances in Electronics, *1*, 347–380, Academic Press, Inc., New York, *Cosmic radio noise.*

Heritage, J. L., Weisbrod, S., and Fay, W. J., **1960**, Inst. Radio Engrs. Trans., *AP-8*, 57–61, *Experimental studies of meteor echoes at 200 Mc.*

Herlofson, N., **1948a**, Repts. Prog. Phys., *11*, 444–454, *The theory of meteor ionization.*

————, **1948b**, Observatory, *68*, 226, *Scattering of radio waves from ionized columns.*

————, **1951**, Arkiv För Fysik, *3*, 247–297, *Plasma resonance in ionospheric irregularities* (in English).

Hey, J. S., Parsons, S. J., and Stewart, G. S., **1947**, Mon. Not. Roy. Astron. Soc., *107*, 176–183, *Radar observations of the Giacobinid meteor shower.*

Hey, J. S., and Stewart, G. S., **1947**, Proc. Phys. Soc., *59*, 858–883, *Radar observations of meteors.*

Hines, C. O., **1955**, Canad. J. Phys., *33*, 493–503, *Diurnal variations in the number of shower meteors detected by the forward-scattering of radio waves. I: Theory.*

————, **1958**, Canad. J. Res., *36*, 117–126, *Diurnal variations in the number of shower meteors detected by the forward-scattering of radio waves. III: Ellipsoidal theory.*

————, **1959**, J. Geophys. Res., *64*, 2210–2211, *An interpretation of certain ionospheric motions in terms of atmospheric waves.*

Hines, C. O., and Forsyth, P. A., **1957**, Canad. J. Phys., *35*, 1033–1041, *The forward-scattering of radio waves from overdense meteor trails.*

Hodge, P. W., and Wildt, R., **1958**, Geochimica et Cosmochimica Acta, *14*, 126–133, *A search for airborne particles of meteoric origin.*

Hoffmeister, C., **1937**, Akademische Verlagsgesellschaft M. B. H., Leipzig, 154 pp., *Die Meteore* (in German).

————, **1948**, Verlag Werden und Werken Weimar, Leipzig, 286 pp., *Meteorströme* (in German, with chapter summaries in English).

————, **1955**, Naturwiss., *42*, 458, *Note on the electrophysical determination of the velocity of meteors* (in German).

Hughes, R. F., **1959**, Smith. Contr. to Astrophys., *3*, 79–94, *Meteor trains.*

Hunter, W., and Parkin, D. W., **1960**, Proc. Roy. Soc., *A255*, 382–397, *Cosmic dust in deep-sea sediments.*

Huruhata, M., **1949**, Publ. Astron. Soc. Japan, *1*, 39–43, *Radar observations of meteors. I* (in English).

Huxley, L. G. H., **1952**, Aust. J. Sci. Res., *5*, 10–16, *The persistence of meteor trails.*

Imoto, S., and Hasegawa, I., **1958**, Smith. Contr. to Astrophys., *2*, 131–144, *Historical records of meteor showers in China, Korea and Japan.*

Jacchia, L. G., **1955**, Astrophys. J., *121*, 521–527, *The physical theory of meteors. VIII: Fragmentation as cause of the faint-meteor anomaly.*

————, **1957**, Astron. J., *62*, 358–362, *On the color index of meteors.*

Jacchia, L. G., Kopal, Z., and Millman, P. M., **1950**, Astrophys. J., *111*, 104–133, *A photographic study of the Draconid (Giacobinid) meteor shower of 1946.*

Jahnke, E., and Emde, F., **1938**, Teubner, Leipzig, and Stechert, New York, 3d rev. ed., 303 pp. + 76 pp., *Tables of functions with formulae and curves.*

Jenkins, A. W., Phillips, C. A., and Maple, E., **1960**, J. Geophys. Res., *65*, 1617–1619, *Observed magnetic effects from meteors.*

Kaiser, T. R., **1953**, Phil. Mag. Supp., *2*, 495–544, *Radio echo studies of meteor ionization.*

——, **1954a**, Mon. Not. Roy. Astron. Soc., *114*, 39–51, *Theory of the meteor height distribution obtained from radio-echo observations. I: Shower meteors.*

——, **1954b**, Mon. Not. Astron. Soc., *114*, 52–62, *Theory of the meteor height distribution obtained from radio-echo observations. II: Sporadic meteors.*

——, **1955a**, Spec. Supp. J. Atmos. Terr. Phys., *2*, 55–64, *The interpretation of radio echoes from meteor trails.*

——, **1955b**, Spec. Supp. J. Atmos. Terr. Phys., *2*, 119–130, *The incident flux of meteors and the total meteoric ionization.*

Kaiser, T. R., and Closs, R. L., **1952**, Phil. Mag., (7) *43*, 1–32, *Theory of radio reflections from meteor trails. I.*

Kaiser, T. R., and Greenhow, J. S., **1953**, Proc. Phys. Soc., *B66*, 150–151, *On the decay of radio echoes from meteor trails.*

Kalashnikov, A. G., **1949**, Dok. Akad. Nauk. SSSR, *66*, 373–376, *On the induction method of observing magnetic effects of meteors* (in Russian).

——, **1952**, Izvestia Akad. Nauk. SSSR, Ser. Geofiz., (No. 6), 7–20, *Magnetic effects of meteors* (in Russian).

Katasev, L. A., **1957**, State Publishing House of Technical Literature, Moscow, 179 pp., *Photographic methods of meteor astronomy* (in Russian).

Keitel, G. H., **1955**, Proc. Inst. Radio Engrs., *43*, 1481–1487, *Certain mode solutions of forward-scattering by meteor trails.*

Kotadia, K. M., **1958**, J. Scien. Indust. Res., *17A*, Supp., 46–49, *Meteors and E, ionization.*

Kresák, L., **1948**, Bull. Astron. Inst. Czech., *1*, 55–59, *Observations of long-enduring meteor trains* and *On the heights of long-enduring noctilucent meteor trains.*

——, **1960**, Bull. Astron. Inst. Czech., *11* (No. 1), 1–9, *The effect of solar corpuscular emission on the magnitude distribution of meteors* (in English).

Kresáková, M., and Kresák, L., **1955**, Contr. Astron. Obs. Skalnaté Pleso, *1*, 40–77, *On the activity of telescopic meteors and some related problems* (in English).

Krinov, E. L., and Fonton, S. S., **1954**, Meteoritica, (No. 11), 122–131, *Meteoric dust from the place of the fall of the Sihkote-Aline iron meteorite shower* (in Russian).

Kvíz, Zd., **1958**, Bull. Astron. Inst. Czech., *9* (No. 2), 70–76, *Probability of the perceptibility of a meteor and the independent counting method* (in English).

——, **1960**, Bull. Astron. Inst. Czech., *11* (No. 6), 251–253, *Atmospheric freezing nuclei and the structure of interplanetary matter* (in English).

Landsberg, H. E., **1947**, Popular Astron., *55*, 322, *A report on dust collections made at Mt. Weather and Arlington, Virginia, 1 October to 20 November, 1946.*

LaPaz, L., **1958**, Advances in Geophysics, *4*, 217–350, Academic Press, Inc., New York, *The effects of meteorites upon the earth (including its inhabitants, atmosphere and satellites).*

Levin, B. J., **1956**, Izd. Akad. Nauk. SSSR, Moscow, 293 pp., *The physical theory of meteors, and meteoric matter in the solar system* (in Russian). The first three chapters of this book are available in English in ASTIA Doc. No. AD 110091.

Liller, W., and Whipple, F. L., **1954**, Spec. Supp. J. Atmos. Terr. Phys., *1*, 112–130, *High-altitude winds by meteor-train photography.*

Lindblad, B. A., **1952**, Medd. från Lunds Astron. Obs., (1), (No. 179), *A radar investigation of the Delta Aquarid meteor shower of 1950* (in English).

——, **1956,** Medd. från Lunds Astron. Obs., (1), (No. 189), *Combined visual and radar observations of Perseid meteors* (in English).

Lindemann, F. A., and Dobson, G. M. B., **1923,** Proc. Roy. Soc., *A102,* 411–437, *A theory of meteors, and the density and temperature of the outer atmosphere to which it leads.*

Lockyer, J. Norman, **1890,** The Macmillan Company, London and New York, 560 pp., *The meteoric hypothesis.*

Lovell, A. C. B., **1947,** Nature, *160,* 670–671, *Electron density in meteor trails.*

——, **1948,** Repts. Prog. Phys., *11,* 415–444, *Meteoric ionization and ionospheric abnormalities.*

——, **1950,** Science Progress, *38,* 22–42, *Meteor ionization in the upper atmosphere.*

——, **1954,** University Press, Oxford, New York, 463 pp., *Meteor astronomy.*

——, **1957,** Handbuch der Physik, Geophysics II, *48,* 427–454, *Geophysical aspects of meteors* (in English).

Lovell, A. C. B., Banwell, C. J., and Clegg, J. A., **1947,** Mon. Not. Roy. Astron. Soc., *107,* 164–175, *Radio echo observations of the Giacobinid meteors 1946.*

Lovell, A. C. B., and Clegg, J. A., **1948,** Proc. Phys. Soc., *60,* 491–498, *Characteristics of radio echoes from meteor trails. I: The intensity of the radio reflections and electron density in the trails.*

McCoy, C. T., **1958,** Proc. Inst. Radio Engrs., *46,* 61–66, *Present and future capabilities of microwave crystal receivers.*

McCrosky, R. E., **1957,** Smith. Contr. to Astrophys., *1,* 215–224, *A rapid graphical method of meteor trail reduction.*

——, **1958,** Astron. J., *63,* 97–106, *The meteor wake.*

——, **1959,** Sky and Telescope, *18,* 440, *American astronomers report—Artificial meteor observations.*

McIntosh, R. A., **1934,** Trans. New Zealand Inst., *63,* 433–456, *Report of the (Meteor) Section (of the New Zealand Astronomical Society) for the observation of meteors, for the years 1929–1931.*

——, **1938,** Pop. Astron., *46,* 516–520, *Meteor rates in the Southern Hemisphere.*

McKinley, Barbara M., and McKinley, D. W. R., **1951,** Canad. J. Phys., *29,* 111–121, *Photoelectric meteor observations.*

McKinley, D. W. R., **1951a,** J. App. Phys., *22,* 202–213, *Deceleration and ionizing efficiency of radar meteors.*

——, **1951b,** Astrophys. J., *113,* 225–267, *Meteor velocities determined by radio observations.*

——, **1951c,** Canad. J. Phys., *29,* 403–426, *Variation of meteor echo rates with radar system parameters.*

——, **1953a,** Canad. J. Phys., *31,* 758–767, *Effect of radar sensitivity on meteor echo durations.*

——, **1953b,** Canad. J. Phys., *31,* 1121–1135, *Meteor echo duration and radio wavelength.*

——, **1954a,** Astrophys. J., *119,* 519–530, *Radio determination of the velocity and radiant of the Delta Aquarid meteors.*

——, **1954b,** Canad. J. Phys., *32,* 450–467, *Dependence of integrated duration of meteor echoes on wavelength and sensitivity.*

——, **1955,** Spec. Supp. J. Atmos. Terr. Phys., *2,* 65–72, *The meteoric head echo.*

——, **1956,** J. Atmos. Terr. Phys., *8,* 76–82, *Radar echo duration and height of a Perseid meteor.*

McKinley, D. W. R., and Bourne, B. E., **1951,** Canad. J. Technology, *29,* 428–434, *A precision radio time signal system.*

McKinley, D. W. R., and McNamara, A. G., **1956**, Canad. J. Phys., *34*, 625–637, *Meteoric echoes observed simultaneously by back scatter and forward scatter.*

McKinley, D. W. R., and Millman, Peter M., **1949a**, Proc. Inst. Radio Engrs., *37*, 364–375, *A phenomenological theory of radar echoes from meteors.*

——, **1949b**, Canad. J. Res., *A27*, 53–67, *Determination of the elements of meteor paths from radar observations.*

——, **1953**, Canad. J. Phys., *31*, 171–181, *Long duration echoes from aurora, meteors and ionospheric back-scatter.*

McNamara, A. G., and McKinley, D. W. R., **1959**, J. Atmos. Terr. Phys., *16*, 156–159, *The effect of trail irregularities on the interpretation of meteor echoes.*

Mainstone, J. S., **1960**, Mon. Not. Roy. Astron. Soc., *120*, 517–529, *The calculation of meteor velocities from continuous-wave radio diffraction effects from trails.*

Manning, L. A., **1948**, J. App. Phys., *19*, 689–699, *The theory of the radio detection of meteors.*

——, **1953**, J. Atmos. Terr. Phys., *4*, 219–225, *The strength of meteoric echoes from dense columns.*

——, **1958**, J. Geophys. Res., *63*, 181–196, *The initial radius of meteoric ionization.*

——, **1959a**, J. Atmos. Terr. Phys., *14*, 82–93, *Oblique echoes from over-dense meteor trails.*

——, **1959b**, J. Atmos. Terr. Phys., *15*, 137–140, *Air motions at meteoric heights.*

——, **1959c**, J. Geophys. Res., *64*, 1415–1425, *Air motions and the fading, diversity and aspect sensitivity of meteoric echoes.*

Manning, L. A., and Eshleman, V. R., **1957**, J. Geophys. Res., *62*, 367–371, *Discussion of the Booker and Cohen paper, "A theory of long-duration meteor echoes based on atmospheric turbulence with experimental confirmation."*

——, **1958**, J. Geophys. Res., *63*, 737–739, *Concerning Booker's theory of meteoric reflections.*

——, **1959**, Proc. Inst. Radio Engrs., *47*, 186–199, *Meteors in the ionosphere.*

Manning, L. A., Helliwell, R. A., Villard, O. G., and Evans, W. E., **1946**, Phys. Rev., *70*, 767–768, *On the detection of meteors by radio.*

Manning, L. A., Peterson, A. M., and Villard, O. G., **1954**, J. Geophys. Res., *59*, 47–62, *Ionospheric wind analysis by meteoric echo techniques.*

Manning, L. A., Villard, O. G., and Peterson, A. M., **1949**, J. App. Phys., *20*, 475–479, *Radio Doppler investigation of meteoric heights and velocities.*

——, **1950**, Proc. Inst. Radio Engrs., *38*, 877–883, *Meteoric echo study of upper atmosphere winds.*

——, **1952**, J. Geophys. Res., *57*, 387–403, *Double-Doppler study of meteoric echoes.*

——, **1953**, Trans. Amer. Geophys. Union, *34*, 16–21, *The length of ionized meteor trails.*

Maveva, G., **1953**, Publ. Acad. Sci. Turkmen S.S.R., (No. 4), 95, *The daily variation of hourly meteor rates from observations in Ashkabad 1942–1945* (in Russian).

Meeks, M. L., and James, J. C., **1957**, Proc. Inst. Radio Engrs., *45*, 1724–1733, *On the influence of meteor-radiant distributions in meteor-scatter communication.*

Millman, P. M., **1932**, Ann. Harvard Coll. Obs., *82*, 113–146, *An analysis of meteor spectra.*

——, **1935**, Ann. Harvard Coll. Obs., *82*, 149–177, *An analysis of meteor spectra: second paper.*

——, **1950a**, J. Roy. Astron. Soc. Can., *44*, 209–220, *Meteoric ionization.*

——, **1950b**, Nature, *165*, 1013–1014, *Spectrum of a meteor train.*

——, **1953**, Nature, *172*, 853–854, *The typical Perseid meteor spectrum.*

——, **1954a**, J. Roy. Astron. Soc. Can., *48*, 193–195, *A provisional list of the major meteor showers.*

——, **1954b**, J. Roy. Astron. Soc. Can., *48*, 226–227, *Meteor showers and rainfall.*

——, **1954c**, Science, *120*, 325–328, *Radio observation of meteors.*

——, **1955**, J. Roy. Astron. Soc. Can., *49*, 171–173, *A provisional supplementary list of meteor showers.*

——, **1957**, J. Roy. Astron. Soc. Can., *51*, 113–115, *The relative numbers of bright and faint meteors.*

——, **1959a**, J. Roy. Astron. Soc. Can., *53*, 15–33, *The Meanook-Newbrook meteor observatories.*

——, **1959b**, J. Geophys. Res., *64*, 2122–2128, *Visual and photographic observations of meteors and noctilucent clouds.*

——, **1959c**, J. Roy. Astron. Soc. Can., *53*, 271–276, *Photographic meteor spectra (Appendix 7).*

Millman, P. M., and Hoffleit, D., **1937**, Ann. Harvard Coll. Obs., *105*, 601–621, *A study of meteor photographs taken through a rotating shutter.*

Millman, P. M., and McKinley, D. W. R., **1956**, Canad. J. Phys., *34*, 50–61, *Meteor echo durations and visual magnitudes.*

Millman, P. M., and Robins, J. A., **1935**, Publ. Amer. Astron. Soc., *8*, 147, *Some properties of enduring meteor trains.*

Minohara, T., and Ito, Y., **1933**, Repts. Radio Res. Japan, *3*, 115, *Effect of Leonid meteors on the ionized upper atmosphere.*

Mitra, S. K., Syam, P., and Ghose, B. N., **1934**, Nature, *133*, 533–534, *Effect of a meteoric shower on the ionosphere.*

Montgomery, G. F., and Sugar, G. R., **1957**, Proc. Inst. Radio Engrs., *45*, 1684–1693, *The utility of meteor bursts for intermittent radio communication.*

Murakami, T., **1955**, Publ. Astron. Soc. Japan, *7*, 49–57 and 58–64, *On the annual variation of sporadic meteors. I and II.*

Murray, E. L., **1959**, Planet. Space Sci., *1*, 125–129, *Ambipolar diffusion of a meteor trail and its relation with height.*

Nagaoka, H., **1929**, Proc. Imp. Acad. Tokyo, *5*, 233, *Possibility of disturbance of radio transmissions by meteoric showers.*

Newton, H. A., **1865**, Amer. J. Science, (II) *39*, 193, *Abstract of a memoir on shooting stars.*

Nicolet, M., **1955**, Spec. Supp. J. Atmos. Terr. Phys., *2*, 99–110, *Meteor ionization and the night-time E-layer.*

Olivier, C. P., **1925**, The Williams & Wilkins Company, Baltimore, 276 pp., *Meteors.*

——, **1942**, Proc. Amer. Phil. Soc., *85*, 93–135, *Long enduring meteor trains.*

——, **1947**, Proc. Amer. Phil. Soc., *91*, 315–327, *Long enduring meteor trains, second paper.*

——, **1950**, Proc. Amer. Phil. Soc., *94*, 327–335, *Some results from data secured by the American Meteor Society.*

——, **1957**, Proc. Amer. Phil. Soc., *101*, 296–315, *Long enduring meteor trains and fireball orbits.*

——, **1960**, Smith. Contr. to Astrophys., *4*, 1–14, *Catalog of hourly meteor rates.*

Oort, J. H., **1951**, Observatory, *71*, 129–144, *Origin and development of comets.*

Öpik, E., **1922**, Publ. Astron. Obs. Tartu, *25* (No. 1), *A statistical method of counting shooting stars and its application to the Perseid shower of 1920.*

——, **1930**, Publ. Astron. Obs. Tartu, *27* (No. 2), *Telescopic observations of meteors at the Tartu Observatory.*

——, **1934**, Harvard Cir., (No. 389), *Results of the Arizona expedition for the study of meteors. III: Velocities of meteors observed visually.*

——, **1937**, Publ. Astron. Obs. Tartu, *29* (No. 5), *Researches on the physical theory of meteor phenomena. III: Basis of the physical theory of meteor phenomena.*

————, **1941,** Publ. Astron. Obs. Tartu, *30* (No. 6), *Observations of meteor velocities 1931–1938.*

————, **1953,** Irish Astron. J., *2,* 193–202, *A vibrating camera for meteor photography.*

————, **1955a,** Mem. Soc. Roy. Sci. Liège, (4) *15,* 125–146, Contr. from Armagh Obs., (No. 14), *The masses of meteors.*

————, **1955b,** Mem. Soc. Roy. Sci. Liège, (4) *15,* 147–173, Contr. from Armagh Obs., (No. 15), *The distribution of meteor stream intensity over the celestial sphere.*

————, **1955c,** Proc. Roy. Soc., *A230,* 463–501, *Meteor radiation, ionization and atomic luminous efficiency.*

————, **1955d,** Irish Astron. J., *3,* 165–181, Armagh Obs. Leaflet, (No. 30), *Meteors and the upper atmosphere.*

————, **1956a,** Irish Astron. J., *4,* 49–59, *Concluding results from the Arizona Expedition for the study of meteors.*

————, **1956b,** Irish Astron. J., *4,* 84–135, *Interplanetary dust and terrestrial accretion of meteoric matter.*

————, **1958a,** Interscience Publishers, Inc., New York and London, 174 pp., *Physics of meteor flight in the atmosphere.*

————, **1958b,** Contr. from Armagh Obs., (No. 26), 1–82, *Statistical results from the Arizona Expedition for the study of meteors.*

Park, F. R., **1958,** Engineering J., *41* (No. 8, Aug.), 68–70, *An observatory for the study of meteors.*

Partridge, W. S., and Harris, L. D., **1957,** J. App. Phys., *28,* 1269–1271, *Ionization in the trail of high-velocity pellets.*

Pettersson, H., and Rotschi, H., **1950,** Nature, *166,* 308, *Nickel content of deep-sea deposits.*

Pierce, J. A., **1938,** Proc. Inst. Radio Engrs., *26,* 892–902, *Abnormal ionization in the E-region of the ionosphere.*

————, **1947,** Phys. Rev., *71,* 88–92, *Ionization by meteoric bombardment*

Pineo, V. C., **1950,** Science, *112,* 50–51, *A comparison of meteor activity with occurrence of sporadic-E reflections.*

————, **1958,** Proc. Inst. Radio Engrs., *46,* 922, *Off-path propagation at VHF.*

Porter, J. G., **1952,** Chapman & Hall, Ltd., London, 123 pp., *Comets and meteor streams.*

Prentice, J. P. M., Lovell, A. C. B., and Banwell, C. J., **1947,** Mon. Not. Roy. Astron. Soc., *107,* 155–163, *Radio echo observations of meteors.*

Rao, M. S., **1958,** Canad. J. Phys., *36,* 840–854, *Analysis of meteoric body Doppler radar records taken during a Geminid shower period.*

————, **1959,** Canad. J. Phys., *37,* 557–568, *Size of irregularities in the E-region of the ionosphere.*

Rao, M. S., and Armstrong, R. L., **1958,** Canad. J. Phys., *36,* 1601–1623, *Investigation of the shifts of the effective point of radio reflection along a meteor train.*

Ridenour, L. N., **1947,** Editor-in-Chief, Radiation Laboratory Series, McGraw-Hill Book Company, Inc., New York, Vol. *1,* 748 pp., *Radar system engineering.*

Rinehart, J. S., Allen, W. A., and White, W. C., **1952,** J. App. Phys., *23,* 132–137, 198–201, 297–299, *Phenomena associated with the flight of ultra-speed pellets. I: Ballistics; II: Spectral character of luminosity; III: General features of luminosity.*

Robertson, D. S., Liddy, D. T., and Elford, W. G., **1953,** J. Atmos. Terr. Phys., *4,* 255–270, *Measurements of winds in the upper atmosphere by means of drifting meteor trains. I.*

Russell, J. A., **1960,** Astrophys. J., *131,* 34–37, *A time-resolved spectrum of the terminal burst of a Perseid meteor.*

Schafer, J. P., and Goodall, W. M., **1932,** Proc. Inst. Radio Engrs., *20,* 1941–1945, *Observations of the Kennelly-Heaviside layer heights during the Leonid meteor shower of Nov. 1931.*

Schiaparelli, J. V., **1866,** Stamferia, Firenze, *Note e riflessioni sulla theoria astronomica della stella cadenti* (in Italian). More available in an amended German translation by G. von Boguslawski, 1871, von der Nahmer, Stettin, *Entwierf einer astronomischen Theorie der Sternschnuppen.*

Skellett, A. M., **1931,** Phys. Rev., *37,* 1668, *The effect of meteors on radio transmission through the Kennelly-Heaviside layer.*

———, **1935,** Proc. Inst. Radio Engrs., *23,* 132–149, *The ionizing effects of meteors.*

———, **1938,** Nature, *141,* 472, *Meteoric ionization in the E-region of the ionosphere.*

Stewart, J. Q., Ference, M., Slattery, J. J., and Zahl, H. A., **1947,** Sky and Telescope, *6* (No. 5), 3–5, *Radar observations of the Draconids.*

Trowbridge, C. C., **1907,** Astrophys. J., *26,* 95–116, *Physical nature of meteor trains.*

Urey, H. C., and Craig, H., **1953,** Geochimica et Cosmochimica Acta, *4,* 36–82, *The composition of the stone meteorites and the origin of the meteorites.*

Van Bladel, J., **1955,** Gauthier-Villars, Paris, 147 pp., *Applications of radar to astronomy and meteorology* (in French).

van der Hulst, H. C., **1947,** Astrophys. J., *105,* 471–488, *Zodiacal light in the solar corona.*

Van Valkenburg, M. E., **1954,** J. Geophys. Res., *59,* 359–364, *The two-helix method for polarization measurements of meteoric radio echoes.*

Vestine, H. E., **1934,** J. Roy. Astron. Soc. Can., *28,* 249–272, 303–317, *Noctilucent clouds.*

Villard, O. G., Eshleman, V. R., Manning, L. A., and Peterson, A. M., **1955,** Proc. Inst. Radio Engrs., *43,* 1473–1481, *The role of meteors in extended-range VHF propagation.*

Villard, O. G., Peterson, A. M., Manning, L. A., and Eshleman, V. R., **1953,** J. Geophys. Res., *58,* 83–93, *Extended-range radio transmission by oblique reflection from meteoric ionization.*

———, **1956,** J. Geophys. Res., *61,* 233–249, *Some properties of oblique radio reflections from meteor ionization trails.*

Vincent, W. R., Wolfram, R. T., Sifford, B. M., Jaye, W. E., and Peterson, A. M., **1957a,** Proc. Inst. Radio Engrs., *45,* 1693–1700, *A meteor burst system for extended range VHF communications.*

———, **1957b,** Proc. Inst. Radio Engrs., *45,* 1701–1707, *Analysis of oblique path meteor-propagation data from the communications viewpoint.*

Vogan, E. L., and Campbell, L. L., **1957,** Canad. J. Phys., *35,* 1176–1189, *Meteor signal rates observed in forward-scatter.*

von Niessl, G., **1878,** Astron. Nachr., *93,* 209–238, *On the daily variation of meteors* (in German).

Watson, F. G., **1956,** Harvard Univ. Press, rev. ed., 188 pp., *Between the planets.*

Webb, E. L. R., **1950,** J. Roy. Astron. Soc. Can., *44,* 110–117, *A mount with chopping shutters for meteor cameras.*

Weiss, A. A., **1955a,** Aust. J. Phys., *8,* 148–166, *Radio echo observations of meteors in the southern hemisphere.*

———, **1955b,** Aust. J. Phys., *8,* 279–288, *Diffusion coefficients from the rate of decay of meteor trails.*

———, **1957a,** Aust. J. Phys., *10,* 77–102, *The distribution of the orbits of sporadic meteors.*

———, **1957b,** Aust. J. Phys., *10,* 299–309, *Meteor activity in the southern hemisphere.*

————, **1957c,** Aust. J. Phys., *10,* 397–411, *The incidence of meteor particles upon the earth.*

————, **1958,** Aust. J. Phys., *11,* 113–117, *The 1956 Phoenicid meteor shower.*

————, **1959,** Aust. J. Phys., *12,* 116–126, *The temporal variation of the heights of reflection points of meteor trails.*

Whipple, F. L., **1938,** Proc. Amer. Phil. Soc., *79,* 499–548, *Photographic meteor studies. I.*

————, **1940,** Proc. Amer. Phil. Soc., *83,* 711–745, *Photographic meteor studies. III: The Taurid shower.*

————, **1943,** Rev. Mod. Phys., *15,* 246–264, *Meteors and the earth's upper atmosphere.*

————, **1947,** Proc. Amer. Phil. Soc., *91,* 189–200, *Photographic meteor studies. IV: The Geminid shower.*

————, **1951,** Astrophys. J., *113,* 464–474, *A comet model. II: Physical relations for comets and meteors.*

————, **1952,** Physics and medicine of the upper atmosphere, 137–170, University of New Mexico Press, Albuquerque, *Meteoric phenomena and meteorites.*

————, **1954,** Astron. J., *59,* 201–217, *Photographic meteor orbits and their distribution in space.*

————, **1955a,** Astrophys. J., *121,* 241–249, *The physical theory of meteors. VII: On meteor luminosity and ionization.*

————, **1955b,** Publ. Astron. Soc. Pacific, *67,* 367–386, *Meteors.*

————, **1957,** I.A.U. Symposium No. 4: Radio astronomy (edited by H. C. van der Hulst), 375–389, Cambridge University Press, New York, *Some problems of meteor astronomy.*

————, **1958,** Proc. Intern. Astronautical Congr. Barcelona, 1957, 418–428, Springer-Verlag, Vienna, *The meteoric risk to space vehicles.*

————, **1959,** J. Geophys. Res., *64,* 1653–1664, *Solid particles in the solar system.*

Whipple, F. L., and Hawkins, G. S., **1956,** J. Meteorology, *13,* 236–240, *On meteors and rainfall.*

————, **1959,** Handbuch der Physik, *52,* 519–564, *Meteors.*

Williams, J. D., **1939,** Proc. Amer. Phil. Soc., *81,* 505–520, *Binocular observations of 718 meteors.*

Wyatt, S. P., and Whipple, F. L., **1950,** Astrophys. J., *111,* 134–141, *The Poynting-Robertson effect on meteor orbits.*

Wylie, C. C., **1947,** Sky and Telescope, *6* (No. 66), 11–12, *American astronomers report—the Draconid meteor maximum.*

Name Index

Subject Index

A scope, 73, 74
  in direction finding, 84–86
  in velocity measurements, 88, 89
Aberration, diurnal, 34
Ablation, 174–176
  heat of, 174
Absorption, in ionosphere, 72, 252–255, 265
  in troposphere, 26, 27
Aerodynamic drag, 173, 185
Air cap, 174
Air-to-ground scatter communications, 260
α, elongation from radiant, 93, 94, 220–223
α_e, recombination coefficient, 211, 212, 269, 270
Alpha Capricornids (see Capricornids)
Ambipolar diffusion, 198–204, 282, 283
Amplitude modulation, 35–38
  in scatter communications, 251, 255–261
Amplitude-range display (A scope), 73, 74
Ancient records, 3–5
Andromedids (see Bielids)
Angstrom unit, 26
Antennas, 41–44
  cross-sectional area of, 44, 188, 215
  height-finding, 84–86
  high-gain, 44, 73, 94–97, 104, 208, 260
  omnidirectional, 43, 44, 77–81, 85, 94
  for radiant and orbit determinations, 97–100
  rotating pattern, 85, 86
  for scatter communications, 257–262
  spaced dipole, 84, 85
Apex, 33, 158–162
Aphelion, 31
Aquarids, Eta, cometary association, 150
  orbital elements, 151
  shower data, 147
  Northern Delta, orbital elements, 154

Aquarids, Northern Delta, shower data, 147
  Northern Iota, orbital elements, 154
  shower data, 147
  Southern Delta, association with Arietids, 154–155
  orbit, 155
  orbital elements, 154
  shower data, 147
  Southern Iota, orbital elements, 154
  shower data, 147
Argument of perihelion, 32
Arietids, association with Southern Delta Aquarids, 154, 155
  echo height distribution, 134
  mass distribution, 124
  orbit, 155
  orbital elements, 154
  shower data, 147
Artificial meteors, 277, 278
Ascending node, 32
Aspect sensitivity, in forward-scatter, 237–240, 247, 248, 251
  in overdense trail, 215, 219–225, 233–235
  in underdense trail, 90, 190–195, 200, 201, 209, 210, 232–235
Asteroidal belt, 276
Asteroidal meteors, 170
Asteroids, 170
Astronomical unit, 32
Atmosphere, adopted model of, 280–283
  gravity waves in, 227
  isothermal, 178, 280–283
Attachment, 211, 212
  and echo duration, 225–232
Attenuation of echo, by absorption (see Absorption)
  by diffusion, 198–210
  by distance, 188, 216
  effect of, on diffraction oscillations, 209, 210
  by initial trail radius, 198–210

301